Classified Examples in

ELECTRICAL ENGINEERING

BY

S. GORDON MONK

M.Sc. (Eng.), B.Sc., M.I.E.E.

Head of Electrical Engineering Department
Plymouth and Devonport Technical College

IN TWO VOLUMES

VOLUME II

ALTERNATING CURRENT

SIXTH EDITION

LONDON
SIR ISAAC PITMAN & SONS, LTD.

First Edition,	1928	Fifth Edition,	1941
Second ,,	1930	Reprinted,	1945
Third ,,	1933	,,	1946
Fourth ,,	1937	Sixth Edition,	1949

SIR ISAAC PITMAN & SONS, Ltd.
PITMAN HOUSE, PARKER STREET, KINGSWAY, LONDON, W.C.2
THE PITMAN PRESS, BATH
PITMAN HOUSE, LITTLE COLLINS STREET, MELBOURNE
27 BECKETTS BUILDINGS, PRESIDENT STREET, JOHANNESBURG

ASSOCIATED COMPANIES

PITMAN PUBLISHING CORPORATION
2 WEST 45TH STREET, NEW YORK
205 WEST MONROE STREET, CHICAGO

SIR ISAAC PITMAN & SONS (CANADA), Ltd.
(INCORPORATING THE COMMERCIAL TEXT BOOK COMPANY)
PITMAN HOUSE, 381–383 CHURCH STREET, TORONTO

MADE IN GREAT BRITAIN AT THE PITMAN PRESS, BATH
D9—(T.5492)

PREFACE

SUNDRY corrections have been made, certain questions have been deleted, and more recent questions added. Questions that are new to this edition have been marked with an asterisk.

S. G. M.

DEVONPORT, 1949.

PREFACE
TO THE FIRST EDITION

THIS work is just an assembly of questions in electrical engineering arranged under the most important heads in that subject. They are taken mainly from the examination papers set during recent years at the London B.Sc. (Eng.) Degree, the A.M.I.E.E., the Final City and Guilds and the Whitworth Examinations of the Board of Education, and the author is indebted to the respective authorities (including the Controller, H.M. Stationery Office) for permission to reproduce these questions. The questions are mainly numerical, but many purely descriptive questions have been included, especially dealing with important principles. Notes have been given with many of the sections to help the student; some examples are worked fully in the answers, and references have been given in many instances where the student can obtain further information. There are, of course, other works than those specifically mentioned, wherein information can be obtained, and it does not follow that the references given are necessarily the best, but they will generally be found to be the most accessible. Questions have been included in design work, and some data have been given in these sections, but such data are given with reserve, and the student must supplement these data with any other to which he has access. The value in design work lies rather more in how to use data when given than in the accuracy of those data. It is thus impossible to give answers to the design questions, but many suggestions are given in the answers for the student's guidance.

The working of many numerical examples is of great assistance to a student of electrical engineering. Many text-books, therefore, give some examples, but they can only give examples that are covered by the text. This collection of examples is not so restricted, and the references given encourage a student to hunt up information, wherever obtainable, and so combines the work of many books and technical publications, and develops that quality of " self-help " so essential in an engineer.

Whereas many lecturers will have their own sets of examination questions, it is felt that such a collection as here given in compact form is readily obtainable by the students, and much time can be saved in lectures by reference to these questions instead of dictating such questions to the class, with the added advantage that the student has the question correctly and in permanent form.

Vol. I deals with the earlier years of the subject and covers the bulk of D.C. work, including D.C. machine design.

Vol. II is more advanced, dealing with more specialized work, and includes A.C. machinery and transmission and distribution. The author is indebted to D. G. Hitt, Esq., B.Sc. (Eng.), for valuable assistance in getting out some of the answers.

S. G. M.

Devonport, 1928.

Publishers' Note

The Publishers' thanks are due to the Syndics of the University Press, Cambridge, for their kind permission to reproduce the Tables on pages 202–205 from Godfrey and Siddons' *Four-figure Tables*.

CONTENTS

VOL. II—ALTERNATING CURRENT, ETC.

Classified Examples in
ELECTRICAL ENGINEERING

VOL. II : ALTERNATING CURRENT, ETC.

36. A.C. Fundamentals and Series Circuits

References. C2, 4; D3; G2; K2; M1, 2.

FOR a sine wave—

Average value $= 2/\pi = 0.637$ of maximum value.

R.M.S. value $= 1/\sqrt{2} = 0.707$ of maximum value.

Form factor $=$ R.M.S./Av. $= 0.707/0.637 = 1.11$.

$R =$ resistance, in ohms,

$L =$ coefficient of self-induction, in henrys,

$f =$ frequency, in cycles per second,

$\omega = 2\pi f$, in radians per second,

$\omega L =$ inductive reactance, in ohms,

$C =$ capacitance, in farads,

$1/\omega C =$ capacitative reactance, in ohms,

$X =$ reactance, in ohms

$\quad = (\omega L \sim 1/\omega C)$.

$Z =$ impedance, in ohms

$\quad = \sqrt{R^2 + (\omega L \sim 1/\omega C)^2}$ for series circuits.

Series resonance occurs when $X = 0$, i.e. when $\omega L = 1/\omega C$ or $f = 1/2\pi\sqrt{LC}$. The current then reaches a *maximum* for a given applied voltage. (*Acceptor Circuit.*)

1

"j" Notation

$j = \sqrt{-1}$ or $j^2 = -1$. As an operator, j turns a vector through 90° counterclockwise.

Thus $Z = R + jX$ when X is inductive;

$\qquad = R - jX$ when X is capacitative.

Numerically, $Z = \sqrt{R^2 + X^2}$ as above.

Impedances are fixed constants of a circuit and do not change with time, i.e. they do not have instantaneous values like alternating currents and voltages.

Alternating currents and voltages may be represented by their in-phase and quadrature components referred to any arbitrary axis of reference. (See Ques. 15 below.)

If the j- or quadrature-component is positive, then the vector is ahead of the reference axis in time. Thus, with volts taken as the axis of reference, a lagging current would be of the form $i = a - jb$, where a is the in-phase or energy component and b is the idle or wattless component. A leading current would have the j component positive. The actual value of the current is

$$I = \sqrt{a^2 + b^2}.$$

The power is the product of volts and in-phase component, i.e. Va. If both volts and current are in symbolic form, the power is the "dot" product; thus if

$$\text{current, } i = a + jb$$
$$\text{voltage, } v = c + jd$$

the power is given by $ac + bd$. Any components that are negative have corresponding effects upon the signs in this product.

Voltage/current, when rationalized, will give the impedance in symbolic form. The result must be the same whatever the axis of reference used for expressing the voltage and current. Similarly, *current/voltage* gives admittance in symbolic form.

Three Voltmeter Method of Measuring Power absorbed by a Series Circuit. (See Fig. 1.)

If V_1 = voltage across the device under test,

V_2 = voltage across a non-inductive resistance connected in series with same,

V_3 = voltage across the whole circuit,

I = current flowing through the circuit,

then, for the given device,

$\cos \phi_1$ = power factor and

$$V_3{}^2 = V_1{}^2 + V_2{}^2 - 2V_1V_2 \cos(180 - \phi_1)$$
$$= V_1{}^2 + V_2{}^2 + 2V_1V_2 \cos \phi_1.$$

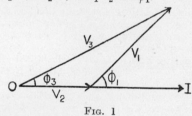

Fig. 1

This enables $\cos \phi_1$ and $V_1 \cos \phi_1$ to be determined, and the power absorbed is $IV_1 \cos \phi_1$.

For the whole circuit,

$\cos \phi_3$ = power factor and

$$V_1{}^2 = V_2{}^2 + V_3{}^2 - 2V_2V_3 \cos \phi_3$$

giving $\cos \phi_3$ and $V_3 \cos \phi_3$ and the total power is $IV_3 \cos \phi_3$. The difference between these two powers must be the I^2R power in the added resistance.

EXAMPLES 36

1. Explain how alternating quantities may be represented by complex numbers. If the potential difference across a circuit is represented by $40 + j25$ volts, and the circuit consists of a resistance of 20 ohms in series with an inductance of 0·06 henry and the frequency is 79·5 cycles per second, find the complex number representing the current in amperes.

(*Lond. Univ.*, 1940, *A.E.*)

2. A resistance of 0·1 ohm, an inductance of 1 henry, and a capacitor of 10·2 microfarads are connected in series and supplied with alternating current at 10 volts, 50 cycles. Find

the voltages across the inductance and the capacitor. Plot the current curve as the frequency varies from 49·5 to 50·5 in steps of 0·1.

3. An alternating-current electromagnet, the winding of which has a negligible resistance, is connected in series with a non-inductive resistance and with a condenser of 50 microfarads capacitance. When connected across an alternating-current supply the current taken is 1·9 amperes, the voltage across the condenser is 120 volts, across the resistance 60 volts, across the electromagnet 85 volts, and across the resistance and the electromagnet, together, 115 volts. Calculate the iron loss in the electromagnet, the supply voltage, and its frequency.   (*C. & G., Final*, 1929.)

4. A circuit is made up of a choking coil having a resistance of 7 ohms and an inductance of 0·4 henry, joined in series with a condenser of 20 microfarads capacity. Find the current in the circuit and the potential difference across the choking coil when an alternating E.M.F. of 230 volts at 50 c.p.s. is applied to the terminals.   (*Lond. Univ.*, 1935, *El. Tech.*)

5. A closed circuit consists of a resistance of 5 ohms, an inductance of 0·2 millihenry and a variable condenser connected in series. An E.M.F. of one volt at a frequency of $10^6/2\pi$ is induced in the circuit. Draw the current locus as the capacitance of the condenser is raised from 220 $\mu\mu$F. below to 200 $\mu\mu$F. above the value giving rise to resonance.
                                              (*Lond. Univ.*, 1938, *El. Tech.*)

6. An inductive coil of value 1·2 millihenrys is shunted by a variable condenser. When the capacity is 0·0003 microfarads, find the wavelength (in metres) and frequency in kilocycles to which this combination is tuned, assuming that all inductance and capacity are concentrated in the respective units.

7. When 30 volts D.C. were applied to a certain coil, the consumption was found to be 150 watts. When A.C. at 230 volts was applied, the consumption was 3,174 watts. Find the reactance of the coil.

8. An inductive coil in series with a non-inductive resistance on 100 volts A.C. takes a current of 5 amperes. The voltage across the coil is 80 volts, and across the resistance 30 volts. Find the power factor and power (*a*) for the whole circuit, (*b*) for the coil alone.

9. An air-gap choking coil has a back E.M.F. of 200 volts when taking a current of 10 amperes from a supply at 50 cycles per second. Calculate the effective length of the air-gap. Assume that (*a*) the number of turns on the coil is 400, (*b*) the

maximum flux density reached in the air-gap is 8000 C.G.S. units, (c) the magnetic reluctance of the iron core is 6 per cent of that of the gap, and (d) the magnetic leakage is negligible.
(*I.E.E.*, 1937.)

10. An inductive circuit supplied with 100 volts at 50 cycles per sec. is found to take 10 amperes. When supplied with 100 volts at 200 cycles per sec. it takes 5 amperes. Determine the circuit constants. Assume sine-wave current in each case.   (*I.E.E.*, *May*, 1932.)

11. A current of 10 amperes at 50 frequency passes through a non-inductive resistance in series with an iron-cored inductance, the winding of which has a resistance of 1·5 ohms. The voltage across the non-inductive resistance is 20 volts, across the coil 30 volts, and across both 45 volts. Find the watts lost in the iron core.

12. An alternating current circuit consists of a constant reactance of 1 ohm in series with a variable resistance. A constant voltage of 100 volts is applied. Show that the current locus is represented by a circle. Calculate (a) the maximum power input to the circuit in watts, (b) the corresponding current and power factor, (c) the value of the resistance required for the power input to be a maximum. (*C. & G.*, 1933.)

13. Two coils, A of inductance 0·2 henry and resistance 50 ohms, and B of inductance 0·5 henry and resistance 200 ohms, are coupled by a mutual inductance of 0·25 henry. Find the voltage at a frequency of 159·5 cycles per sec. that must be maintained across the terminals of A in order that a current of 10 milliamperes may flow in B when the terminals of B are connected to a resistance of 100 ohms. Draw a vector diagram to scale showing the currents and voltages in the coils.   (*Lond. Univ.*, 1933, *El. Tech.*)

14. A choke coil has a resistance of 3 ohms and a reactance of 1 ohm at 50 cycles. In series with it is placed an adjustable choke of negligible resistance, and reactance varying from zero to 3 ohms. Draw the locus diagram of the current taken from a 100-volt supply at 50 cycles and find its minimum and maximum values, and the corresponding power factors.

15. Explain the method of representing a vector quantity by the j notation. The current in a circuit is given by $4·5 + j12$ when the applied voltage is $100 + j150$. Determine (a) the complex expression for the impedance, stating whether it is inductive or capacitative, (b) the power, (c) the phase angle between the current and the voltage. (*C. & G.*, *Final*, 1948.)

16. A circuit consisting of a condenser of capacitance 318

microfarads in series with a coil of inductance 0·07 henry and resistance 15 ohms is connected to an A.C. supply of 230 volts, 50 cycles per sec. Calculate the energy stored in the electric field of the condenser and in the magnetic field of the coil at the instant when the supply voltage is zero.

(Lond. Univ., 1936.)

17. The low-voltage release of an A.C. motor starter consists of a solenoid into which an iron plunger is drawn against a spring. The resistance of the solenoid is 28·5 ohms. When connected to 100-volt, 50-cycle mains the current taken is at first 1·12 amperes and it falls to 0·43 ampere when the plunger is drawn into the full-in position. Calculate the inductance of the solenoid and the maximum flux-turn linkages for both positions of the plunger. Explain fully why these values vary with the position of the plunger, and discuss the factors that determine the magnitude of the current and the flux-turn linkages for a constant applied voltage.

(Lond. Univ., 1938, A.E.)

*18. A coil having a resistance of 2 ohms and an inductance of 10 millihenrys is connected in series with a condenser of 20 microfarads to a supply of 100 volts at 400 cycles per second. Find (a) the current taken, (b) the voltage across the coil, and (c) that across the condenser. Draw a complete vector diagram.

*19. Two coils having inductances of 0·01 henry and 5 henrys respectively and corresponding resistances of 5 ohms and 100 ohms have a coefficient of coupling of 0·8. Calculate the percentage change in the effective resistance of the first coil at a frequency of 50 cycles per second when a resistance of 200 ohms is connected across the terminals of the second coil. Deduce any formula used.   *(C. & G., Final, 1943.)*

*20. Explain the symbolic method of vector representation and express the vector $4 + j5$ in its various forms. Draw the following vectors to a scale of inches:

(1) $(1 + j2) - (j1·5 - 1)$,
(2) $(j - 1) \times (j0·5 - 2)$,
(3) $(1·5 \underline{/\pi/3})^2$.   *(C. & G., Final, 1942.)*

*21. A coil having an inductance of 0·12 henry and a resistance of 4 ohms is connected in series with a variable non-inductive resistance having a maximum value of 200 ohms across a 110 volt, 50-cycle supply. Derive from first principles the locus of the extremity of the current vector. From the locus diagram, estimate the value of the current when the power factor is 0·3 and the value of the variable resistance then in circuit.   *(Lond. Univ., 1943, Ap. Elect.)*

37. A.C. Circuits in Parallel

References. C2, 4; D3; G2; K2; Ml, 2.

With loads in parallel, final energy current is the sum of the individual energy currents, and final idle or wattless current is the sum of the individual idle currents.

"j" Notation for Parallel Circuits.
Conductance $= G = R/Z^2$ mhos,
Susceptance $= B = X/Z^2$ mhos,
Admittance $= Y = 1/Z$ mhos,
            $= G - jB$ for inductive reactance,
            $= G + jB$ for capacitative reactance.
Numerically
$$Y = \sqrt{G^2 + B^2}$$
With volts as axis of reference, then
Current $= I = VY$ amperes,
Energy current $= I_e = VG$ amperes,
Idle current $= I_i = VB$ amperes,
Power factor $= \cos\phi = G/Y$,
Power $= V^2G$ watts,
            $\text{kVA} = V^2Y \times 10^{-3}$,
            $\text{kVAR} = V^2B \times 10^{-3}$.

Parallel resonance occurs when $B = 0$, i.e. $X = 0$ as in series resonance, but in this case the admittance Y, and consequently the current I, is a *minimum* for a given applied voltage. (*Rejector Circuit.*)
To obtain the equivalent circuit of any number of parallel circuits, sum the G's and the B's of each. Thence find $Y^2 = G^2 + B^2$. Then the equivalents, $R = G/Y^2$ and $X = B/Y^2$.

Three Ammeter Method of Measuring Power Absorbed by a Parallel Circuit. (See Fig. 2.)

$I_1 =$ current in the device under test,
$I_2 =$ current in a non-inductive resistance connected in parallel with the same,
$I_3 =$ current in the above circuits combined,
$V =$ voltage common to both circuits,

then, for the given device,

cos ϕ_1 = power factor, and

$$I_3{}^2 = I_1{}^2 + I_2{}^2 - 2I_1I_2 \cos(180 - \phi_1)$$
$$= I_1{}^2 + I_2{}^2 + 2I_1I_2 \cos \phi_1$$

which enables cos ϕ_1 and I_1 cos ϕ_1 to be determined, and the power absorbed is given by $VI_1 \cos \phi_1$.

For the whole circuit,

cos ϕ_3 = power factor, and

$$I_1{}^2 = I_2{}^2 + I_3{}^2 - 2I_2I_3 \cos \phi_3$$

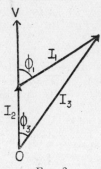

Fig. 2

giving cos ϕ_3 and I_3 cos ϕ_3, and the total power absorbed is given by $VI_3 \cos \phi_3$.

The difference between these two powers must be the I^2R power in the added resistance.

TABLE OF CORRESPONDING SINES AND COSINES

| Cos ϕ | 0·95 | 0·9 | 0·87 | 0·85 | 0·8 | 0·75 | 0·71 | Sin ϕ |
| Sin ϕ | 0·316 | 0·435 | 0·5 | 0·53 | 0·6 | 0·66 | 0·71 | Cos ϕ |

More accurately 0·87 should be 0·866 = $\sqrt{3}/2$ (i.e. 60° - 30° $\triangle$) and 0·71 should be 0·707 = $1/\sqrt{2}$ (i.e. 45° $\triangle$).

EXAMPLES 37

1. Coil A has resistance 4 ohms and coefficient L of ·02 henry, while coil B has resistance 2 ohms and coefficient L of ·04 henry,

With a supply of 100 volts at 50 frequency, find the current taken and its power factor when the coils are (a) in series, and (b) in parallel.

2. A resistance of 23 ohms, an inductance of 0·4 henry with a resistance of 13 ohms, and a condenser of 90 μF. are connected in parallel across a 50-cycle, 230-volt supply. Find the values of the total current, the current in the condenser and in the inductance at the instants when the current in the resistance is 8 amps.   (*Lond. Univ.*, 1937, *El. Tech.*)

3. Three circuits having impedances $10 + j30$, $20 + j0$, and $1 - j20$ ohms are connected in parallel across a 200-volt supply. Find the total current flowing and its phase angle.

4. A condenser of 5 microfarads capacity is shunted by a variable resistance R. Draw the vector locus of the impedance of the combination at 50 cycles per sec. as R varies from zero to infinity. Read off the impedance when the value of R is 500 ohms.   (*Lond. Univ.*, 1934, *El. Tech.*)

5. A coil having a resistance of 5 ohms and an inductance of 0·02 henry is connected in parallel with another coil of resistance 1 ohm and inductance 0·08 henry. Find the equivalent impedance of the combination. If this combination be connected in series with an impedance of 2 ohms resistance and 0·005 henry inductance, find the percentage by which the voltage must be raised to keep the current unchanged. Frequency 50 cycles per sec.   (*C. & G., Final*, 1931.)

6. Two reactive conductors when traversed by alternating currents of frequency 50 have the same impedance and also the same power factor of $1/\sqrt{2}$. The first consists of a condenser shunted by a non-inductive resistance of 200 ohms. The second consists of a choking coil. Find the capacitance of the first and the inductance and resistance of the second. These conductors are placed in series across 400-volt 50-cycle mains. Draw a vector diagram for the voltages and currents in the circuit.   (*I.E.E., Nov.*, 1937.)

7. A coil having a resistance of 50 ohms and an inductance of 0·2 henry is connected in series with a condenser. The current is a maximum when the frequency is 50. Calculate the capacitance of the condenser to be connected in parallel with this combination so that the total current taken from the mains is a minimum when the frequency is 100.

If the p.d. is 200 volts, find the current taken from the mains in each case and illustrate the conditions by vector diagrams.
                    (*C. & G., Final*, 1935.)

8. Two impedances $4 + j5$ and $8 + j10$ are connected in

parallel across 200-volt, 50-frequency mains. Find (a) the admittance, conductance and susceptance of each branch, and of the entire circuit; (b) the total current and its power factor. What value of capacitance must be connected in parallel with this combination to raise the resultant power factor to unity?

(C. & G., 1937.)

9. A and B are in parallel, and together are in series with C. $A = 3 + j4$; $B = 5 - j12$; $C = 3 + j5$. If 100 volts A.C. is applied to the whole, find the currents in and voltages across each item, and draw the vector diagram.

10. An alternating p.d. of 200 volts at 50 cycles is applied to a circuit consisting of a non-inductive resistance of 10 ohms in parallel with a choking coil of self-induction 0·02 henry and negligible losses. Determine either graphically or by calculation, the values of the total current and of the two branch currents at the instant the applied p.d. is 100 volts and increasing. (I.E.E., Nov., 1934.)

11. Two inductive coils, A and B, are in parallel on a 100-volt supply. The coil A is found to be taking 12 amperes at 0·9 power factor, while the total load for both coils is 20 amperes at 0·8 power factor. Find the individual resistances and reactances and the equivalent resistance and reactance, and the current and power factor in coil B.

12. A coil of resistance 2 ohms and inductive reactance of 4 ohms is shunted by a variable resistance. Draw the locus of the impedance of this combination, and determine therefrom the value of this impedance when the adjustable shunt resistance has values of 2, 2·5, 3·33, 5 and 10 ohms.

13. A circuit consists of a resistance of 20 ohms in series with an inductance of 0·05 henry. Find the characteristics of a circuit to be placed in parallel with the above such that when the pair are connected to a supply of 100 volts, a total current of 5 amperes shall be passed at all frequencies.

14. A lamp takes 3·05 amperes at unity power factor and consumes 410 watts. Calculate the inductance of a choke-coil which, when connected in series with the lamp to 230-volt, 50-frequency mains, will ensure that it runs under these conditions. What is the capacitance of the condenser which, when connected across the supply terminals, will raise the power-factor of the supply to unity? Draw a vector diagram, roughly to scale, of the currents and voltages in the lamp, the choke and the condenser. (Lond. Univ., 1936, El. Tech.)

*15. A factory load supplied by an alternator consists of lighting 500 kW., induction motors 3000 kVA. at power-factor

0·707, and a synchronous motor which operates at a leading power-factor of 0·6 when loaded to 1000 kVA. Calculate the total kVA. loading of the alternator, and its power-factor.

(I.E.E., Nov., 1943.)

*16. The impedance of two parallel circuits can be represented by $(20 + j15)$ and $(10 - j60)$ ohms respectively. If the supply frequency is 50 cycles per second, find the resistance and the inductance or capacitance of each circuit. Also, derive a symbolic expression for the admittance of the combined circuits, and thence find the phase angle between the applied voltage and the resultant current. State whether this current is leading or lagging relatively to the voltage.

(Lond. Univ., 1944, Ap. Elect.)

*17. A coil of 10 ohms resistance and 0·02 henry inductance is connected in parallel with a capacitor of 60 microfarads. Calculate the frequency at which the reading of the ammeter in the main circuit is unaffected when the coil is disconnected.

(C. & G., Final, 1945.)

*18. A coil having a resistance of 5 ohms and a reactance of 12 ohms is shunted by another coil of 8 ohms reactance which is in series with a resistance variable from 2 ohms to 10 ohms and the combination is connected across 200 volts mains. Draw to scale the locus diagram of the current taken from the mains and determine the two extreme phase angles between this current and the applied voltage. *(C. & G., Final, 1945.)*

38. Reactive Circuit Time Constant

References. C2, 4; G2.

Growth of Current in Inductive Circuit.

If R = resistance of circuit,

V = applied pressure, assumed constant,

I = final steady current = V/R,

L = coefficient of self-induction in henrys,

then, after the expiry of time t seconds, the value of the current is

$$i = I\left(1 - e^{-\frac{Rt}{L}}\right)$$

L/R = time constant = T,

Q = energy stored in the magnetic field = $IT = \frac{1}{2}LI^2$.

After time L/R, $i = I\ (1 - e^{-1}) = 0.632I$, or 63.2 per cent of final value.

Decrease of Current in Inductive Circuit.

$$i = I e^{-\frac{R}{L}t}$$

i.e. the complement of the above expression.

Discharge Limiting Resistances or Condensers.

If I = steady current through coil at moment of breaking circuit,

R = shunt resistance across coil,

$V = RI$ will be the voltage reached immediately after break.

With a condenser in shunt, its capacity C must be of such a value that the energy it stores when raised to the desired limiting voltage V is equal to the energy stored in the magnetic field, i.e.

$\frac{1}{2}LI^2 = \frac{1}{2}CV^2$, from which C is obtainable.

Charge and Discharge of Condensers through Resistance.

q = quantity stored in coulombs,

v = voltage difference of plates,

C = capacity in farads,

q = Cv and also $\int i \cdot dt$,

T = time constant = RC.

EXAMPLES 38

1. Establish the formula for the growth of a current in a coil of resistance R and inductance L when connected to a D.C. supply at V volts, and show that after the elapse of a time L/R, the current has reached a value 63·2 per cent of its final value. Deduce also the fact that the energy stored in the magnetic field is given by $\frac{1}{2}LI^2$.

2. If a coil has a resistance of 10 ohms and a self-inductance of 1 henry, what are the values of the current 0·1 and 1 second after switching on a 100-volt D.C. supply?

(*I.E.E., May*, 1935.)

3. The inductance of a certain 5000 ohm resistance is 250 microhenrys. What is the time constant of this coil? What is the phase difference between the voltage across the coil and the current in it, at a frequency of 3000 c.p.s.?

(*Lond. Univ.*, 1935, *El. Tech.*)

4. A condenser of capacity 10 microfarads is shunted by a neon lamp, the striking voltage of which is 170 volts. A resistance of 10 megohms is connected in series with this combination, and the whole connected to 200-volt D.C. mains. Find how long it will take for the neon lamp to strike after closing the main switch.

5. Describe the various methods employed for limiting the voltage rise on disconnecting a highly inductive coil, such as a field coil, from the supply. If a coil of 50 ohms resistance is suddenly disconnected from a supply at 80 volts, find what discharge resistance must be connected across it to limit the voltage rise to 200 volts.

6. The initial rate of rise of current on switching on an inductive circuit to a D.C. supply is 1600 amperes per sec. and the rate after 2 milli-seconds is 1000 amperes per sec. Find the final value of the current.

(*Lond. Univ.*, 1934, *El. Tech.*)

7. If a condenser of 20 microfarads be charged to a potential difference of 15,000 volts, and then be suddenly shorted by a coil of negligible resistance and of inductance 0·002 henry, ascertain the frequency and maximum amplitude of the resultant current oscillations.

8. Derive an expression for the current in an inductive circuit at any instant after the application of a steady voltage. A coil has a time constant of 1·0 and an inductance of 10 henrys. What is the value of the current 0·1 second after switching on to a steady p.d. of 100 volts. Find also the time taken for the current to reach one-half of its steady value.

(*C. & G.*, 1939.)

9. A condenser is charged through a large non-inductive resistance by connecting it to a battery of constant E.M.F. Obtain an expression by which the rate at which the condenser receives its charge may be calculated. A condenser of 3 microfarads capacity is connected through a resistance of 1 megohm to a constant E.M.F. Find how long it will take before the condenser receives 99 per cent of its final charge.

(*Lond. Univ.*, 1923, *El. Tech.*)

10. Each field coil of a 10-pole machine is wound with 1500 turns, all the coils being connected in series. The exciting voltage is 200 volts and the field current 10 amperes. The flux per pole being 5,000,000 lines, calculate (*a*) the time constant of the circuit, (*b*) the time required for the current to reach 90 per cent of its final value. Assume that the inductance of the coils remains constant.　　　(*C. & G., Final*, 1926.)

11. A resistance and a 2-microfarad condenser are connected in series across a 200-volt D.C. supply. A neon lamp, which has a "striking" voltage of 120, is connected in parallel with the condenser. Calculate the value of resistance required to make the lamp strike 5 seconds after the switch has been closed. Draw a curve, approximately to scale, showing how the voltage across the condenser varies during the first 10 or 15 seconds.　　　(*Lond. Univ.*, 1937, *El. Tech.*)

39. Rectifiers (other than Mercury-Arc)

References. *Electrolytic Rectifiers,* by De Bruyne (Pitman) ;
A.C. Rectification, by L. B. W. Jolley (Chapman & Hall).

EXAMPLES 39

1. A sine wave of alternating E.M.F. of maximum value
100 volts (50 frequency) is applied to a circuit consisting of a
50-volt battery in series with a half-wave rectifier which has
an effective resistance of 10 ohms to a current discharging the
battery and an infinite resistance to a current in the opposite
direction. Assuming that the internal resistances of the battery
and A.C. generator are negligible, determine the energy dissipated in the rectifier in 1 hour.

(Lond. Univ., 1934, El. Tech.)

2. Describe a vibrating reed half-wave rectifier and show
how it is possible automatically to obtain correct charging
half of wave irrespective of which way round the accumulator
is connected.

3. Explain how rectification for charging purposes may be
obtained by means of a "synchronous commutator" and say
how synchronous running is obtained.

4. Describe the Lodge-Cottrell method of precipitating fine
dust, giving an idea of the voltages and currents used, and the
size of the installations for specific purposes.

(See *Electrical Precipitation,* by Sir Oliver Lodge. *Physics
in Industry,* Vol. III (Oxford University Press.)

5. The characteristic of a metal rectifier is as follows—

Volts	+ 1·0	+ 0·8	+ 0·6	+ 0·48	− 0·5	− 1·0
Milliamps	+ 12	+ 7	+ 2	+ 1	− 0·1	− 0·2

A sinusoidal alternating voltage of 2 volts R.M.S. is applied to
this rectifier with a non-inductive resistance of 100 ohms and
a moving-coil milliammeter of negligible resistance in series.
What will be the ammeter reading? *(Lond. Univ., 1937, A.E.)*

6. A moving-coil ammeter, a hot-wire ammeter, and a
resistance of 100 ohms are connected in series with a rectifying
device across a sinusoidal alternating supply at 200 volts. If
the device has a resistance of 100 ohms to current in one
direction, and of 500 ohms to current in the opposite direction,
calculate the readings on the two ammeters, the power taken
from the mains, and that dissipated in the rectifying device.

(Lond. Univ., 1926, El. Tech.)

40. Harmonics

References. C2; 4; D3; G2; K2; M1.

General Expression.

$$e = E_1 \sin \omega t + E_3 \sin (3\omega t + \alpha) + E_5 \sin (5wt + \beta) \ . \ .$$

and a similar expression for current.

R.M.S. Value. $E = \sqrt{\tfrac{1}{2}(E_1{}^2 + E_3{}^2 + E_5{}^2 + \text{etc.})}$

Effect of Harmonics on Reactance.

Inductive. $X = \omega L \sqrt{\dfrac{E_1{}^2 + E_3{}^2 + E_5{}^2 + \cdots}{(E_1/1)^2 + (E_3/3)^2 + (E_5/5)^2 \cdots}}$

Capacity $X = \dfrac{1}{\omega C} \sqrt{\dfrac{E_1{}^2 + E_3{}^2 + E_5{}^2 + \cdots}{(E_1)^2 + (3E_3)^2 + (5E_5)^2 \cdots}}$

EXAMPLES 40

1. A circuit consists of a choking coil of coefficient 0·4 henry and resistance 12 ohms in series with a condenser of 4 micro-farads capacity. A supply represented by

$$v = 800 \sin \omega t + 400 \sin 3\omega t + 200 \sin 5\omega t$$

is applied, the fundamental frequency being 50. What will be the maximum p.d. across the coil due to the fundamental, and that across the condenser due to the fifth harmonic ?

2. A charging current represented by

$$i = 200 \sin \omega t + 60 \sin 3\omega t + 15 \sin 5\omega t$$

flows through a condenser having an effective resistance of 5 ohms and a capacity of 20 microfarads, the frequency of the fundamental being 50. Find the p.d. produced across it due to the fundamental and each of the harmonics.

3. An alternator having a pressure wave represented by

$$e = 5500 \sin \omega t + 250 \sin 13\omega t$$

is connected to an open cable. If the reactance of the alternator at the fundamental frequency of 50 is 1 ohm, and the resistance of machine and half run of cable is ·5 ohm, find the capacity of the cable that will give resonance with the thirteenth harmonic, and the voltage across it due to this harmonic.

4. If in Ques. 2 a hot-wire ammeter had been inserted in the circuit, what reading would it have given ? Similarly, what

would an electrostatic voltmeter read across the terminals of the alternator in Ques. 3 ?

5. A current of 50 frequency (fundamental), containing first, third, and fifth harmonics of crest values 100, 15, and 12 amperes respectively, is sent through an ammeter and an inductive coil of negligibly small losses. A voltmeter connected to the terminals shows 75 volts. What will be the current indicated on the ammeter, and what is the value of the inductance of the coil expressed in henrys ? (*C. & G.*, 1918.)

6. A potential difference represented by the formula

$$v = \sqrt{2} \cdot 100 \cdot \sin 2\pi \cdot 50 \cdot t + \sqrt{2} \cdot 20 \cdot \sin 2\pi \cdot 150 \cdot t$$

is applied to the terminals of a circuit made up of a resistance of 5 ohms, an inductance of 0·0318 henry, and a capacity of 12·5 microfarads all in series. Calculate the effective current and the power supplied to the circuit.

(*Lond. Univ.*, 1926, *El. Tech.*)

7. In a 3-phase system containing fifth and seventh harmonics in the pressure waves, prove that, with respect to the fundamental, the seventh harmonic has the same and the fifth the opposite cyclic rotation in the phases. Apply this to explain the blackening of the commutator at six places in each pole-pair of a rotary convertor fed from such a pressure.

(*C. & G.*, *Final*, 1923.)

8. An electromotive force

$$e = 2000 \sin \omega t + 400 \sin 3\omega t + 100 \sin 5\omega t$$

is connected to a circuit consisting of a resistance of 10 ohms, a variable inductance, and a capacity of 30 microfarads, arranged in series with a hot-wire ammeter. Find the value of the inductance which will give resonance with the triple frequency component of the pressure ; and estimate the readings on the ammeter and on a hot-wire voltmeter connected across the supply when resonant conditions exist ; $\omega = 300$. (*Lond. Univ.*, 1922, *El. Tech.*)

9. Explain what is meant by a harmonic in alternating current working. An alternating voltage given by the expression $1000 \sin 314t + 100 \sin 942t$ is applied to a circuit having a resistance of 100 ohms and an inductance of 0·5 henry. Calculate the R.M.S. value of the current and the power factor. (*C. & G.*, *Final*, 1931.)

41. Three-Phase Circuits and Power Measurement.

References. C2, 4; D3; G2; K2; M1.

Two wattmeters are connected with current coils in each of two of the lines, and the pressure coils connected from their respective current coils to the third line. For balanced loads only, one wattmeter may be used, the free end of the pressure coil being connected to the other two lines successively.

If W_1 and W_2 = readings thus obtained, so chosen that W_1 is the greater, and $r = W_2/W_1$, then

$$\cos \phi \quad = \frac{1 + r}{2\sqrt{1 - r + r^2}}$$

For an angle of lag or lead of 60°, one of the wattmeters will read zero.

For angles in excess of these values, the respective wattmeters will read backwards or negatively. It is thus possible for r to range from -1 through zero to $+1$, corresponding to power factors of 0, 0·5, and unity respectively, lagging and leading.

EXAMPLES 41

1. A 10 h.p., 500-volt, 3-phase star-connected induction motor, running at full load, has an efficiency of 0·8 and a power factor of 0·75. Find the current in each phase at an instant when the voltage across two of the terminals is 300 volts.
(*Lond. Univ.*, 1938, *El. Tech.*)

2. In using two wattmeters to measure 3-phase power, what are the possible power factors when one wattmeter reads one half as much as the other? Give vector diagrams illustrating all four possible cases.

3. Explain, with connection and vector diagrams, how the power input and power factor of a 3-phase induction motor can be measured. A 440-volt 3-phase motor has an output of 80 b.h.p., an efficiency of 90 per cent, and a power factor of 0·87. Find the line current and the readings on each of the two wattmeters connected to measure the input. Express the power factor in terms of the wattmeter readings.
(*C. & G., Final*, 1933.)

4. In a test on an induction motor running light on

3-phase mains, it was found that the two wattmeters read respectively 2·5 and 2 kW., but on slowly applying a load, the reading on the second wattmeter decreased. Explain this phenomenon, and find the power factor of the motor when thus running light.

5. In a test to determine the phase sequence of a 415-volt, 50-cycle, 3-phase supply, a non-inductive resistance of 430 ohms was connected in series with a 5μF. condenser between two of the line terminals A and B. The voltage between the junction of the resistance and the condenser and the third line terminal C was found to be 182 volts. Draw the vector diagram and determine the phase sequence. If the phase sequence is reversed what will be the new reading on the voltmeter? (*Lond. Univ.*, 1937, *El. Power.*)

6. A 3-phase mesh connected motor operating on a 3300-volt circuit is coupled to a pump raising 3000 gallons of water per minute against a head of 2000 feet. The motor has a power factor of 0·85 and an efficiency of 92 per cent. The pump efficiency is 75 per cent. Calculate the line current and the phase current of the motor. (*I.E.E.*, *May*, 1937.)

7. The axes of three identical coils are in the same plane, are 120 degrees apart, and meet in a point. The inductance of each coil separately is 0·5 henry and its resistance is 200 ohms, and the mutual inductance between each pair of coils is 0·2 henry. What current will flow in each coil if the three are connected in star to a 3-phase 50-cycle supply of 440 volts? (*Lond. Univ.*, 1933, *El. Tech.*)

8. Three non-inductive resistances, each of 100 ohms, are connected in star to a 3-phase 440-volt supply. Three equal choking coils are also connected in delta to the same supply, the reactance of one coil being equal to 100 ohms. Calculate (*a*) the line current, and (*b*) the power factor of the system. (*I.E.E.*, *Nov.*, 1934.)

*9. An electrically-driven boiler-feed pump delivers 300,000 lb. of water per hour at a pressure of 500 lb. per sq. in. Calculate the current input to the 3000-volt, 3-phase driving motor assuming the efficiencies of pump and motor to be 85 per cent and 93 per cent respectively, the power-factor 0·93, and the weight of 1 cub. ft. of hot water 59 lb. (*Lond. Univ.*, 1947, *El. Power.*)

42. Unbalanced Three-Phase Loads

References. D3; G2.

Symmetrical Components.

The operator a rotates a vector through 120° counter-clockwise. In "j" notation,

$$a = -0.5 + j0.866$$
$$a^2 = -0.5 - j0.866$$

and $\qquad a^3 = 1$ and $1 + a + a^2 = 0$.

In positive phase sequence,

$$E_{a1} = E_{a1}; \; E_{b1} = a^2 E_{a1}; \; E_{c1} = aE_{a1}.$$

In negative phase sequence

$$E_{a2} = E_{a2}; \; E_{b2} = aE_{a2}; \; E_{c2} = a^2 E_{a2}.$$

In zero phase sequence

$$E_{a0} = E_{b0} = E_{c0}.$$

In any 3-phase system,

$$E_a = E_{a0} + E_{a1} + E_{a2}$$
$$E_b = E_{b0} + E_{b1} + E_{b2} = E_{a0} + a^2 E_{a1} + aE_{a2}$$
$$E_c = E_{c0} + E_{c1} + E_{c2} = E_{a0} + aE_{a1} + a^2 E_{a2}.$$

Positive sequence components,

$$E_{a1} = E_{b1} = E_{c1} = \tfrac{1}{3}(E_a + aE_b + a^2 E_c).$$

Negative sequence components,

$$E_{a2} = E_{b2} = E_{c2} = \tfrac{1}{3}(E_a + a^2 E_b + aE_c).$$

Zero sequence components,

$$E_{a0} = E_{b0} = E_{c0} = \tfrac{1}{3}(E_a + E_b + E_c).$$

In the above, E can be replaced by I or Z. If a 3-phase system is unbalanced, but of resultant zero, e.g. the currents in a 3-line supply, or the voltages in a delta connection, then the zero sequence components are zero.

EXAMPLES 42

1. What are the advantages of the 3-phase, 4-conductor system for a distribution network?

In such a system there is a balanced 3-phase motor load taking 200 kilowatts at a power factor of 0·8 lagging, while lamps connected between phase conductors and the neutral take 50, 70, and 100 kilowatts respectively. The voltage between phase conductors is 430 volts. Calculate the current in each phase conductor and in the neutral wire of the feeder supplying these loads.   (*Lond. Univ.* 1928, *El. Power.*)

2. What are the advantages of the 3-phase, 4-wire system of distribution? Compare the weight of copper required for the distributor cables in such a system with that required in a 3-wire D.C. system. State exactly the basis of comparison. A 440/254-volt, 3-phase, 4-core cable supplies an unbalanced load represented by the following impedances in ohms connected between the R, Y, and B phases respectively and the neutral: $16 + j12$, $14 - j21$ and 25. The phase sequence is RYB. Calculate the current in each conductor of the cable and the readings on each of three wattmeters connected in each line to neutral.   (*C. & G.*, 1938.)

3. A 3-phase supply with the neutral point earthed and with a constant p.d. of 430 volts between lines, supplies the following unbalanced loads connected in delta: 65 kVA. power factor 0·7 leading between lines 1 and 2, 100 kVA. power factor unity between lines 2 and 3, and 75 kVA. power factor 0·6 lagging between lines 3 and 1. Give a graphical representation of the line and phase voltages and currents, and find, graphically or otherwise, the current in each line conductor of the supply system.   (*C. & G.*, *Final*, 1929.)

4. A resistance of 50 ohms, a choke coil of reactance 50 ohms, and a condenser of reactance 50 ohms are connected in star and connected to a 3-phase supply at 100 volts between lines. Find the voltage across each unit of the load.

5. Three equal star-connected air-core inductive resistances together take 8·0 kilowatts at a power factor of 0·8 when connected to a 460-volt, 3-phase, 3-wire, 50-cycle supply. Find the line currents if one of the inductive resistances is completely short-circuited.   (*Lond. Univ.*, 1931, *El. Tech.*)

6. A building is supplied by a 3-phase 4-wire service main, the resistance of each line wire being 0·25 ohm, and of the neutral 0·5 ohm. The main is fed with 3-phase voltages at a line voltage of 420. Determine (*a*) the current in the neutral wire, and (*b*) the voltage, phase I to neutral, at the building end of the main, when the power *input* to the main comprises: 5kVA. at 0·866 power factor lagging for phase I, 5kVA. at 0·866 power factor leading for phase II, and 5kVA. at 1·0 power factor for phase III. (*Lond. Univ.*, 1933, *El. Power.*)

7. A factory is fed by a 3-phase 4-wire service main with

a balanced 3-phase line voltage of 400. The resistance of the neutral of the service main is 0·4 ohm, and of each line wire 0·15 ohm. The load includes one 12·5 h.p. motor of 0·8 power factor, lagging, and 85 per cent efficiency, across the outers, and lighting loads of 20 amperes, 15 amperes, and 5 amperes respectively between lines 1, 2, 3 and neutral. Determine the voltage of phase 3 to neutral at the sending end of the main.

(*Lond. Univ.*, 1934, *El. Power.*)

8. A 4-wire, 3-phase distributor is fed with a balanced 3-phase voltage system of 420 volts between lines. The loads, at the sending end, are: Phase I, 40 amperes at 0·8 power factor, lagging; Phase II, 30 amperes at unity power factor; Phase III, 20 amperes at 0·87 power factor, leading. The resistance of each outer is 0·2 ohm, and of the neutral 0·4 ohm. Determine (*a*) the voltage phase I to neutral, at the receiving end; and (*b*) the voltage between lines I and III at the receiving end. (*Lond. Univ.*, 1935, *El. Power.*)

9. Three loads are mesh connected to a symmetrical 3-phase 440-volt system. Load A takes 20 kW. at unity power factor, load B takes 30 kVA. at power factor 0·8 lagging, and load C takes 20 kVA. at power factor 0·6 leading. Calculate the three line currents and the readings of two wattmeters connected to measure the input, the current coils being connected respectively in the line going to the junction of A and C and in the line going to the junction of B and C. The phase sequence is A, B, C. (*C. & G.*, *Final*, 1934.)

10. Give a diagram of the connections of a balancing transformer for supplying a 3-phase, 4-wire network from 3-phase, 3-wire lines. A 440-volt, 3-phase, 4-wire cable supplies a motor load taking 500 kW. at a power-factor of 0·71 and lighting loads connected between the phase conductors and the neutral of 100 kW., 120 kW., and 250 kW. respectively. Find the power-factor of the system and the current in each of the four conductors. (*C. & G.*, *Final*, 1935.)

11. In Ques. 3 above, find the symmetrical components of the phase currents in the mesh, taking V_{12} as axis of reference.

43. Alternator Voltage Calculations

References. B1; C2, 4, 5, 6; D3; M1; S4; W2.

Always work to phase values, and find terminal volts afterwards.

E.M.F. $= 4k_1k_2k_3 \Phi Sf \times 10^{-8}$, or $2Z$ instead of $4S$,

where $k_1 =$ the field form factor, i.e. 1·11 for sinusoidal distribution of the flux Φ,

$k_2 =$ the *breadth* or *distribution* factor $= \dfrac{\operatorname{Sin} m\beta/2}{m \operatorname{Sin} \beta/2}$,

where β is the angle in electrical degrees between adjacent slots and $m =$ number of slots over which the coil side is spread,

$k_3 =$ the *coil-span* factor $= \cos(\alpha/2)$, where α is the electrical angle by which the coil span differs from the pole pitch,

$\Phi =$ the flux per pole,

$S =$ the number of turns in series (per phase),

$Z =$ the number of conductors in series (per phase),

$\quad =$ the frequency $= np$, where $n =$ the r.p.sec.

$\qquad\qquad\qquad p =$ the pairs of poles.

EXAMPLES 43

1. A 3-phase, 8-pole alternator has a star-connected winding with 120 slots and 8 conductors per slot. The flux per pole is 5 megalines, sinusoidally distributed. Find the phase and line voltages when the frequency is 50 cycles per sec. Prove any formula used. (*Lond. Univ.*, 1932, *El. Tech.*)

2. The field system of a 50-cycle alternator has sinusoidal flux per pole of 10^7 lines. Calculate the E.M.F. generated in one turn which spans $\frac{2}{3}$ of a pole pitch.

(*Lond. Univ.*, 1937, *A.E.*)

3. Discuss—with the aid of diagrams—the nature of armature reaction in single-phase generators. Deduce an expression for the E.M.F. generated in a full-pitched armature coil of a 2-pole machine, if the useful flux is $\Phi \cos \omega t$ and the speed of rotation is n r.p.sec. The flux distribution is sinusoidal. (*Lond. Univ.*, 1939, *El. Mach.*)

4. Define, and obtain an expression for, the " coil-span factor " of a fractional-pitch winding for an alternator. Show

how a fractional-pitch winding can be employed to suppress a given harmonic in the " phase electromotive force." The resultant air-gap flux of a 16-pole, 3-phase alternator is 6×10^6 lines per pole and is distributed sinusoidally over the pole. The stator has 2 slots per pole per phase, and 4 conductors per slot accommodated in two layers. The coil span is 150 electrical degrees. Calculate the electromotive force generated in each phase when the machine runs at 375 r.p.m.

(*Lond. Univ.*, 1923, *El. Mach.*)

5. Why may an alternator winding be chorded? Find the no load terminal E.M.F. of a 4-pole A.C. generator from the following data: Flux per pole (sinusoidally distributed) 12·0 megamaxwells; slots per pole per phase, 4; conductors per slot, 4; two-layer winding; coil span, 150°; connection, star.

(*I.E.E.*, *Nov.*, 1938.)

*6. A 4-pole machine has an armature with 60 slots and 10 conductors per slot and revolves at 1500 r.p.m., the flux per pole being 5×10^6 lines. Calculate the E.M.F. generated (*a*) as a D.C. machine if the winding is lap connected, and (*b*) as a 3-phase, star-connected machine if the winding factor is 0·96 and all the conductors in each phase are in series. Deduce the expression used in each case.

(*Lond. Univ.*, 1946, *A.E.*)

7. Explain carefully how the line voltage of a 3-phase alternator is affected by a third harmonic in the phase voltage when the machine is (i) star connected; (ii) delta connected. A 3-phase alternator is connected in star, one phase being inadvertently reversed. If each phase gives 230 volts, determine the line voltages in magnitude and phase.

(*Lond. Univ.*, 1935, *El. Tech.*)

*8. Derive an expression for the voltage induced in an alternator winding consisting of a number of similar full-pitch coils joined in series, the air-gap flux having sine distribution. Calculate the induced voltage of a 6-pole, single-phase alternator running at 1200 r.p.m. The machine has 108 slots of which two-thirds are wound with full-pitch coils of 20 turns each; the flux per pole is 5 megalines. (*C. & G.*, *Final*, 1945.)

44. Cooling of Alternators, Transformers, etc.

References. B1; C5, 6; K1; R2; S1, 4; W2.

Data Required.

Specific heat of air at constant pressure $= 0\cdot2375$ (calories per grm.).

Volume of 1 kg. of dry air at $0°$ C. and normal atmospheric pressure $= 0\cdot775$ cub. m. (or $1\cdot29$ kg. per m.³).

Volume of air changes with *temperature* in the proportion of the absolute temperatures, i.e. $273 + °$C. Thus, 1 cub. m. at $15°$ C. would at $35°$ C. become

$$1 \times \frac{273 + 35}{273 + 15} = \frac{308}{288} = 1\cdot07 \text{ cub. m.}$$

(*Increased* temperature gives *increased* volume.)

Volume changes with *pressure* on the basis that pressure × volume is constant for constant temperature. Thus 1 cub. m. at the normal pressure of 760 mm. becomes at 765 mm. of pressure

$$1 \times \frac{760}{765} = 0\cdot994 \text{ cub. m.}$$

(*Increased* pressure gives *reduced* volume.)

Combined changes of temperature and pressure: 1 cub. m. at $20°$ C. and 760 mm. would become, at $40°$ C. and 770 mm.,

$$1 \times \frac{273 + 40}{273 + 20} \times \frac{760}{770} = 1\cdot055 \text{ cub. m.}$$

Weight of water—

1 cub. ft. $= 62\cdot35$ lb. $= 1000$ oz.

1 gallon $= 10$ lb.

Joule's equivalent—

1 calorie (grm. -° C.) $= 4\cdot2$ joules.

When circulating air against a definite head, the work done is given in ft.-lbs. per minute, with sufficient accuracy by the product of the head in lbs. per sq. ft., and the volume of air circulated in cubic ft. per minute. Take the height of the water barometer as 34 ft. or 1 cubic ft. of water = 1000 oz.

EXAMPLES 44

1. Describe in detail how the efficiency of an alternator in a central station can be determined by measurements made on the cooling air. Mention all the precautions that must be taken. Find the amount of cooling air in cubic metres per second at the inlet temperature of 15° C., for a 10,000 kW. alternator on full-load, if the efficiency be 96 per cent and the temperature rise of the cooling air 35° C.

(C. & G., Final, 1930.)

2. Determine the efficiency of a 6000-kVA. alternator from the following test figures taken at unity power factor and full load: Volume of cooling air at outlet, 12 m.³ per sec.; outlet temperature, 40° C.; inlet temperature, 15° C.; barometer pressure, 750 mm. (Air data as above.)

(C. & G., 1940.)

3. A 25,000 kVA. alternator has a full-load efficiency of 96 per cent. If the inlet and outlet cooling air temperatures are to be 25° C. and 50° C. respectively, find the volume of air required per second. *(C. & G., Final, 1933.)*

4. Find the amount of cooling water in litres per minute required by a 5000-kW. transformer having an efficiency of 98·8 per cent, when the water has to carry off 80 per cent of the heat.

Take the temperature of the water at inlet .   .   .   15° C.
And the temperature of the water at outlet.   .   .   35° C.

(I.E.E., Oct., 1922.)

5. Describe the closed-circuit, air-cooling system used for turbo-alternators. Calculate the volume of cooling air in cubic metres per second required for a 20,000-kVA. turbo-alternator running at full-load, 0·8 power factor, with an efficiency of 96 per cent. The inlet and outlet air temperatures are to be 15 and 35° C. respectively. Calculate also the amount of cooling water in gallons per minute to cool the air, assuming the temperature rise of the water to be 8° C.

(Lond. Univ., 1932, El. Mach.)

6. Give an account of modern methods of air cooling a large turbo-alternator. How is the volume of air circulated measured? Calculate the volume required to cool a 10,000-kVA. machine running on full-load at 0·8 power factor with an efficiency of 96·5 per cent, with an air temperature rise of 25° C. from 25°. Find also the horse-power absorbed in circulating the air against a head of 6 in. of water.

(*Lond. Univ.*, 1924, *El. Power.*)

7. A 15,000 kVA. alternator has a full-load efficiency of 0·96, and the cooling air was found to be entering at a temperature of 22° C., and 760-mm. pressure, and issuing at 40° C. Calculate the volume of the inlet air that must have been circulating through the machine. Had the inlet air been reduced to 20° C. and the pressure raised to 765 mm., what change in the volume of inlet air would be occasioned, the outlet temperature remaining unchanged?

8. A ventilating fan supplies 700,000 cub. ft. per minute of air against a pressure of 8 in. of water. The efficiency of the fan is 0·9 and of the electric motor driving it 0·92 ; find the power required. Discuss the type of motor best suited for this purpose, the supply being 3-phase at 500 volts, with direct current available.   (*Lond. Univ.*, 1927, *El. Power.*)

45. Alternators—General

EXAMPLES 45

1. Describe the connections usually employed in a generating station for the purpose of synchronizing any one of the machines with the busbars, and describe the whole operation of synchronizing a turbo-alternator, starting from rest. After connecting the machine to the bars, how will you get it to take over its share of the load, and adjust the power factor of the machine to any desired value ?

2. Describe an automatic regulator for maintaining constant voltage on the busbars of a generating station to which are connected a number of alternators. Why are such regulators rendered necessary ?

3. A simple bipolar single-phase alternator, giving a sine wave of E.M.F., has one coil of 20 turns upon its armature. It feeds an air-cored choking coil having 500 turns of negligible resistance. Show that there must be an exact relation at every instant between the flux linked with the armature coil and that linked with the choking coil. Say what this relation is. Sketch the combination, indicating the position of the armature coil with respect to the field and the direction of each flux and current when the choking coil flux is a maximum. Neglect hysteresis.   (*I.E.E.*, *May*, 1935.)

4. Explain how the speed of a turbo-generator is governed, and what is meant by inherent regulation of an alternator. What happens to the alternator voltage if full-load is tripped off a generator ? How much of the resulting effect is explainable because the governor is not perfectly isochronous ? What apparatus is commonly fitted to control this effect, and how does it act ?   (*I.E.E.*, *April*, 1921.)

46. Alternators in Parallel

References. *Journal, I.E.E.*, Vol. 47. Paper by Barr (page 276). *Journal, I.E.E.*, Vol. 50. Paper by Everest (page 520). *A.C. Machinery*, by Silvanus P. Thompson. B1; C2, 4; D3; M2; S5.

Synchronizing Torque.

Synchronizing watts $W_s = \dfrac{mE_p{}^2\alpha}{\omega L}$ or $mE_p I_o \alpha$

Synchronizing torque

$$= \frac{mE_p{}^2\alpha}{\omega L.2\pi N} \times \frac{33000}{746} \text{ lb.-ft.}$$

where m = number of phases, N = r.p.m.,

E_p = phase volts,

α = electrical angle of displacement in radians,

ωL = reactance of machines per phase when only two are in parallel. When running on a large system, the reactance of the one machine under consideration alone is taken.

Periodic Time of Swing of an Alternator.

$$T = kN \sqrt{\frac{K}{kVA(I_o/I)f}}$$

where K = moment of inertia of the whole moving system,

I_o/I = short-circuit current/full load current,

f = frequency,

and k = 0·0017 if K is expressed in lb./ft.^{2}

$= 0·0083$ if K is expressed in kgm./m.^{2}

Sharing of Loads in Parallel.

If two alternators run in parallel to feed a common load on bus-bars of voltage V, or two transformers, connected on the primary side to a common supply, feed in parallel a common load on bus-bars of voltage V, then, if

E_1 and E_2 = E.M.F.'s generated in each, on open circuit,

Z_1 and Z_2 = synchronous or leakage impedances of each,

I_1 and I_2 = currents supplied by each,

V = common load voltage,

I = total load current = $I_1 + I_2$,

Z = load impedance,

I_s = synchronizing or circulating current; then

$$I_1D = E_1Z_2 + (E_1 - E_2)Z$$
$$I_2D = E_2Z_1 - (E_1 - E_2)Z$$
$$ID = E_1Z_2 + E_2Z_1$$
$$I_sD = (E_1 - E_2)Z$$
$$VD = ZID = (E_1Z_2 + E_2Z_1)Z$$

where $\quad D = Z_1Z_2 + (Z_1 + Z_2)Z$

all the above vectors being in symbolic form.

The total loads on the machines (including losses) are given by the dot products of E_1I_1 and E_2I_2, while the portions of the external load supplied by each are the dot products of VI_1 and VI_2. See also solution to Ques. 11.

(*Note.* The "dot" product of $(a + jb)(c + jd)$
$$= ac + bd.)$$

EXAMPLES 46

1. What is meant by the synchronizing power of an alternator armature when running in parallel with others ? Calculate the synchronizing torque per unit mechanical angle of phase displacement for a 5000-kVA. alternator running at 1500 r.p.m. when connected to 6600-volt, 50-frequency busbars. The armature has a short-circuit reactance of 15 per cent.
(*C. & G., Final,* 1925.)

2. Calculate the synchronizing torque for one mechanical degree of phase displacement in a 6000 kVA. 50-cycle alternator when running at 1500 r.p.m. with a generated E.M.F. of 10,000 volts. The machine has a synchronous impedance of 25 per cent. (*C. & G., Final,* 1934.)

3. Prove that the maximum load (before dropping out of step) that an alternator can supply, when connected to constant voltage and frequency busbars, depends on the value of the

excitation.   A 6600-volt, 10,000-kVA., 3-phase alternator has a steady short-circuit current equal to five times its normal rated value.   Calculate the maximum load the machine can deliver when connected up to 6600-volt, constant-voltage busbars, with its field excited to give an open-circuit voltage of 7000 volts.   Find also the armature current and power factor corresponding to this load.   (*Lond. Univ.*, 1931.)

4.   Two 3-phase star-connected 50-cycle alternators of equal capacity are paralleled with a phase displacement of 2 degrees (electrical), the terminal voltage being 6600, and there being no external load.   Calculate approximately the synchronizing current if the synchronous reactance of each machine is 8·5 ohms.   (Resistance negligible.)   (*I.E.E.*, *May*, 1935.)

5.   Two 3-phase synchronous mechanically-coupled generators operate in parallel on the same load.   Determine the kW. output and power factor of each machine under the following conditions :   Synchronous impedance of each generator, $0·2 + j2$ ohms per phase.   Equivalent impedance of the load, $3 + j4$ ohms per phase.   Induced E.M.F. per phase, $2000 + j0$ volts for machine I and $2200 + j100$ for II.   (*L.U.*, 1940.)

6.   Explain the action of the induction generator and the advantages and disadvantages of the use of this type of machine.   An induction generator requiring a reactive excitation of 1000 kVA. is intended to be used in parallel with a synchronous turbo-alternator rated at 5000 kW. at 0·71 power factor.   If the original load supplied by the latter was 5,000 kW. at 0·87 power factor, find the additional load at 0·87 power factor that can be supplied by the two machines in parallel without overloading the synchronous machine.
        (*C. & G.*, *Final*, 1932.)

7.   Two similar 6600-volt, 3-phase generators are running in parallel on constant voltage and frequency bus-bars.   Each has an equivalent resistance and reactance of 0·05 ohm and 0·5 ohm respectively and supplies one-half of a total load of 10,000 kW. at a lagging power-factor of 0·8, the two machines being similarly excited.   If the excitation of one machine be adjusted until the armature current is 438 amperes, and the steam supply to the turbine remain unchanged, find the armature current, the E.M.F. and the power-factor of the other alternator.   Give a vector diagram in illustration.   (*C. & G.*, '35.)

8.   A turbo-alternator having a reactance of 10 ohms has an armature current of 220 amperes at unity power factor when running on 11,000 volt constant frequency busbars.   If the steam admission be unchanged and the E.M.F. raised by

25 per cent determine graphically or otherwise the new value of the machine current and power factor. If this higher value of the excitation were kept constant and the steam supply gradually increased, at what power output would the alternator break from synchronism? Find also the current and power factor to which this maximum load corresponds. State whether this power factor is lagging or leading.   (*C. & G.*, 1937.)

9. A 3-phase, star-connected alternator connected to 6600-volt busbars has a synchronous impedance of 10 ohms and a resistance of 2 ohms per phase. The excitation is such that on open circuit the E.M.F. would be 6000 volts. Determine the maximum load the machine can supply to the external circuit before dropping out of synchronism and the corresponding armature current and p.f. Criticize all assumptions made. State clearly what happens if the machine is left connected to the busbars after dropping out of synchronism.
     (*Lond. Univ.*, 1937, *El. Mach.*)

10. A single-phase alternator connected to 6600 volt busbars has a synchronous impedance of 10 ohms and a resistance of 1 ohm. If its excitation is such that on open circuit the p.d. would be 5000 volts, calculate the maximum load the machine can supply to the external circuit before dropping out of step and the corresponding armature current and power factor.
     (*Lond. Univ.*, 1926, *El. Power*.)

11. Calculate the rotational inertia in lb.–ft.^{2} units of the moving system of a 10,000-kVA., 6600-volt, 4-pole turbo-alternator driven at 1500 r.p.m. for the set to have a natural period of 1 second when running in parallel with a large number of other machines. The steady short-circuit current of the alternator is five times the normal full-load value.
     (*C. & G.*, 1940.)

*12. Determine the terminal voltage and the kW. output of two alternators in parallel if $E_1 = 100$, $E_2 = 110$ volts, $Z = 3 + j4$, and $Z_1 = Z_2 = 0.2 + j1$ ohms.   (*L. U.*, 1945.)

13. Show that an alternator running in parallel on constant voltage and frequency busbars has a natural time period of oscillation. Deduce a formula for the time of one complete oscillation and calculate its value for a 5000 kilo-volt-ampere, three-phase 10,000-volt machine running at 1500 revolutions per minute on constant 50-frequency bus-bars.

The moment of inertia of the whole moving system is 150 ton-feet^2 units and the steady short-circuit current of the alternator five times the normal full-load value.
     (*Lond. Univ.*, 1929, *El. Power*.)

47. Alternators—Tests and Regulation

References. B1; C2, 4, 5, 6; D3; K2; M1; S1, 3; W2.

The Rothert Ampere-turn Method is illustrated by the solution given to Ques. No. 5. In this method it is assumed that the whole of the excitation used on short-circuit is demagnetizing effect. Given the internal resistance and

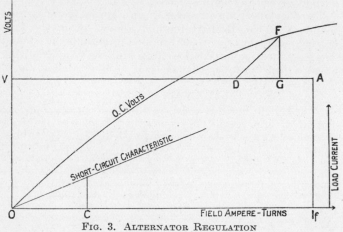

FIG. 3. ALTERNATOR REGULATION

reactance, it is possible to find the internal drops on short-circuit and find from the O.C. volts curve the excitation required to generate this drop, and subtract this excitation from the total employed to obtain the true demagnetizing excitation.

Potier's Method deduces the reactance and demagnetizing effects from a load test at low power factor, in which terminal volts, load current, excitation, and power factor are read. The method is illustrated in Fig. 3. On the O.C. volts curve mark the point A corresponding to the terminal volts and excitation in the above test. Find the wattless current in the above load test, and from the short-circuit characteristic determine the field ampere-turns O.C. corresponding to this wattless load, and set off AD horizontally to represent this excitation. Through D draw DF parallel to the O.C. volts curve at the origin to cut the O.C. volts curve in F, and drop the perpendicular FG. Then AG is the demagnetizing ampere-turns produced by the wattless component of the test load, and AG divided by this current gives the demagnetizing constant K_d. Similarly FG is the reactance drop, and this divided by the same wattless current gives the reactance constant ωL.

The regulation for any load at any power factor is then found as in the Rothert method above. From the load current and the above determined constants are found the reactance (or impedance) drop and the demagnetizing ampere-turns for use in that method, as illustrated in Fig. 5. (See Answers.)

EXAMPLES 47

1. A straight-line law connects terminal voltage and load current of a 3-phase, star-connected alternator delivering current at 0·8 power factor lagging. At no-load the terminal voltage is 3500 and at full load of 2280 kW. it is 3300. Calculate the terminal voltage when delivering current to a balanced star-connected load having a resistance of 8 ohms and a reactance of 6 ohms per phase. Assume constant speed and field excitation. *(Lond. Univ., 1939, A.E.)*

2. The open-circuit characteristic of a 3-phase, 50-cycle synchronous machine is given by—

| Exciting current, amperes . | 20 | 40 | 60 | 84 | 105 | 133 |
| Terminal E.M.F., volts . | 850 | 1700 | 2460 | 3000 | 3300 | 3600 |

Determine the excitation necessary for full-load operation at 0·9 power factor, leading, on a 3000-volt supply. When short-circuited and driven at normal speed an excitation of 50 amperes gives normal full-load stator current. The resistance drop is 2 per cent and the leakage reactance drop 15 per cent. *(Lond. Univ., 1939, El. Mach.)*

3. Deduce the exciting current for a 3-phase 3300-volt generator when supplying 1000 kW. at 0·8 power factor, lagging, given magnetization curve, on open circuit—

| Line voltage . . . . | 3300 | 3600 | 3900 |
| Exciting current (amps.) . | 80 | 96 | 118 |

There are 16 poles; 144 slots; 5 conductors per slot; single circuit full-pitched winding, star-connected. The stator winding has a resistance per phase of 0·15 ohm and a leakage reactance of 1·2 ohm. The field coils have each 108 turns.

(*Lond. Univ.*, 1936, *El. Mach.*)

4. The following data relate to a 6600-volt, 10,000-kVA. 50-cycle, 3-phase turbo-alternator—

Voltage on open circuit	4,250	5,450	6,600	7,300	8,000	9,000
Exciting ampere-turns	60,000	80,000	100,000	120,000	145,000	220,000

Excitation needed to circulate full-load current on short-circuit: 117,000 ampere-turns. Inductive drop in stator winding at full load: 15 per cent. Find the voltage regulation at full load 0·8 power factor. Explain any assumptions made in the method employed. (*C. & G.*, *Final*, 1936.)

5. A 600-kVA., 3300-volt, 8-pole, 3-phase, 50-cycle alternator has the following characteristics—

Ampere-turns per pole			4000	5000	7000	10,000
Terminal E.M.F.			2850	3400	3850	4400

There are 200 conductors in series per phase.

Find the short-circuit characteristic, the field ampere-turns for full-load 0·8 power factor (lagging), and the voltage regulation, having given that the inductive drop at full-load is 7 per cent and that the equivalent armature reaction in ampere-turns per pole = 1·06 × ampere-conductors per phase per pole. (*Lond. Univ.*, 1923, *El. Mach.*)

6. During a full-load test on a 3-phase alternator driven by a water turbine the following measurements are made: Head of water registered on pressure gauge, 277 ft. Height of pressure gauge above nozzle, 5 ft. Quantity of water, 629 cub. ft. per sec. The output is measured electrically by the 2-wattmeter method, and the following readings are taken: Voltmeter 1, 110 volts. Voltmeter 2, 110 volts. Ammeter 1, 3·97 amps. Ammeter 2, 3·97 amps. Wattmeter 1, 438 watts. Wattmeter 2, 191 watts. The ratio of the potential transformer is 11,000/110 volts, and that of the current transformer is 1000/5 amp. Determine the overall efficiency of the turbo-alternator, and the power factor of the load.

(*I.E.E.*, *Nov.*, 1932.)

7. Estimate the percentage regulation at full load and

power factor 0·8 lagging of a 1000-kVA., 6600-volt, 3-phase, 50-cycle, star-connected salient-pole synchronous generator. The open-circuit characteristic is as follows—

Terminal voltage . .	4000	6000	6600	7200	8000
Field amp.-turns . .	5200	8500	10,000	12,500	17,500

Leakage reactance, 10 per cent; resistance, 2 per cent. Short-circuit characteristics: full-load current with a field excitation of 5000 amp.-turns. Take the permeance to cross armature reaction as 35 per cent of that to direct reaction. (Refs. C5, p. 213, and S1, p. 392.) (*I.E.E.*, *Nov.*, 1936.)

8. The following test results were obtained on a 275-kW., 3-phase, 6600-volt, non-salient-pole type alternator.

Open-circuit characteristic—

Volts . . .	5600	6600	7240	8100
Exciting amperes .	46·5	58	67·5	96

Short-circuit characteristic: stator current 35 amperes with an exciting current of 50 amperes. Leakage reactance on full load: 8 per cent. Neglect armature resistance. Calculate as accurately as possible the exciting current (for full load) at power factor 0·8 lagging and at unity. (*C. & G.*, 1935.)

9. The following figures give the open-circuit and full-load zero power factor saturation curves for a 15,000-kVA., 11,000-volt 3-phase, 50-cycle, star-connected turbo-alternator—

Field ampere-turns in 10^3 . .	10	18	24	30	40	45	50
O.C. line kV. . .	4·9	8·4	10·1	11·5	12·8	13·3	13·65
Zero p.f. full-load, line kV. . .	—	0	—	—	—	10·2	—

Find the armature reaction, the armature reactance, and the synchronous reactance. Deduce the regulation for full load at 0·8 power factor lagging. (*I.E.E.*, *May*, 1936.)

48. Alternator Design—General

References. A2; B1; C5, 6; S1, 4, 5; W2.

EXAMPLES 48

1. It is proposed to manufacture a line of alternators from about 250 kVA. at 500 r.p.m. to about 1000 kVA. at 200 r.p.m. Draw up a schedule showing the number of standard frames you would adopt, giving outside diameters of stampings, bores, and core lengths, together with the maximum and minimum number of poles covered by the various standard frames.

(I.E.E., April, 1923.)

2. Describe and sketch methods of construction of large 2-pole turbo-alternator rotors. Point out the most highly-stressed parts. Describe the process of balancing and explain what is meant by the critical speed. *(I.E.E., May, 1935.)*

3. What is meant by the *distribution factor* of an alternator winding? Neglecting friction and iron losses, the torque of a 3-phase alternator on balanced load may be put in the form: $T = ANIP\Phi \cos \phi$ where N = the stator turns in series per phase, I = stator R.M.S. current per phase, P = pairs of poles, Φ = flux per pole in volt-seconds, $\cos \phi$ = power factor upon which the machine is working, and A is a constant. Prove this statement and derive the value of A if T is to be in lb.-ft.

(I.E.E., May, 1935.)

4. Discuss the differences in the regulating properties and short-circuit characteristics of salient and non-salient pole alternators. What features in the design of these machines are mainly responsible for the differences ?

(I.E.E., April, 1924.)

5. Outline the design of the field magnet of a 3-phase turbo-alternator. Show the effect of the design of the air-gap and slots upon the behaviour of the machine on sudden large variations in the load. What are the outstanding features in the design of the field magnet circuit of a machine with a low first cost ? *(I.E.E., Oct., 1925.)*

49. Alternator Design—Harmonics

References. A2; C5; S1, 3; W2.

EXAMPLES 49

*1. Neglecting the slot ripple, the flux distribution curve of a 16-pole, 50 cycles per second, three-phase alternator is given by—

Distance from neutral axis, cm. . . .	0	3	6	9	12	15	18
Flux density in air-gap, kilo-gauss	9	8·9	8·7	8·2	4	0·4	0

The pole-pitch is 36 cm. and the effective core length 30 cm. There are 12 slots per pole, with 4 conductors in each forming a single-circuit, full-pitched, star-connected winding. Determine and plot to scale the wave shape of the E.M.F. between terminals.   (*Lond. Univ.*, 1945, *El. Mach.*)

2. Explain what is meant by a harmonic in alternating current working. Three coils, each having a resistance of 100 ohms and an inductance of 0·5 henry, are connected in delta across the terminals of a 4-pole alternator running at 1500 r.p.m. The machine is star-connected and has a phase voltage represented by $v = 1000 \sin \omega t + 200 \sin 3\omega t + 100 \sin 5\omega t$. Calculate the power factor of the load.

(*C. & G., Final*, 1934.)

3. Determine and plot the wave shape of (*a*) the phase E.M.F., and (*b*) the terminal E.M.F. for a 3-phase star-connected alternator having a pole-pitch of 36 cm., 9 slots per pole and a normal full-pitch winding. The flux distribution curve is given by—

Distance from neutral axis, cm. . .	0	4	8	12	16	18
Flux density, gauss .	0	1500	8000	8700	8900	8950

(*Lond. Univ.*, 1935, *El. Mach.*)

4. Discuss the steps that are taken in the design of salient-pole alternators to ensure a good wave-form for the E.M.F. How may tooth ripples be minimized? Explain the advantages of using the two-layer type of winding for A.C. generators.

(*Lond. Univ.*, 1940, *El. Mach.*

*5. Show that the wave-form of the E.M.F. induced in a full-pitch coil on the stator of an alternator will be identical with the air-gap flux distribution curve. A 4-pole alternator having a stator bore of 50 cm. and a core length of 35 cm. is wound with single-turn full-pitch coils. The R.M.S. value of the E.M.F. induced in each coil is 18 volts when the speed is 1500 r.p.m., and the E.M.F. is constant over the middle two-thirds of each half-cycle and varies uniformly over the remainder. Calculate the maximum flux density in the air-gap and the total flux per pole. (*Lond. Univ.*, 1945, *Ap. Elect.*)

*6. The flux-distribution curve of a smooth core three-phase, 50 cycles per second generator is $B = 10 \sin \theta + 2 \sin 3\theta + 2 \sin 5\theta + 2 \sin 7\theta$ kilogauss, when θ is measured from the neutral axis. The pole pitch is 35 cm., the active core length 32 cm., and the stator coil-span four-fifths of the pole pitch. Determine the instantaneous and R.M.S. values of the E.M.F. induced in each turn of the winding, explaining the principles involved. (*Lond. Univ.*, 1943, *El. Mach.*)

*7. The rotor of a 3-phase alternator has 16 poles and runs at 375 r.p.m. The flux distribution in the air-gap is symmetrical about the centre line of the pole, the values over half a pole pitch being as follows—

Angle, elect.°	0	15	30	45	60	75	90
B, lines/cm.²	0	2250	5850	7900	8800	9000	9000

The axial length of the stator core is 35 cm. and the internal diameter is 180 cm. Determine the flux per pole. Plot to scale the E.M.F. waveform in a single-turn, full-pitch coil on the stator and determine the frequency and R.M.S. value of this E.M.F. (*Lond. Univ.*, 1944. *Ap. El.*)

50. Alternator Design—Windings and Slot Design

References. A2; B1; C2, 5, 6; D3; F1; H2; K2; M1; S1, 3, 4; W2.

EXAMPLES 50

*1. A 3-phase, 6600-volts, 50-cycle, star-connected alternator is to run at 750 r.p.m. There are to be 36 conductors per slot, the flux per pole is about 4·2 megalines and the distribution factor is 0·97. The winding is to be concentric, with the overhang arranged in two planes. Calculate the number of slots required and draw the winding for 4 pole pitches.   (*C. & G., Final*, 1941.)

2. Determine a suitable number of slots, and conductors per slot, for the stator winding of a 3-phase, 3300-volt, 50-cycle, 300 r.p.m. alternator. The diameter of the core is 230 cm., and the axial core length 35 cm. The maximum flux density in the air gap should be approximately 9000 lines per cm.[2] Assume sinusoidal flux distribution. Give a sketch showing the arrangement of the conductors in the slot, and their insulation.   (*Lond. Univ.*, 1934, *El. Mach.*)

3. Design the slots and winding for a 3-phase alternator from the following particulars: output 2000 kVA., 11,000 volts, 24 poles, 250 r.p.m. Bore of stator 275 cm., axial length 32 cm.   (*I.E.E.*, *May*, 1934.)

4. A 3-phase alternator has 12 poles, 72 slots on the stator and 4 conductors per slot. There are to be two distinct windings per phase so arranged that the two windings may be connected in series or parallel. The windings are wave-connected with full-pitch coils. Draw up a winding table and indicate clearly the start and finish of each phase. (A winding diagram is not required.)   (*Lond. Univ.*, 1935, *El. Mach.*)

5. A 3-phase machine has 4 poles, 9 slots per pole and 4 conductors per slot arranged in two-layer wave-connected winding with full-pitch coils. There are to be two distinct circuits per phase arranged for series or parallel connection. Draw up a winding table, indicating clearly the start and finish of each winding, and a circuit diagram for parallel connection with the phases in star.   (*Lond. Univ.*, 1938, *El. Mach.*)

6. A stator has 48 slots. Using a single-layer winding with one coil-side per slot, show, diagrammatically, the coils and connections for (*a*) a 6-pole, 2-phase winding, (*b*) a 4-pole, 3-phase, mesh-connected winding.   (*C. & G.*, 1939.)

*7. Discuss the considerations which determine the number of stator slots per pole per phase to use in the design of a 3-phase alternator. Two preliminary designs are made for a 3-phase alternator, the two designs differing only in the number and size of the stator slots and the dimensions of the stator conductors. The first design used 2 slots per pole per phase, there are 9 conductors per slot, each slot being 3 in. deep, ¾ in. wide, and the mean width of each stator tooth is 1 in. The thickness of the slot insulation is 0·08 in.; all other insulations may be neglected. The second design is to have 3 slots per pole per phase. Retaining the same flux density in the teeth and current density in the stator conductors as for the first design, calculate the dimensions of the stator slots. Compare the space factors in the stator slots for the two designs.   (*Lond. Univ.*, 1943, *El. Mach.*)

8. A 3-phase alternator has a stator bore of 170 cm. and a core-length of 35 cm. The average flux density over the whole pole-pitch is to be approximately 5500 lines per sq. cm. on open-circuit. Determine a suitable number of slots and conductors per slot for a terminal voltage of 6600, 50 frequency, 375 r.p.m.   (*Lond. Univ.*, 1940, *El. Mach.*)

*9. A 4-pole, 2-circuit wave winding has 135 coils and 6 coil-sides per slot. Find the points to be opened to obtain a 3-phase winding with a phase-spread of 60°. Determine the relative output of the machine as compared with a winding having a phase-spread of 120°.   (*C. & G., Final*, 1943.)

51. Alternator Design—Short-Circuit Properties and Armature Reaction

References. A2; B1; C2, 5, 6; D3; H2; K2; M1; S1, 4; W2.

EXAMPLES 51

*1. A 3-phase, 6600 volts, 4000 kVA. alternator has the following open-circuit characteristic—

Field amperes . .	0	32	73·5	88	120	170
Terminal volts . .	0	3000	6000	6600	7500	8300

The leakage reactance is 12 per cent, and full-load current flows in the short-circuited armature winding when the field current is 70 amperes. When the machine is supplying full load at normal voltage 0·8 power-factor lagging, a symmetrical short-circuit occurs across the terminals. Determine the peak values of the instantaneous and steady short-circuit currents. Explain what factors determine the value of the instantaneous short-circuit current and its rate of decay with time.

(*Lond. Univ.*, 1945, *El. Mach.*)

*2. A 3-phase armature has 9 slots per pole, 4 conductors per slot each carrying an alternating current of 200 amperes (R.M.S.). Assuming the slots to be skewed by 1 slot pitch, plot curves to scale of the m.m.f. distribution of the winding over two pole pitches (a) when the current in one phase has its maximum value, and (b) $\frac{1}{12}$ of a cycle later. Show that the fundamental moves two pole pitches in space while the current passes through one cycle. (*Lond. Univ.*, 1947, *El. Mach.*)

3. From a developed 3-phase stator winding, deduce the distribution over a pole-pair of the M.M.F. wave due to armature reaction at the instant when the current in any selected phase has its maximum value. Express the value of the maximum ordinate of the M.M.F. wave in terms of: q = slots per pole per phase; u = conductors per slot; I = r.m.s. phase current. Show also two salient poles of the field system, the left-hand being an N-pole. If the field system moves from left to right, give the polarity of the armature reaction poles, and show their position relative to the main poles at the instant chosen. The operating power factor is 0·8 lagging, resistance and armature leakage reactance are negligible.

(*Lond. Univ.*, 1938, *El. Mach.*)

52. Alternator Design—Leading Dimensions

References. A2; B1; C5, 6; F1; S1, 4; W2.

Output $kVA = 2 \cdot 22 \ k \ . \ m \ . \ \Phi \ . \ Z_p \ . \ f \ . \ 10^{-11} \ I_p.$

$$= 2 \cdot 22 \ k \ m \ B_{mean} \cdot \frac{\pi DL}{2p} \cdot \frac{ac\pi D}{mI_p} \cdot \frac{Np}{60} \ 10^{-11} \ . \ I_p$$

$$= \frac{1 \cdot 11 \ k \ \pi^2 \ B_{mean} \ ac}{60 \times 10^{11}} \cdot N \ . \ D^2 L$$

whence output coefficient,

$$G = \frac{kVA}{N \ . \ D^2 L} = \frac{1 \cdot 11 \ k \ \pi^2 \ B_{mean} \ ac}{60 \times 10^{11}}$$

$$= \frac{B_{mean} \ ac}{6 \times 10^{11}} \text{ approx.}$$

where $B_{mean} = \Phi/YL =$ about 5500–6000 gauss,

Φ = total pole flux,
Y = pole pitch in cm.,
L = gross length of core in cm.,
D = core diameter in cm.,
k = winding factors, combined (Section 43)
m = number of phases,
ac = specific electric loading in ampere-conductors per cm., usually about 250 for slow machines up to 650 for large turbo-alternators,
p = pairs of poles,
I_p = phase current,
N = r.p.m.; $n =$ r.p.s.

In a turbo-alternator, the peripheral speed should not in general exceed 160 m. per second, and D should be selected accordingly. For a 2-pole machine, this gives D about 1 m.

EXAMPLES 52

1. Determine the main dimensions and number of slots for the stator of a 3-phase. 3300-volt, 8-pole, 50-cycle alternator developing 400 kVA. at 0·8 power factor.

Maximum flux density under pole arc = 8500 lines/cm.^{2}
Ampere conductors per cm. of periphery = 260.

(Lond. Univ., 1937, El. Mach.)

2. The leading dimensions for a 1000-kVA., 6600-volt, 1500 r.p.m., 3-phase, 50-cycle alternator are to be $D = 27$ in., $L = 19$ in. The stator winding is star connected. Calculate: (a) the number and size of the stator conductors, (b) the full-load resistance loss in the stator winding, (c) the flux density in the stator teeth. Make whatever assumptions are necessary but use the following data: $ac = 280$ per cm. Tooth-width at stator periphery = slot-width. Slot depth = 2 in., space-factor in slots = 0·5, $\rho = 0·8\mu\Omega$-in.

(Lond. Univ., 1938, El. Mach.)

3. Give approximate values for maximum flux density in the air-gap, and specific current loading for a 50-cycle generator of 750 kVA. running at 500 r.p.m., and hence deduce a suitable size for this machine. *(I.E.E., May, 1934.)*

4. Obtain the main dimensions of the rotor for a 50,000-kVA., 2-pole, 50-cycle generator, where the peripheral speed is limited to 160 metres per sec. Take an electric loading of 650 amp.-cond. per cm. of periphery, and a mean flux-density in the gap of 5750 gauss. *(I.E.E., Nov., 1935.)*

5. The following particulars relate to a 3-phase, 50-cycle turbo-alternator running at 3000 r.p.m. Mean flux-density in gap over whole armature surface = 6000 lines per cm.^{2} Ampere-conductors per cm. of armature periphery = 600. Armature core-length = 200 cm. Peripheral speed = 140 m. per second. Find the rating in kVA., showing completely the derivation of any expressions employed. Find a suitable star-connected armature winding for developing 11,000 V., stating the type of winding, the number of slots, and the number of turns per phase. *(C. & G., Final, 1930.)*

6. The following are design data for a 1800-kW., 0·8 power factor, 3300-volt, 50-cycle, 200-r.p.m., 3-phase generator: Stator: Internal diameter 327 cm., core length 35 cm., 270 slots, 6 conductors per slot, full-pitched winding, star connected with two parallel circuits. Deduce corresponding data for a 1200-kW., 0·8 power factor, 3300-volt, 50-cycle, 300-r.p.m., 3-phase generator. *(Lond. Univ., 1940, El. Mach.)*

7. The field coils of a salient-pole alternator are wound with a single-layer winding of bare copper strip 3 cm. deep, with separating insulation 0·15 mm. thick. Determine a suitable winding length, number of turns and thickness of conductor to develop 12,000 ampere-turns with a p.d. of 5

volts per coil, and with a loss of power of 0·12 watt per cm.² of the total surface of the coil (internal + external + ends). The mean length of turn is 120 cm.

(*Lond. Univ.*, 1940, *El. Mach.*)

8. Obtain suitable main dimensions for the stator of a 3-phase, 3300-volt, 16-pole, 50-cycle alternator developing 1500 kW. at 0·8 power factor. The maximum flux density in the air gap is about 9000 gauss, and the amp.-cond. per cm. circumference about 280. (*Lond. Univ.*, 1935, *El. Mach.*)

9. Design the field winding for the following low-speed alternator: 16 poles; excitation voltage 110; maximum ampere-turns per coil, 16,000 approx.; full-load ampere-turns per coil, 12,000. Permissible loss at full load, per sq. cm. of the total surface of the coil, 0·18 watt. The field coil is rectangular, with rounded corners, the internal dimensions being 30 cm. × 18 cm. with corners 4 cm. radius. The total height of the coil is 17 cm. (*Lond. Univ.*, 1933, *El. Mach.*)

*10. Estimate the kVA. rating of a 3-phase alternator for 50 cycles per second at 3000 r.p.m. Core length 160 cm., peripheral speed 140 metres per sec., *ac* 525 per cm., B_{av} 5200 lines per cm². Derive from first principles the output expression used. (*C. & G., Final*, 1945.)

*11. The following are design data for a 3-phase, 25,000 kW., 6600 volts, 50 cycles per second, 2-pole turbo-alternator, working at 0·8 power-factor. Stator: internal diameter 100 cm., core length 210 cm., number of slots 72, two-layer winding with 2 conductors per slot. Coil span 27 teeth; two paths in parallel, star-connected.

Deduce the loading constants. Using the same loading constants, determine the corresponding data for a three-phase, 30,000 kW., 6600 volts, 50 cycles per second, 2-pole turbo-alternator to work at 0·8 power-factor. Sketch and explain a typical arrangement of the slot and its contents for such turbo-alternators. (*Lond. Univ.*, 1945, *El. Mach.*)

53. Transformers—Efficiency and Regulation

References. A2; B1; C2, 4; D2, 3; K1, 2; M1, 6; R2; S1, 5, 6.

Open-circuit Test. Normal pressure and frequency applied to primary, secondary open, wattmeter in primary gives constant iron losses.

Short-circuit Test. Very reduced pressure at normal frequency applied to primary, secondary short-circuited. For any current loading given by primary ammeter and adjusted by altering the applied pressure, wattmeter in primary reads the copper losses in both windings. (The iron losses are negligible because of the considerably reduced exciting pressure.) Test is usually taken for full-load current.

Efficiency. If w_i = iron loss watts (constant)

$$w_c = \text{copper loss watts at full-load}$$

$$W = \text{watts output at full-load}$$

then full-load efficiency $= \dfrac{W}{W + w_i + w_c}$

At any other load current I, the copper losses are changed in the proportion of the square of this current to the square of full-load current, both being either primary or secondary currents. This new value of the copper losses is used in the efficiency formula above, together with the appropriate watts output.

Equivalent Resistance, Impedance, and Leakage Reactance.

If w_c = full-load copper loss watts (primary and secondary, as above)

I_2 = secondary full-load current

then $\overline{R}_2 = \dfrac{w_c}{I_2{}^2} = $ " equivalent " resistance of the whole transformer, referred to the secondary side.

If $V_1 =$ the reduced voltage applied to the primary side in the short-circuit test above, when full-load current is flowing in both windings

$s \ =$ the winding ratio (primary turns/secondary turns)

then $V_2 = V_1/s =$ equivalent secondary voltage, i.e. the voltage that would have been required if the "secondary" side had been fed, with the "primary" shorted†

then $\overline{Z}_2 = V_2/I_2 =$ "equivalent" impedance, referred to secondary side

and $\overline{X}_2 = \sqrt{\overline{Z}_2{}^2 - \overline{R}_2{}^2} =$ "equivalent" leakage reactance referred to secondary side.

By using in the above work primary values for full-load current and the primary pressure as used in the short-circuit test above, the "equivalent" values referred to the primary side will be obtained. They will be s^2 times the secondary values.

At full-load current, the *resistance drop* will be $I_2\overline{R}_2$, and this expressed as a percentage of the open-circuit voltage of the secondary gives the *percentage resistance drop*, r, or

$$r = \frac{I_2\overline{R}_2}{E_2} \times 100 = \text{percentage resistance drop}$$

$$z = \frac{I_2\overline{Z}_2}{E_2} \times 100 = \text{percentage impedance drop}$$

$$x = \frac{I_2\overline{X}_2}{E_2} \times 100 = \text{percentage leakage reactance drop}$$

Primary values will give the same percentage drops.

† In such circumstances, what was previously the *secondary* now really becomes the *primary*. The original designations are retained to avoid confusion.

Regulation. The following formula is approximate, but sufficiently accurate for all ordinary calculations.

Corresponding to any given load at given power factor (cos ϕ), find the secondary current I_2. Then the secondary drop will be given by

$$I_2 \left(\overline{R}_2 \cos \phi \pm \overline{X}_2 \sin \phi \right)$$

At full-load, the "regulation down" is given as a percentage by

$$r \cos \phi \pm x \sin \phi$$

the $+$ sign being used for lagging power factors and the $-$ sign for leading power factors.

EXAMPLES 53

1. With the help of a vector diagram, explain carefully the significance of the following quantities in the open- and short-circuit tests of a transformer: (i) power consumed, (ii) input voltage, (iii) input current. When a 100-kVA. single-phase transformer was tested in this way, the following data were obtained: on open-circuit the power consumed was 1300 watts and on short-circuit at full-load current the power consumed was 1200 watts. Calculate the efficiency of the transformer on (i) full load, (ii) half load, when working at unity power factor.

(*Lond. Univ.*, 1936, *El. Tech.*)

2. The following figures refer to tests on a 100-kVA. single-phase transformer : open-circuit, primary volts 1000, secondary volts 100, wattmeter in primary 975 watts ; short-circuit, full-load current, primary volts 22, watts 1050. Find (*a*) the percentage resistance, impedance, and leakage reactance drops, (*b*) the efficiency at three-quarters full-load current at 0·8 lagging power factor, and (*c*) the regulation at full-load current at 0·9 lagging power factor.

3. A 50-cycle, single-phase transformer has a turn ratio of 6. The resistances are 0·9 ohm and 0·03 ohm, and the leakage reactance 5 ohms and 0·13 ohm for the high-voltage and low-voltage windings respectively. Find (*a*) the voltage to be applied to the high-voltage winding to obtain full-load current of 200 amperes in the low-voltage winding on short-circuit; (*b*) the power factor on short-circuit.

(*I.E.E.*, *May*, 1931.)

4. A single-phase transformer has an output of 2·3 volts,

300 mA., 0·8 power factor (lagging). Ratio of transformation—
15/1. Particulars of windings are—

Primary: resistance 384 ohms, leakage reactance 200 ohms.
Secondary: resistance 1·3 ohms, leakage reactance 0·9 ohm.
Calculate the voltage at the primary terminals. Illustrate by
means of a vector diagram drawn to scale showing primary
and secondary voltages and currents. Neglect magnetizing
current.   (*Lond. Univ.*, 1938, *A.E.*)

5. What are the principal sources of energy loss in a transformer and how do they vary with the load? What is under-
stood by the "all-day" efficiency? Two 100-kW. transformers
each have a maximum efficiency of 98 per cent, but in one the
maximum efficiency occurs at full-load, while in the other it
occurs at half-load. Each transformer is on full-load for 4
hours, on half-load for 6 hours and on one-tenth load for
14 hours per day. Which has the greater all-day efficiency?
                                  (*I.E.E.*, *May*, 1935.)

6. Prove that the magnetically coupled circuits of a transformer can be represented by an equivalent electric circuit,
and deduce the constants for this circuit.

A 4-kVA., 200/400-volt, 50-cycle, 1-phase transformer gave
the following test results: No-load—low-voltage data, 200 V.,
0·7 A., 60 W. Short-circuit—high-voltage data, 9 V., 6 A.,
21·6 W. Calculate (*a*) the current components on no-load;
(*b*) the efficiency and the regulation at full load and power
factor 0·8 lagging.   (*Lond. Univ.*, 1934, *El. Mach.*)

7. Draw the equivalent circuit for a 3000/400-volt,
single-phase transformer on which the following test results
were obtained: input to the high-voltage winding when the low-
voltage winding is open-circuited, 3000 volts, 0·5 ampere,
500 watts; input to the low-voltage winding when the high-
voltage winding is short-circuited, 11 volts, 100 amperes, 500
watts. Insert the appropriate values of resistance and reactance.   (*I.E.E.*, *May*, 1939.)

8. Describe the back-to-back tests for determining the
regulation and efficiency of a pair of similar transformers,
giving the circuit diagrams, and indicating what readings will
be necessary. Give what you think might be typical readings
for transformers of 1000 kVA. for 11,000/550 volts.

9. Show how the operation of a transformer can be fully
represented by an equivalent circuit. Draw the equivalent
circuit for a loaded transformer and calculate the circuit
constants from which the efficiency and voltage regulation of
a 250/500-volt transformer can be determined from the

following test results: Open-circuit test 250 V., 1 A., 80 W. on low-voltage side; short-circuit test, 20 V., 12 A., 100 W. on high-voltage side. *(C. & G., Final, 1936.)*

*10. A 200-kVA., 6600/384 volts, single-phase transformer has a unity power-factor efficiency of 98 per cent at full-load and at one-half full-load. The no-load power-factor is 0·2 and the full-load voltage regulation at a lagging power-factor of 0·8 is 4 per cent. Draw the equivalent circuit referred to the low-voltage side and insert all values.

(C. & G., Final, 1946.)

*11. A 3-phase transformer, rated at 1000 kVA., 11/3·3 kV., has its primary windings star-connected and its secondary windings delta-connected. The actual resistances per phase of these windings are: primary 0·375 ohm, secondary 0·095 ohm; and the leakage reactances per phase are: primary 9·5 ohms, secondary 2 ohms. Calculate the voltage, at normal frequency, which must be applied to the primary terminals in order to obtain full-load current in the windings when the secondary terminals are short-circuited. Calculate also the power input under these conditions. *(I.E.E., Nov., 1943.)*

*12. Discuss fully the energy losses in single-phase transformers. Such a transformer, working at unity power-factor, has an efficiency of 90 per cent at both one-half load and at the full load of 500 watts. Determine the efficiency at 75 per cent of full load. *(Lond. Univ., 1945, Ap. Elect.)*

54. Transformers—Three-Phase and "Scott"-Connected Pair

References. C2, 4; D2, 3; K2; M1, 6; R2; S1, 5, 6.

In 3-phase transformers with the windings connected one star and the other delta, there is a phase displacement of 90° between primary and secondary line values instead of the customary 180°. Hence care must be taken to parallel only those "mixed" transformers in which these secondary phase displacements are in agreement.

"*Scott*"-*Connected Transformers.* A pair of similar single-phase transformers, with the windings intended for the three-phase side (usually the primary) provided with a centre tapping (C) and two tappings ($E_1 E_2$) each 6·7 per cent in from the ends, giving 86·6 per cent turns between them. The main transformer uses the whole (primary) winding, connected between a pair of the 3-phase lines, while the "teaser" has one terminal (E_1) connected to centre tapping (C) of the first, and the other terminal (E_2) to the third 3-phase line. The two secondaries supply 2-phase currents, which, if balanced, will draw a balanced load from the 3-phase supply. If the normal winding ratio of the transformers is S, the second or teaser transformer will have a ratio of 0·866 S. If the 2-phase load is unbalanced, use the transformation ratios of each transformer to find its primary current, and then vectorially add the current of the main transformer to half that of the teaser, displaced 90°, to give the load on the first two of the 3-phase lines, while the third line will obviously carry the load current of the teaser transformer. (See Example 6 below.)

EXAMPLES 54

1. What are the advantages of using three single-phase transformers instead of one 3-phase transformer? Two single-phase transformers with voltage tappings are connected to a 2-phase 200 volt alternator for testing polyphase motors in a factory. Show the connections required in each case, and indicate the voltage tappings for testing: (*a*) 400-volt 2-phase motors, (*b*) 200-volt 3-phase motors, (*c*) 400-volt 3-phase motors. If the alternator has a 2-phase mesh winding, explain

why the Scott 2- to 3-phase transformation cannot be effected by auto-transformers. *(I.E.E., Nov., 1932.)*

2. A 500-kVA., 3-phase, 50-cycle transformer has a voltage ratio (line voltages) of 33,000/11,000, and is delta/star connected. The resistances per phase are: high voltage 35 ohms, low voltage 0·876 ohm; and the iron loss is 3050 watts. Calculate the values of the efficiency at full load and one-half of full load respectively, (a) at unity power factor, (b) at 0·8 power factor. *(I.E.E., May, 1934.)*

3. Three-phase current is transformed to 400 volts in two ways, (a) by a 10,000/400 volt transformer, (b) by a 10,000/2000 volt transformer and then by a 2000/400 volt transformer. In each case the primary windings are delta-connected, and the secondary windings star-connected.

If two similarly placed terminals of the 400 volt windings in (a) and (b) are connected together, what potential difference will exist between the remaining terminals of the two transformers ? Illustrate by means of a vector diagram.

(C. & G., Final, 1921.)

4. Two electrical furnaces are supplied with single-phase current at 80 volts from a 3-phase 11,000 volt system by means of two single-phase, Scott-connected transformers with similar secondary windings. When the load on one furnace is 500 kW. and on the other 800 kW., what current will flow in each of the 3-phase lines, (1) at unity power factor, (2) at 0·5 power factor ? Neglect phase displacement in, and efficiency of, the transformers. *(I.E.E., Nov., 1938.)*

5. A Scott-connected (2-to 3-phase) transformer links a 6000 volt, 2-phase system with a 440 volt, 3-phase system. The frequency is 50 cycles per second, the gross core area is 300 square centimetres, while the maximum flux density is to be about 12,000 lines per square centimetre. Find the number of turns on each winding, and the point to be tapped for the neutral wire on the 3-phase side. If the load is balanced on one side of such a transformer, find whether it will also be balanced on the other side. *(Lond. Univ. 1929, El. Mach.)*

6. A 3-phase, 4-wire distribution network with 240 volts between the phase conductors and neutral is supplied from a 5000 volt 2-phase high-voltage transmission line through a step-down transformer. Explain, with connection and vector diagrams, how this transformation is effected, and calculate the number of turns in each section of the secondary winding if there are 2000 turns on each high-voltage primary.

(C. & G., Final, 1927.)

55. Transformers—Sharing of Loads in Parallel

References. C2; D2, 3; M2, 6; S1.

Analytical Method. See notes on p. 29, as for alternators in parallel.

Graphical Method. (See solution to Ques. 2, p. 179.)

EXAMPLES 55

1. Two transformers A and B are joined in parallel to the same load. Determine the current delivered by each transformer, having given: open circuit E.M.F., 6600 volts for A and 6400 volts for B. Equivalent leakage impedance in terms of the secondary $= 0.3 + j3$ for A, and $0.2 + j1$ for B. The load impedance is $8 + j6$.   (*Lond. Univ.*, 1934, *El. Power.*)

2. Two 100 kW. single-phase transformers are connected in parallel both on the primary and secondary. One transformer has an ohmic drop of $\frac{1}{2}$ per cent at full-load and an inductive drop of 8 per cent at full-load current, zero power factor. The other has an ohmic drop of $\frac{3}{4}$ per cent and an inductive drop of 4 per cent. Show how they will share the following loads : (*a*) 180 kW. at 0.9 power factor, (*b*) 120 kW. at 0.6 power factor.   (*C. & G., Final*, 1920.)

*3. Two 250-kVA. transformers supplying a network are connected in parallel on both primary and secondary sides. The voltage ratios are the same, their resistance drops are 1.5 and 0.9 per cent and their reactance drops 3.33 and 4 per cent respectively. Calculate the kVA. loading of each transformer and its power-factor when the total load on the transformers is 500 kVA. at 0.707 lagging power-factor.

(*C. & G.*, 1941.)

4. Two single-phase transformers supply, in parallel, a secondary load of 1000 amperes at 0.8 power factor, lagging. For each transformer the secondary E.M.F. on open circuit is 3300 volts, and the total leakage impedances—in terms of the secondary—are $0.1 + j0.2$ and $0.05 + j0.4$ ohm respectively. Determine the output current for each transformer, and the ratio of the kW. output of the two transformers.

(*Lond. Univ.*, 1936, *El. Power.*)

*5. Two single-phase transformers rated at 500-kVA. and 400-kVA. respectively are connected in parallel to supply a load of 1000 kVA. at 0·8 lagging power-factor. The resistance and reactance of the first transformer are 2·5 and 6 per cent respectively, and of the second transformer 1·6 and 7 per cent respectively. Calculate the kVA. loading and the power-factor at which each transformer operates.   (C. & G., 1943.)

*6. Determine the kW. output and power-factor of the load on each of two transformers, A and B, operating in parallel on a load of 500 amps at 0·8 power-factor, lagging.

No-load test: 11,000/3000 volts for each transformer.
Short-circuit test, with primary short-circuited:

Transformer A, 150 volts, 200 amps, 10 kW.
      ,,   B, 150 volts, 300 amps, 12 kW.

(Lond. Univ., 1941, El. Power.)

*7. For two transformers connected in parallel, $Z_1 = 1 + j5$, $Z_2 = 1 + j8$, load $Z = 80 + j60$, $V = 6400$ volts (the voltage across Z). Calculate the primary voltage of the transformers if for both the secondary winding has three times as many turns as the primary.

(Lond. Univ., 1942, El. Power.)

*8. A 3-phase transformer, A, rated at 1000 kVA., 33/11 kV., is connected in parallel with a similar transformer, B, rated at 1500 kVA., to supply a load of 2000 kVA. at 0·8 power-factor (lagging). At full load the equivalent voltage-drops per phase, referred to the secondary, due to resistance and leakage reactance, are 2 and 5 per cent respectively for transformer A, and 1·7 and 6 per cent respectively for transformer B. Calculate the load on each transformer and the power-factor at which it operates.   (I.E.E., Nov., 1943.)

56. Transformer Design—General

References. B1; C5; K1; S1, 4, 6.

Hysteresis loss $= 1 \cdot 95 \, B^{1 \cdot 6} f / 10^{10}$ watts per cm^3.
Eddy Current loss $= 0 \cdot 78 \, B^2 f^2 t^2 / 10^{12}$ watts per cm^3.

EXAMPLES 56

1. A transformer core is made up of iron plates having a relative permeability of 850. If the average length of the magnetic circuit is $0 \cdot 4$ m. and its cross-section 26 cm.^{2}, and the primary coil has 1000 turns, estimate the maximum flux density and the magnetizing current taken by the core. Primary voltage, 600 volts. Frequency, 50 cycles per sec. The iron loss at the working flux density is 3 watts per kg., and the density of the iron is $7 \cdot 8$ g. per cm.^{3}

(I.E.E., Nov., 1939.)

2. Describe a method of separating the eddy-current from the hysteresis losses in a transformer. Determine the hysteresis loss and the eddy-current loss at normal voltage and frequency from the following test results taken on a 200 volt, 50 frequency transformer—

Applied voltage	200	180	160	140	120	100
Total iron losses (watts) . .	68·5	61·6	53·6	45·8	39·0	32·3
Frequency	50	45	40	35	30	25

(C. & G., Final, 1929.)

3. An oil-immersed power transformer of 2000 kVA. rating has a full-load efficiency of 98·5 per cent at a power factor of 0·8. The $I^2 R$ loss is 2·5 times the core loss. The mean temperature rise on continuous full load is 45° C. Estimate the temperature rise for (a) half-load and (b) 25 per cent over-load.

(I.E.E., Nov., 1935.)

4. For what uses are auto-transformers suitable? A 5-kVA. single-phase 230/100-volt transformer is connected as an auto-transformer for 230/630 volts. Find the load current and the current in each winding at the full permissible output.

(C. & G., Final, 1933.)

5. It is desired to feed a 360-volt 3-phase motor from 400-volt 3-phase lines. Three similar transformers with 400-volt windings are available. What portion of these windings could be tapped off so that, when the three coils are arranged in delta, the necessary 360 volts would be available from the tappings, acting as an auto-delta transformer?

6. In what circumstances has the auto-transformer advantages over the double-wound transformer? Calculate for full-load and unity power-factor the I^2R losses in a 50-kVA., 500/250-volt, 50-cycle single-phase auto-transformer. Volts per turn, 4; mean length of turn, 60 cm.; current density, 2·25 A. per mm.^{2}; resistivity of copper 0·021 ohm per m. and mm.^{2} at 75° C. (*I.E.E.*, *May*, 1935.)

7. What do you understand by the terms *eddy current loss* and *hysteresis loss*? To what extent are these losses affected by changes in the thickness of the core plates and their composition? A transformer when connected to a 2000-volt, 25-cycle supply has a core loss of 1500 watts, of which 1000 watts are due to hysteresis and 500 watts to eddy currents. Find the core loss if the transformer is connected to a 4000-volt, 50-cycle supply. (*I.E.E.*, *Nov.*, 1935.)

8. The average daily load on a transformer which is permanently connected to the supply mains is: full load at 0·9 power factor for 5 hours, half load at 0·8 power factor for 9 hours and no load for 10 hours. Find the ratio of full load copper loss to iron loss in the economical design of the transformer. (*Lond. Univ.*, 1933, *El. Tech.*)

9. The cylindrical winding of a core-type, oil immersed transformer is 3 cm. thick, and is wound on an insulating former, the thermal conductivity of which may be neglected. The I^2R loss is 15 W. per kg., the radial thermal resistivity is 20° C. per W. per cm., and the copper space factor is 0·6. Calculate the maximum temperature difference between the copper and the oil. Prove any formula used.
(*Lond. Univ.*, 1933, *El. Mach.*)

10. Describe any arrangements for doubling and trebling the frequency of an A.C. supply on a small scale. What method would you employ to obtain a relatively small supply at 50 frequency for lighting from a 3-phase power supply at 25 frequency?

*11. A transformer has 1000 primary and 10,000 secondary turns. The primary applied voltage is 3000 volts at 50 cycles per second and the primary current is 10 amperes at a power-factor of 0·8 lagging. The primary winding has a leakage reactance of 3 ohms and negligible resistance. Calculate the maximum value of the flux in the core and the E.M.F. generated in the secondary by this flux.
(*Lond. Univ.*, 1943, *Ap. Elect.*)

12. The following data relate to the hysteresis loop of a certain transformer iron—

B, lines per cm.²	10,000	9500	8000	6000	4000	2000	0
H, increasing	2·7	2·3	1·52	0·95	0·74	0·62	0·51
H, decreasing	—	1·75	0·47	− 0·17	− 0·34	− 0·42	− 0·51

Determine the wave shape of the magnetizing current for the transformer, working with sinusoidal applied voltage, in accordance with the above loop. In what cases is the star-star connection unsuitable for three-phase transformers?

(*Lond. Univ.*, 1934, *El. Mach.*)

*13. The core of a Variac variable-ratio transformer is constructed of circular steel laminations of inner diameter 4·0 cm. and outer diameter 10·0 cm., piled to a height of 7·0 cm. The insulation accounts for 10 per cent of the thickness, and the maximum flux-density is to be 12,000 gauss. Calculate the number of turns needed if the supply is 230 volts, 50 cycles per second and the output is to be variable up to 260 volts. What is the maximum permissible insulated diameter of the wire with which the Variac is wound?   (*I.E.E.*, *May*, 1945.)

*14. The following results were obtained on an iron-cored choking coil: Input when connected across (*a*) 250 volts, 50 cycles per second supply; 10 amperes, 500 watts. (*b*) 500 volts, 100 cycles per second; 900 watts. (*c*) 20 volts D.C. supply; 10 amperes. Calculate the approximate values of the hysteresis and eddy-current losses in case (*a*).

(*C. & G.*, *Final*, 1945.)

*15. Deduce, from first principles, the equation relating the voltage, the core flux, the frequency and the number of turns in a transformer winding. Calculate the number of turns in each phase of a 20,000/2,000-volt, 3-phase, 50-cycle delta/star-connected transformer. The net core section is 500 cm.² per limb, and the maximum permissible flux density is 12,000 lines/cm².   (*I.E.E.*, *April*, 1946.)

57. Transformer Design—Leading Dimensions

References. B1; C5; K1; S1, 4, 6.

Volts per turn $= 4.44fB_{max}A_i\,10^{-8} = k\sqrt{\text{kVA.}}$, taking for

Single-phase, core, $k = 0.75$; shell, $k = 1$.

Three-phase, core, power, $k = 0.6$; lighting, $k = 0.4$; shell, $k = 1.3$.

$$A_iA_w = \frac{\text{kVA.} \times 10^{11}}{2.22 \times f \times B_{max} \times \delta \times k_w}$$

for single-phase.   Use 3·33 for three-phase

where $A_i =$ net area of limb iron section, cm.^{2}

$A_w =$ area of window opening, cm.^{2}

$f =$ frequency.

$B_{max} =$ max. flux density in core

$\quad = 10,000$ to $14,000$ gauss.

$\delta =$ current density

$\quad = 230$ to 500 A./cm.^{2}, according to cooling.

$k_w =$ copper space factor in window, averaging about 0·3 for high voltage ordinary, and 0·6 for auto.

If $d =$ diameter of limb circumscribing circle, given approx. by

$A_i = 0.45\,d^2$ for plain square limb section

$\quad = 0.56\,d^2$ for cruciform

$\quad = 0.6\,d^2$ for three-stepped core

$\quad = 0.62\,d^2$ for four-stepped core.

If $D =$ distance between centres of cores

then $D - d =$ width of window opening.

If $L =$ length of window opening,

then $A_w = L(D - d)$.

Window proportions, approximately 3×1 for core type, and 2×1 for shell type, in the absence of data requiring otherwise.

EXAMPLES 57

1. A 50-cycle, 1-phase, oil-cooled auto-transformer is required to transform 500 kVA. from 5000 to 6600 volts. Find suitable dimensions for the magnetic circuit and the winding.   (*C. & G., Final*, 1931.)

2. The window in the core of a 2200/440-volt, 15-kVA., 50-cycle, single-phase transformer has a gross available area of 340 cm.^{2}, the space-factor being 0·35. Assuming a maximum core density of 10 kilogauss and a current density in the conductors of 2·1 A. per mm.^{2}, estimate the sectional area of the iron in the limb and the diameter of the circumscribed circle round the square core section. Find also the numbers of primary and secondary turns and conductor cross-sections.
(I.E.E., May, 1938.)

*3. Calculate the core and the window area and make an estimate of the weights of copper and iron required for a 125-kVA., 2000/400-volt, 50-cycle, single-phase, shell-type transformer from the following particulars—

$B_{max} = 11,000$ gauss, current density $= 2·2$ amperes per mm.^{2}, volts per turn $= 11·2$, window area constant $= 0 33$. Specific gravity of copper and iron, 8·9 and 7·8 respectively. The core is rectangular and the stampings are all 7 cm. wide. Sketch the core, inserting dimensions. *(C. & G., Final, 1946.)*

4. Find suitable main demensions (core, yoke, and window sizes) for a 5000-kVA., 6600/440-volt, star-star, 3-phase core-type power transformer. Take flux- and current-densities of 14,000 gauss and 3 amperes per mm.^{2} respectively.

*5. Work out the proportions of the cruciform section of maximum area for the core of a transformer. What is the space factor of the circle circumscribing such a core? A 500-kVA., 6600/400-volt, 50-cycle, single-phase transformer has 380 turns in the high-voltage winding. If the maximum flux density is 13,000 gauss, design the section of the core, giving a sketch to scale. *(C. & G., Final, 1944.)*

6. Obtain suitable values for the number of turns and the cross-section of the conductors and the core of a 100-kVA., 6600/440-volt, 3-phase, 50-cycle, mesh/star, core-type transformer. Assume a current density of 2·5 amp. per mm.^{2}, a window factor of 0·3, and a flux density of 12,000 gauss in the core. Make the window area approximately 1½ times the core area. *(I.E.E., May, 1939.)*

7. Obtain the chief dimensions of the core, yoke, and window for a 1000-kVA., 6600/400-volt, 50-cycle, single-phase, core-type transformer. Assume flux and current densities of 13,000 gauss and 2·8 amperes per mm.^{2} respectively, and a window space-factor of 0·33. State any further assumptions made. *(I.E.E., May, 1935.)*

8. Work out the main dimensions of a single-phase

core-type power transformer rated at 100 kVA., 6600/440 volts, 50 cycles. A suitable core in a circumscribing circle of diameter 25 cm. is available, and the E.M.F. is 8·1 volts per turn. Assume a current density of 2·5 amps. per mm.^{2} and a window space-factor of 0·25. (*I.E.E., Nov.*, 1937.)

*9. Estimate the main core dimensions for a 50-cycles-per-second, three-phase, 200-kVA., 6600/500-volts, star/mesh core type transformer. Use the following data: Core limb section to be 4-stepped cruciform, for which the area factor may be taken as = 0·62. Window space-factor = 0·27. Height of window/width of window = 2. Current density = 2·8 A/mm^2. Volts per turn = 8·5. Maximum flux density = 12,500 gauss.

(*Lond. Univ.*, 1946, *El. Mach.*)

58. Synchronous Motors

References. C2, 3, 4, 5; D3; H4; M1, 2; S1, 4.

For the method of plotting the " V " curves of a synchronous motor, see solutions to Ques. 6 and Ques. 7.

EXAMPLES 58

1. If a salient pole synchronous motor connected to the line, but without any secondary windings at all, is brought up to speed by an outside source, will it keep in step by itself, and if so, why ?   (*I.E.E.*, *April*, 1923.)

2. A 3-phase synchronous motor, when driven at normal synchronous speed as an alternator, has the following magnetization curve—

Exciting current	5	10	15	20	25
Line voltage	370	655	830	950	1050

An exciting current of 10 amperes produces a short-circuit current of 200 amperes. Calculate the power-factor of this machine when operating as a synchronous motor and taking a load of 75 kW. at 800 volts, the exciting current being 20 amperes.   (*C. & G.*, *Final*, 1931.)

3. Compare the performances of a salient pole synchronous motor and a synchronous induction motor with respect to (a) starting torque, (b) synchronizing torque, (c) efficiency, and (d) exciting E.M.F. Give reasons for your conclusions.
                     (*I.E.E.*, *April*, 1923.)

4. Explain with vector diagrams how the power factor of a synchronous motor working on a constant mechanical load depends on its excitation. A synchronous motor has an equivalent armature reactance of 3·3 ohms. The exciting current is adjusted to such a value that the generated E.M.F. is 950 volts. Find the power-factor at which the motor would operate when taking 80 kW. from 800-volt supply mains.
                     (*C. & G.*, *Final*, 1936.)

5. Show that in a synchronous motor, running on constant voltage and frequency mains, the overload torque which the machine can furnish increases with the value of the field excitation.

A 6-pole synchronous motor has an armature impedance of 10 ohms and a resistance of 0·5 ohm. When running on 2000 volts, 25 frequency supply mains its field excitation is such that the electromotive force induced in the machine is 1600 volts.

Calculate the maximum total torque in pounds-feet developed before the machine drops out of step.   (*C. & G.*, 1926.)

6. The following gives the no-load curve for a synchronous motor—

| Excitation amperes . | 5 | 10 | 15 | 20 | 25 |
| Generated volts . . | 155 | 276 | 368 | 435 | 478 |

Armature resistance is 1 ohm and synchronous reactance 5 ohms, and the machine runs on 250 volt mains, single-phase. Plot the " V " curve for a constant input of 10 kW.

7. Plot the " V " curve of the above motor for a constant output of 10 kW.

8. A 200 volt, single-phase synchronous motor has an O.C. volts curve given by the following figures—

| Field amperes . . | 2 | 4 | 6 | 8 | 10 |
| O.C. volts . . . | 144 | 215 | 267 | 304 | 333 |

It has an armature resistance of 2 ohms and reactance of 8 ohms. Plot the " V " curve for a constant input of 4 kW.

9. Plot the " V " curve for the above motor for a constant output equivalent to 4 kW., and also plot the curve of power factor against excitation.

10. Assuming constant synchronous impedance, show that the locus diagram of the current input to a synchronous motor is a circle if the excitation and supply voltage are constant. Draw the locus diagram, and determine the current and power factor for an input of 750 kW. for a 3-phase star-connected synchronous motor, the terminal voltage being 3300, and the synchronous impedance $0 \cdot 25 + j2$ ohms per phase. The excitation corresponds to an induced E.M.F. of 3500 volts.

(*Lond. Univ.*, 1940, *El. Mach.*)

59. Induction Motors—General .

References. A1, 2; C1, 2, 4, 5, 6; D1, 3, 4, 5; H4; K2;
M1, 2, 7; S1, 4; V1; W2, 3.

The following is per phase, and rotor values are "referred"
to the stator if used in conjunction with stator values.

If V = applied mains voltage,

R_1 = stator resistance,

R_2 = rotor resistance,

X_1 = stator leakage reactance,

X_2 = rotor leakage reactance, at standstill,

E_2 = rotor standstill voltage,

s = fractional slip,

R_2/s = apparent resistance of rotor on load

= $R_2 + R_L$,

where R_L = resistance equivalent to rotor load*,

T = torque, which in synchronous watts

= rotor input

= $\dfrac{\text{rotor input (watts)} \times 33{,}000}{2 \times \text{synch. r.p.m.} \times 746}$ lb.-ft.

$$\text{Rotor input} = \frac{V^2(R_2/s)}{(R_1 + R_2/s)^2 + (X_1 + X_2)^2}$$

$$\text{or} = E_2 I_2 \cos \phi$$

$$\text{or} = I_2{}^2(R_2/s)$$

$$\text{or} = \frac{E_2{}^2 s R_2}{R_2{}^2 + (sX_2)^2}.$$

For maximum input or torque,

$$(R_2/s)^2 = R_1{}^2 + (X_1 + X_2)^2$$

which reduces to $R_2 = sX_2$ for R_1 and $X_1 = 0$.

Slip for maximum torque

$$s = \frac{R_2}{\sqrt{R_1{}^2 + (X_1 + X_2)^2}}$$

or $\dfrac{R_2}{X_2}$ if stator losses are neglected.

* See Fig. 4, page 74.

Maximum input or torque

$$= \frac{V^2}{2\left\{R_1 + \sqrt{R_1{}^2 + (X_1 + X_2)^2}\right\}}$$

which reduces to $\dfrac{V^2 \text{ or } E_2{}^2}{2X_2}$ if stator losses neglected.

Output of rotor (including mechanical losses)

$$= I_2{}^2(R_2/s)\,(1 - s)$$
$$= \frac{V^2 R_L}{(R_1 + R_2/s)^2 + (X_1 + X_2)^2}$$

Maximum output occurs when $R_L = \overline{Z}_1$ (numerically), where $\overline{Z}_1 =$ total impedance of motor, referred to stator, and $\overline{R}_1 =$ total resistance of motor, referred to stator.

$$\text{Max. Output} = \frac{V^2}{2\left\{\overline{R}_1 + \overline{Z}_1\right\}}.$$

$$\frac{\text{Torque, standstill}}{\text{Torque, full load}} = \text{Slip}_{\text{fl}} \cdot \left(\frac{I_{\text{ss}}}{I_{\text{fl}}}\right)^2.$$

Torque at standstill $\propto$ (applied voltage)^2.

For the full use of the circle diagram, see Examples 64, Ques. 6, p. 74, and Answers, Fig. 10, p. 187.

EXAMPLES 59

1. A squirrel-cage motor is guaranteed to give 40 b.h.p. at 1450 r.p.m. when supplied with 400-volt 3-phase current. The guaranteed efficiency is 89 per cent, and the guaranteed power factor is 0·9 at full load. On brake test the following results are obtained: Speed, 1458 r.p.m.; length of torque arm (radius), 36 in.; mean weight at end of torque arm, 49 lb.; line volts, 400 volts; line current, 54 amperes; kW. input, 33·9 kW. Compare the guarantees and test-results.

(*I.E.E., May,* 1932.)

2. Show that if a 3-phase induction motor is connected to a 3-phase supply and driven above synchronous speed, the machine will generate electrical energy. A load of 800 kW. at 0·8 power factor, lagging, is shared by two generators, X and Y. X is an asynchronous generator, and develops 300 kW., its power factor is 0·9. Determine the kVA. output and the power factor of Y.　　　(*Lond. Univ.,* 1933, *El. Mach.*)

3. Show that full-load power is required to obtain full-load torque in a polyphase induction motor, neglecting stator losses. A 500-volt, 50-frequency, 3-phase induction motor develops 20 h.p. inclusive of mechanical losses when running at 995 r.p.m., the power factor being 0·87. Calculate (a) the slip, (b) rotor copper losses, (c) total input if the stator losses are 1500 watts, (d) line current, (e) number of cycles per minute of the rotor E.M.F.   (C. & G., 1937.)

4. Describe two methods of measuring the slip of an induction motor. A 3-phase induction motor has a synchronous speed of 250 r.p.m. and a 4 per cent slip at full-load. The rotor has a resistance of 0·02 ohms per phase and a standstill leakage reactance of 0·15 ohm per phase. Calculate: (a) the ratio of maximum to full-load torque, (b) the speed at which maximum torque is developed. Neglect resistance and leakage reactance of the stator winding.   (Lond. Univ., 1939, El. Mach.)

5. Explain the action of the 3-phase induction motor, show how the slip varies with the load torque, with constant supply voltage. If a motor has a slip of 2 per cent at normal voltage, deduce approximately the slip when developing the same torque at 10 per cent above normal voltage.

(Lond. Univ., 1939, A.E.)

6. Discuss methods of suppression of the effect of harmonics in the M.M.F. curve on the speed-torque curve of an induction motor and explain, by means of sketches, the effect of harmonics on the running speed of the motor.

(I.E.E., April, 1925.)

7. If an 8-pole induction motor running from a supply of 50 cycles per sec. has an E.M.F. in the rotor of frequency 1½ cycles per sec., determine (i) the speed of the motor, (ii) the slip.   (Lond. Univ., 1934, El. Tech.)

*8. A 6-pole, 3-phase induction motor runs at a speed of 960 r.p.m. when the shaft torque is 100 lb.-ft. and the frequency 50 cycles per sec. Calculate the rotor I^2R loss if friction and windage losses are 150 watts.

(Lond. Univ., 1948, Ap. Elect.)

60. Induction Motors—Starting

References. D4, 5; G1; H4; J1; M7; V1; W3, 4, 5.

EXAMPLES 60

1. Determine approximately the starting torque of an induction motor in terms of full-load torque when started by means of (a) a star/delta switch, (b) an auto-transformer with 50 per cent tapping. Ignore the magnetizing current. The short-circuit current of the motor at normal voltage is 5 times the full-load current, and the full-load slip is 5 per cent.
(*I.E.E.*, Nov., 1939.)

2. Find the ratio of starting to full-load current in a 15-h.p., 400-volt, 3-phase induction motor with star-delta starter, given full-load efficiency, 0·88; full-load power factor, 0·85; short-circuit current, 40 amperes at 200 volts, and neglecting magnetizing current. (*I.E.E.*, Nov., 1935.)

3. A 3-phase, 50-cycle induction motor with its rotor star-connected gives 500 volts (r.m.s.) at standstill between the slip-rings on open circuit. Calculate the current and power factor in each phase of the rotor winding at standstill when joined to a star-connected circuit each limb of which has a resistance of 10 ohms and an inductance of 0·03 henry. The resistance per phase of the rotor winding is 0·2 ohm and its inductance 0·03 henry. Calculate also the current and power factor in each rotor phase when the slip-rings are short-circuited and the motor is running with a slip of 4 per cent. Neglect the impedance of the stator winding. (*Lond. Univ.*, 1938, *A.E.*)

4. A 4-pole, 50-cycle, 3-phase induction motor has a slip-ring rotor with a resistance and stand-still reactance of 0·04 ohm and 0·2 ohm per phase respectively. Find the amount of resistance to be inserted in each rotor phase to obtain full-load torque at starting. What will be the approximate power factor in the rotor at this instant? The slip at full load is 3 per cent.
(*Lond. Univ.*, 1930, *El. Mach.*)

5. Calculate the steps in a 5-step starter for a 3-phase slip-ring induction motor given that the slip at the maximum starting current is 2 per cent, and the resistance per rotor phase is 0·015 ohm. (Ref. M7.) (*I.E.E.*, April, 1922.)

6. Discuss the advantages and disadvantages of auto-transformer, star-delta and resistance starters for squirrel-cage, 3-phase induction motors. A 10-h.p. motor when started at normal voltage with a star-delta switch in the star position is found to take an initial current of 1·7 × full-load current and

give an initial starting torque of 35 per cent of full-load torque. Explain what happens when the motor is started under the following conditions: (a) an auto-transformer giving 60 per cent of normal voltage; (b) a resistance in series with the stator reducing the voltage to 60 per cent of the normal; and calculate in each case the value of the starting current and torque in terms of the corresponding quantities at full load.

(*Lond. Univ.*, 1935, *El. Power.*)

7. Describe briefly how a high starting torque is obtained with a double-cage induction motor. The resistance and reactance (equivalent) values of such a motor for stator, outer and inner cages are 0·25, 1·0 and 0·15 ohms resistance and 3·5, zero and 3·0 ohms reactance respectively. Find the starting torque, if the phase voltage is 250-volt and the synchronous speed is 1000 r.p.m. (Ref. M7.) (*I.E.E.*, 1940.)

8. Explain the phenomenon of "crawling" in cage induction motors, and describe methods of avoiding it. A 3-phase, 4-pole, 50-cycle cage motor has 24 stator and 44 rotor slots, and has a crawling speed at 115 r.p.m. What are the precise causes of this?   (*I.E.E.*, *May*, 1935.)

*9. Estimate the total resistance per phase required to limit to approximately 40 amperes the line current of a 30-h.p., 50-cycle, 6-pole, 400-volt, 3-phase induction motor having delta/star connections, unity line voltage ratio, and the following stator and rotor values respectively: resistance, 0·5 ohms and 0·167 ohm; leakage reactance, 1·5 ohms and 0·5 ohm. On no-load the motor takes 1·5 amperes active and 13 amperes reactive current per line.   (*I.E.E.*, *Nov.*, 1940.)

*10. A 3-phase slip-ring induction motor gives a reading of 55 volts across slip-rings on open-circuit when at rest with normal stator voltage applied. The rotor is star-connected and has an impedance of 0·7 + j5 ohms. Find the rotor current when the machine is (a) at standstill with the slip-rings joined to a star-connected starter with a phase impedance of 4 + j3 ohms; (b) running normally with a 5 per cent slip.

(*I.E.E.*, *Nov.*, 1943.)

*11. A 3-phase, cage induction motor takes a starting current at normal voltage of 5 times full-load value, and its full-load slip is 4 per cent. What auto-transformer ratio would enable the motor to be started with not more than twice full-load current drawn from the supply? What would be the starting torque under this condition, and how would it compare with that obtained using a stator resistance starter under the same limitations of line current?   (*I.E.E.*, *Nov.*, 1943.)

61. Induction Motors—Speed Control

References. G1; M7; V1; W3.

EXAMPLES 61

1. What are the advantages of electric ship propulsion? Describe the principal power equipment for propelling a ship requiring 30,000 shaft horse-power for a cruising speed of 21 knots. How is the speed regulated if only 10,000 horse-power is required for 15 knots, and how is the plant operated to secure maximum economy? (*I.E.E., Nov.*, 1932.)

2. In what way does the speed vary with the load when resistance is inserted in the rotor circuit of a polyphase induction motor? The voltage at standstill between the slip-rings of the star-connected rotor of a 100-h.p. motor is 273 volts and the slip at full load is 2 per cent. Calculate the resistance of a controller to reduce the speed by 25 per cent when the torque of the drive varies as the square of the speed. Neglect mechanical loss. (*Lond. Univ.*, 1934, *El. Mach.*)

3. Describe with diagrams either a cascade induction motor combination or a cascade motor converter. Explain the action and show that synchronous speed of the set is given by

$$\text{R.P.M.}_{syn} = 120 \times f_1 \div (p_1 + p_2)$$

where f_1 is the line frequency and p_1 and p_2 are the number of poles in the two machines. (*I.E.E., April*, 1921.)

4. The stator of a 6-pole motor is joined to a 50-cycle supply, and the machine is mechanically coupled and joined in cascade with a 4-pole motor. Neglecting all losses, determine the speed and output of the 4-pole motor when the total load on the combination is 100 h.p., deducing any formula used. (*Lond. Univ.*, 1940, *El. Power.*)

5. It is required to obtain gradual and economical control of the speed of a 3-phase 50-cycle induction motor within 10 per cent of synchronous speed. The maximum output is 1000 h.p. and the load requires a constant torque over the speed range. Describe a method whereby this can be done with simultaneous compensation of power factor, indicating clearly what auxiliary machines and apparatus are needed and their rating. (*C. & G., Final*, 1930.)

62. Induction Motor Design—Stator Windings

References.   A2;   B1;   C1, 5, 6;   F1;   H4;   M7;   S1, 3; 4, V1;   W2.

EXAMPLES 62

1. Design the stator winding of a 5 h.p., 220-volt, 3-phase, 50-cycle squirrel cage induction motor with a synchronous speed of 1500 r.p.m. Assume mesh connection and the following magnetic and electric loadings: mean flux density in gap, 4800 lines/cm.[2]; ampere conductors per cm. of stator periphery, 200.   (*I.E.E., Nov.*, 1932.)

2. A 400-volt, 3-phase, squirrel-cage motor is required for present operation at about 730 r.p.m. on a 25-cycle supply. Ultimately, the motor has to operate at the same speed—and voltage—when the supply frequency is changed to 50 cycles. Explain in detail how this can be arranged.

(*Lond. Univ.*, 1933, *El. Power.*)

3. Explain fully how to arrange the stator windings of a 3-phase squirrel-cage motor so that it can operate with either 4 poles or 8 poles off a constant voltage supply.

(*Lond. Univ.*, 1935, *El. Mach.*)

4. Design the stator winding of a 15 h.p., 4-pole, 400-volt, 50-cycle, 3-phase induction motor intended for star-delta starting. Mean flux density in gap, about 4000 gauss; ampere-conductors per cm. about 250. Obtain the number of slots, conductors per slot, and approximate conductor size.

(*I.E.E., Nov.*, 1934.)

5. Design the stator winding of a 3-phase, 4-pole, 440-V., 50-cycle mesh-connected induction motor with a bore of 20 cm., a core-length of 15 cm. and a mean gap-density of 4400 gauss. State the number of slots, conductors per slot, coil-pitch, type of winding and flux per pole.   (*I.E.E., May*, 1936.)

6. A 10-h.p., 220-volt, 4-pole, 50-cycle, star-connected, 3-phase induction motor with a bore of 18 cm. and a core-length of 13·5 cm. is to have an average air-gap flux density of about 4000 gauss. Find particulars of a suitable stator winding, stating the number of slots, conductors per slot, coil pitch, and flux per pole.   (*I.E.E., May*, 1940.)

*7. A three-phase, 10-pole, single circuit, star-connected winding is arranged in two layers in 126 slots. Give full details of a suitable winding scheme for the case of 2 conductors per slot. What advantages arise from the use of such slottings?

(*Lond. Univ.*, 1942, *El. Mach.*)

*8. A stator is wound with 12 similar concentric type coils arranged symmetrically. Show how to arrange the winding for: (a) 3-phase, 8-poles, star-connection, and (b) 2-phase, 6-poles.   (*Lond. Univ.*, 1943, *El. Mach.*)

*9. A wave-winding for the stator of a 4-pole induction motor is accommodated in 39 slots with 6 coil-sides per slot. Indicate clearly the connections to be made in order to produce a 3-phase, star-connected winding with a 60° phase spread.

(*C. & G., Final*, 1944.)

*10. Draw developed diagrams showing (a) a 4-pole star-connected, single-layer winding comprising 24 conductors with the overhang in 3 planes; (b) a 6-pole, mesh-connected, single-layer winding with 36 conductors and the overhang in 2 planes. In each case mark the phases and the terminals.

(*I.E.E., May*, 1939.)

*11. An 8-pole 3-phase induction motor has 45 slots and 45 coils. Show diagrammatically, or with a connection table, how to connect the coils so as to produce a symmetrical star-connected wave winding, with 60° phase spread.

(*I.E.E., Nov.*, 1939.)

63. Induction Motor Design—Rotor Windings and Power Factor Improvement

References as for Section 62. For cage rotors, $Z_2 I_2 \doteqdot Z_1 I_1$ or in average cases about 93 per cent of $Z_1 I_1$. End ring current $= Z_2 I_2/2p\pi$.

EXAMPLES 63

1. Design a suitable 3-phase rotor winding for the following 3-phase induction motor : output, 20 h.p. ; supply voltage, 440 volts ; frequency, 50 periods ; speed (synchronous), 750 r.p.m. ; efficiency, 0·82 ; power factor, 0·8 ; stator bore, 30 cm. , length, 20 cm. There are 72 stator slots with 10 conductors per slot and the phases are star-connected.

(*I.E.E.*, *Oct.*, 1922.)

2. The equivalent standstill impedances per phase of the first cage and of the second cage respectively of a double-cage induction motor are $5 + j1$, and $1 + j5$ ohms. Compare the torques of the two cages (*a*) at standstill, (*b*) at a slip of 4 per cent. Sketch approximately the total torque/speed curve.

(*Lond. Univ.*, 1933, *El Mach.*)

3. The armature of a 2-pole D.C. machine, free to move in its bearings, is supplied with a sine-wave alternating current of low frequency, while a constant direct current is passed through its field windings. Explain what happens and show by means of diagrams the relation between current, velocity, displacement and generated E.M.F. Compare the method of improving the power factor of induction motors employing armatures of this kind with other methods of obtaining the same result.   (*Lond. Univ.*, 1935, *El. Mach.*)

4. Under what conditions is the use of a phase advancer justified ? Describe the construction and action of one type of rotary phase advancer suitable for use with a large induction motor driving a factory load. A 3-phase induction motor at 2000 h.p. has an efficiency of 0·97, a power factor of 0·9 and a slip of 0·016. Calculate the rating of a phase advancer for insertion in the rotor circuit to raise the motor power factor at this load to unity.   (*Lond. Univ.*, 1934, *El. Power.*)

5. A 90 h.p., 1000-volt, 50-cycle, 3-phase induction motor with a synchronous speed of 750 r.p.m. has a star-connected winding in 72 slots with 8 conductors per slot. Find a suitable rotor winding to give about 400 volts at the slip-rings on open circuit. State the number of slots and conductors per slot, the

open-circuit slip-ring voltage, and the approximate full-load rotor current per phase. (*I.E.E.*, *Nov.*, 1935.)

6. Calculate the resistance loss in each end-ring of the 4-pole cage induction motor to which the following particulars apply—

Number of stator conductors = 432.

Number of rotor conductors = 83.

Stator current per conductor = 230 amps.

Mean diameter of end-rings = 60 cm.

Section of end-rings = 5 cm. by 2 cm.

Resistivity of end-ring material = $1 \cdot 8 \mu\Omega$-cm.

(*Lond. Univ.*, 1937, *El. Mach.*)

7. In a double-cage induction motor, if the outer cage has an impedance at standstill of $2 + j2$ ohms, and the inner cage an impedance of $0 \cdot 5 + j5$, determine the slip at which the two cages develop equal torques.

(*Lond. Univ.*, 1939, *El. Mach.*)

8. A 6-pole, 3-phase, squirrel-cage induction motor has 72 stator slots with 15 conductors in each. There are 55 rotor slots. Determine the current in the rotor bars and in the end rings if the "equivalent" stator current is 20 amp. Deduce the formulae used. (*Lond. Univ.*, 1940, *El. Mach.*)

*9. If the equivalent impedances of the two cages of a double-cage induction motor at standstill are $0 \cdot 1 + j1$ and $0 \cdot 4 + j0 \cdot 3$ respectively, compare the torque developed by the two cages (*a*) at starting, and (*b*) at 4 per cent slip.

(*Lond. Univ.*, 1942, *El. Mach.*)

*10. Show how a phase advancer may be used to improve the power-factor of an induction motor. A three-phase induction motor with a winding ratio of 1 : 1, and having a mesh-connected rotor and stator, gave a rotor E.M.F. at standstill of 150 volts per phase. The rotor resistance was 0·2 ohm per phase, and the rotor reactance at stator frequency 1·2 ohms per phase. This motor was connected to a mesh-connected phase advancer which gave an E.M.F. between brushes of 5 volts for a brush current of 10 amperes at all frequencies. The resistance of the advancer was 0·3 ohm per phase and the reactance per phase 0·8 ohm at stator frequency of the induction motor. Calculate (*a*) the diameter, in amperes, of the circle diagram of the motor alone, and (*b*) the diameter, in amperes, of the circle diagram of the combined motor and phase advancer. (*Lond. Univ.*, 1946, *El. Mach.*)

64. Induction Motor Design—The Circle Diagram

References. A1; C1, 5, 6; M1, 7; S1, 4; V1.
See answers to Q. 1 for drawing and use of Circle Diagram.

EXAMPLES 64

1. A 3-phase, 440-volt, 4-pole, 50-cycle induction motor has a wound rotor, the ratio of turns on stator to rotor being 3·6/1. When running light on 440 volts, it took a current of 8 amperes at 0·2 power factor, and on standstill, with the rotor short-circuited, and an applied voltage of 110 volts, the current taken was 23 amperes at 0·3 power factor. The stator and rotor copper losses in this test were equal. The full-load current is 20 amperes. Draw the circle diagram, and from it ascertain the following: (a) full-load power factor, torque, horse-power, efficiency and slip; (b) the maxima for torque and horse-power; (c) the standstill torque; (d) the resistance to be inserted in the rotor circuit to give 150 per cent full-load torque at starting, and the current and power factor under these conditions.

*2. A 3-phase, 220-volt, 12-pole, star-connected induction motor has a cage-type rotor with 67 conductors; the stator has 720 conductors. The rotor end-rings have a section of 1·3 cm.² and a mean diameter of 25 cm. They are made of material having a resistivity of 7 microhm-cm. At full-load of 14 h.p. the rotor conductor current is 360 amperes. Calculate the resistance loss in each end-ring. At no-load the stator current is 8 amperes at 0·2 power-factor, lagging. At full-load the rotor and stator resistance losses are equal, each being 5 times the loss in one rotor end-ring. Draw the circle diagram for the motor and obtain from it the starting torque in terms of full-load torque. (*Lond. Univ.*, 1942, *El. Mach.*)

3. The following are test figures for a 25 h.p., 3-phase, 440-volt slip-ring induction motor: light load: 440 volts, 7·5 amperes, 1350 watts (including 650 watts friction loss). Short-circuit, at stand-still: 100 volts, 32 amperes, 1800 watts. Draw the locus diagram of the stator current, and hence obtain the current, power factor, and slip on full load. On short-circuit, the rotor and stator copper losses are equal.
(*Lond. Univ.*, 1935, *El. Mach.*)

4. Draw the circle diagram for a 10-h.p., 230-volt, 50-cycle, 4-pole, 3-phase, mesh-connected induction motor from the

following data (line values): no-load test: 9 amperes, power factor 0·17. Short-circuit test at one-third voltage; 57 amperes, power factor 0·46. Find the full-load current and power factor, and the maximum output.   (*I.E.E.*, *Nov.*, 1934.)

5. The following particulars apply to a 200-h.p., 3-phase, 25-cycle, 5000-volt induction motor with stator and rotor windings star-connected—

Turns per phase, stator = 576, rotor = 56. Resistance per phase, stator = 3·6 ohms, rotor = 0·03 ohms. Reactance per phase, stator = 16 ohms, rotor = 0·07 ohms. No-load current = 6 amperes at 0·07 power factor. Draw the circle diagram and determine from it the starting torque on full voltage with

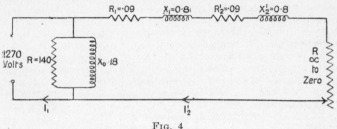

Fig. 4

the rotor short-circuited, and the value of the resistance to be added to each phase of the rotor circuit to give twice full-load torque at starting. Determine the starting current and power factor for each case.

(*Lond. Univ.*, 1936, *El. Mach.*)

6. The following figures were obtained from tests on a 1600-h.p., 3-phase, 50-cycle, 3000-volt, 24-pole induction motor: running light: volts, 3000; amperes, 100; watts, 30,000. With short-circuited rotor locked: volts, 1000; amperes, 445; watts, 86,000. The resistance of one leg of the star-connected stator is 0·075 ohm, and of the rotor 0·013 ohm. Ratio of transformation 2·4. Draw the circle diagram of the motor. Find the power factor at full load. What resistance must be inserted in the rotor circuit to give full-load starting torque?   (*I.E.E.*, *May*, 1934.)

7. Show that the performance of a polyphase induction motor operating with constant applied voltage and frequency can be approximately represented by the equivalent circuit of Fig. 4. Point out the assumptions made, and develop a vector

diagram for this circuit which enables the currents I_1 and I'_2 to be directly determined for any conditions of working.

With the values given in the figure, which relate to one winding of a star-connected, 3-phase motor, determine : (a) the maximum power input to the motor from the supply ; (b) the maximum power expended in the resistance R ; (c) the value of R which gives the maximum power factor.

(Lond. Univ., 1925, El. Mach.)

8. Draw the circle diagram for a 20 h.p., 440 volt, 50-cycle, 3-phase induction motor from the following test figures (line values)—

No-load : 440 volts, 10 amp., p.f. 0·2.

Short-circuit : 200 volts, 50 amp., p.f. 0·4.

From the diagram estimate (a) the line current and p.f. at full load, (b) the maximum horse-power, (c) the stalling torque. Assume the rotor and stator I^2R losses on short circuit to be equal.   *(Lond. Univ., 1931, El. Mach.)*

9. A 40-h.p., 440-volt, 50-cycle, 3-phase induction motor gave the following test results : no-load : 440 volts, 16 amperes, power factor 0·15. Short-circuit : 100 volts, 55 amperes, power factor 0·225. Ratio of rotor to stator losses on short-circuit, 0·9. Find the full-load current and power factor, the pull-out torque, and the maximum horse-power.

(I.E.E., May, 1935.)

10. A 220 volt, 3-phase, star-connected 15 b.h.p. induction motor has a winding ratio of 4/1, and the resistances per phase are : stator, 0·32 ohm ; rotor, 0·0176 ohm. The no-load current is 8 amperes per phase, at a power factor of 0·18, while on standstill test the current is 100 amperes per phase at 0·45 power factor. What resistance must be added per phase to the rotor to give maximum torque at starting ?

11. A 40-h.p., 50-cycle, 6-pole, 420-volt, 3-phase slip-ring induction motor furnished the following test figures : no-load : 420 volts, 18 amperes, power factor 0·15. Short-circuit : 210 volts, 140 amperes, power factor 0·25. The ratio of stator to rotor I^2R losses on short circuit was 7 : 6. Draw the circle diagram and find from it (a) the full-load current and power factor ; (b) the maximum torque and horse-power.

(I.E.E., Nov., 1935.)

12. Draw the " no-load and short-circuit diagram " for a mesh-connected, 30 h.p., 4-pole, 3-phase, 500 volt, 50-cycle squirrel-cage induction motor, from the following data—

No-load run : line voltage, 500 ; line current, 8·3 amperes ; wattmeter readings, + 2·85 kW., – 1·35 kW.

Short-circuit test : line voltage, 100 ; line current, 32 amperes ; wattmeter readings, $- 0.75$ kW., $+ 2.35$ kW.

Find for full-load conditions (a) the stator line current, (b) the power factor, (c) the efficiency. Find also the maximum horse-power the machine will give.

(*Lond. Univ.*, 1927, *El. Mach.*)

13. The following are test figures for a 5-h.p., 500-volt, 3-phase induction motor: No load: 500 volts, 3·0 amperes, 350 watts. Short-circuit at standstill: 120 volts, 5·9 amperes, 460 watts. Connected in parallel with the motor are condensers such that the total power factor is 0·95 at a load of 3·75 h.p. Draw the locus diagram for the total current input, and from it determine the total power factor at full load.

(*Lond. Univ.*, 1939, *El. Mach.*)

14. A 3-phase induction motor has a full-load output of 25 b.h.p. at 220 volts, 720 r.p.m. The full-load power factor is 0·83 and efficiency is 85 per cent. When running light the motor takes 5 amperes at 0·2 power factor. Draw the circle diagram and use it to determine the maximum torque which the motor can exert (a) in lb.-ft., (b) in terms of the full-load torque, (c) in terms of the starting torque.

(*Lond. Univ.*, 1940, *El. Mach.*)

*15. A 3-phase, 5 h.p., 440-volt, cage induction motor has the following test figures :

No-load :	440 volts	4·3 amperes	430 watts
Standstill :	100 volts	7 amperes	490 watts

Static condensers are joined in parallel with the motor, and the total power-factor on full-load is 0·95, lagging. Draw the locus diagram for the total current, and determine the total current and power-factor at half-load.

(*Lond. Univ.*, 1942, *El. Mach.*)

*16. A 3-phase, 400-volt, 50-cycle, delta-connected, cage-rotor induction motor gave the following test readings :

No-load :	400 volts	5 amperes	0·1 power-factor.
Standstill :	100 volts	12·5 amperes	0·4 power-factor.

Stator resistance 0·9 ohm per phase. A 3-ohms resistor is joined in each line wire connecting the motor terminals to 400-volt, 50-cycles mains. Draw the locus diagram of the current taken by the motor. (*Lond. Univ.*, 1943, *El. Mach.*)

*17. Draw, and explain, the conventional equivalent circuit diagram for one phase of a three-phase induction motor. In such a circuit for a 4-pole, 400-volt, 50-cycle, squirrel-cage motor the primary leakage impedance is $1 + j2$ ohms, the secondary leakage impedance at standstill is $1.2 + j1.5$ ohms, and the impedance of the magnetization branch is $4 + j40$ ohms. Determine the output current, efficiency and power-factor at a slip of 5 per cent. Frictional losses = 250 watts. The winding is star-connected.

(Lond. Univ., 1944, El. Mach.)

*8. The following particulars apply to a 5-h.p., 110-volts, 4-pole, 50-cycle, 3-phase induction motor, the stator and rotor windings being star-connected—

	Turns	Reactance	Resistance
Stator, per phase :	48	0.25 ohm	0.065 ohm
Rotor, per phase :	64	0.45 ohm	0.27 ohm

No-load current 10 amperes, power-factor 0.15.

Draw the circle diagram to scale and determine (a) the current and power-factor at full-load and (b) the starting torque in lb.-ft. if full voltage is switched on with the rotor short-circuited.

(Lond. Univ., 1946, El. Mach.)

65. Induction Motors—Designing

References. A2; B1; C5, 6; S1, 4; V1; W2.

Output Coefficient.

$$G = \frac{H.P.}{N \cdot D^2 L} = \frac{B_{mean} \, ac \cdot \eta \cos \phi}{4 \cdot 1 \times 10^{11}} \text{ for 3-phase}$$

where B_{mean} = mean flux density in air-gap

ac = ampere-conductors per cm.

N = r.p.m. synchronous speed

$\cos \phi$ = power-factor, full-load

η = efficiency, full-load

D = core diameter in cm.

L = core length (gross) in cm.

= $1 \cdot 2 \times$ Pole pitch in many cases.

For 2-phase, use $4 \cdot 3$ instead of $4 \cdot 1$ above.

Average values—

B_{mean} = about 4500 lines per sq. cm.

B_{max} = $1 \cdot 7 \, B_{mean}$ for 3-phase machines, and

= $1 \cdot 94 \, B_{mean}$ for 2-phase machines (see H4)

ac = about 300 per cm., fair size, well ventilated

Cos ϕ and η assume about $0 \cdot 9$ each for initial working.

EXAMPLES 65

1. A 3-phase, 220-volt, 50-cycle induction motor is to have a full-load output of 10 b.h.p. Its synchronous speed is 1000 r.p.m. Assuming a full-load current of 25 amperes and the stator core-length is equal to the pole-pitch, calculate: (i) the internal diameter and length of the stator core, (ii) the number of stator conductors if delta connected. Assume $ac = 200$ and $B_{mean} = 7000$.   (*Lond. Univ.*, 1939, *El. Mach.*)

2. A 3-phase, 4-pole, 400-volt, 50-frequency, squirrel-cage induction motor is to be started by a star-delta switch. Determine suitable values for the number of stator slots, and the conductors per slot, having given: Internal diameter of stator = 25 cm.; axial core length = 15 cm.; mean flux density in

air-gap = 4200 to 4500 lines per cm.^{2} State also a suitable number of rotor slots, giving reasons for your choice.

(Lond. Univ., 1933, El. Mach.)

3. Determine the starting torque in lb.-ft. of a 4-pole, 25-frequency, cage type, 3-phase motor, having given: stator: 96 slots, 12 conductors per slot. Rotor: 70 slots, 1 conductor per slot. Resistance of each rotor conductor = 0·035 × 10^{-3} ohm. Resistance of each end-ring = 0·06 × 10^{-3} ohm. The short-circuit current at full voltage (with delta connection) is 170 amperes in each stator conductor, and the equivalent rotor current is 93 per cent of the stator current. The motor is started with a star-delta switch.

(Lond. Univ., 1934, El. Mach.)

4. Find the main dimensions and a suitable stator winding for a mesh-connected 10-h.p., 220-volt, 4-pole, 50-cycle, 3-phase induction motor of the open ventilated type. Indicate briefly the several factors which influence the choice of the gap density and the ampere-conductors per cm. *(C. & G., Final, 1933.)*

*5. A 3-phase, 440-volt, 750-r.p.m., 50-cycle, star-connected induction motor has a stator with an internal diameter of 25 cm. and an axial length of 15 cm. It has 16 slots per phase, 24 conductors per slot. Calculate the air-gap flux per pole of the rotating field. Indicate any assumptions made in the calculation. The area of each stator conductor is to be 0·05 cm^2. Calculate the width and depth of a slot to accommodate the stator conductors. The maximum flux density in the stator teeth is to be about 18,000 gauss. Conductor insulation is 0·08 mm. thick. Slot insulation is 0·8 mm. thick.

(Lond. Univ., 1942, El. Mach.)

*6. Derive from first principles an expression for the output coefficient of an induction motor. Obtain the approximate core dimensions for a 25-h.p., 3-phase, 50-cycle, 4-pole induction motor. Take the power-factor and the efficiency to be 90 per cent, and B_{av} = 5000 lines per cm.^{2}, and the specific electric loading = 240 ampere-conductors per cm.

(C. & G., Final, 1946.)

*7. Determine the approximate core dimensions, number of stator turns and number of stator slots for a 15 h.p., 400-volt, 3-phase, 50-cycle, 4-pole induction motor, the stator winding of which is to be delta-connected for normal running. Assume: specific magnetic loading = 4500 lines per cm.^{2}; specific electric loading = 250 amp-conductors per cm.; full-load efficiency = 85 per cent; full-load power-factor = 0·87. Sketch the shape of the slot. *(Lond. Univ., 1947, El. Mach.)*

65a. Induction Regulators

References. *English Electric Journals.*

EXAMPLES 65a

*1. A 4-pole, auto-connected, 3-phase, induction regulator is to maintain a constant output voltage of 400, when the input voltage varies between 350 and 450. Calculate (i) the minimum ratio of secondary to primary turns; (ii) the angular movement of the core for the given range of input voltage; and (iii) the maximum range of input voltage for which the output could be maintained constant at 400 volts.

(*I.E.E., April*, 1947.)

2. Describe the action of the induction regulator and explain any differences between the design of single- and 3-phase regulators. Given a 3-phase 440-volt supply, show how to arrange the windings for varying the voltage (*a*) from 0 to 440 volts, (*b*) from 220 to 660 volts.   (*C. & G., Final*, 1931.)

3. Draw the diagram of connections for a 3-phase induction regulator for regulating the voltage at the receiving end of a transmission line. The voltage at the end of a feeder transmitting 100 kW. varies between 475 and 525 volts. For how many kilovolt-amperes must an induction regulator be designed to maintain the pressure constant at 500 volts ?

(*C. & G., Final*, 1923.)

4. Describe the operation of an induction regulator. Calculate the rating of a regulator to regulate the voltage between 10,000 and 12,000 at the receiving end of a 3-phase feeder loaded up to 1500 kVA.   (*I.E.E., Nov.*, 1935.)

5. Explain the purpose of the twin induction regulator. An induction regulator is to give a 10 per cent up and down voltage regulation for a nominal 500-volt, 50-cycle, 1000-kW., 6-ring synchronous convertor supplying a 3-wire d.c. system. Draw a diagram of connections between the secondary side of the transformer and the d.c. bus-bars. Find the approximate voltage and current ratings of each of the regulator windings, and the capacity of the regulator in kVA. Assume unity power factor and an efficiency of 90 per cent.

(*I.E.E., May.* 1942.)

66. Rotary and Motor-Convertors— General Principles

References. A2; C4, 5; D3; H3; M1; S1, 2, 4.

Conversion Ratios.

(1) *Volts.* $\dfrac{\text{A.C. volts between slip rings}}{\text{D.C. volts}} = \dfrac{\sin \pi/m}{\sqrt{2}}$

where m = number of rings or tappings per pole-pair (two-phase to be taken as 2).

(2) *Current.* $\dfrac{\text{A.C. line current}}{\text{D.C. current}} = \dfrac{2\sqrt{2}}{m \cos \phi}$

(3) *A.C. line current* $= 2 \sin \pi/m \times$ phase current.

Phases or m .	.	1	2	3	6	12
(1) Volt ratio	.	·707	·707	·612	·354	·183
(2) Current ratio	.	1·414	·707	·943	·472	·236

Above current ratios at unity power factor and 100 per cent efficiency. For other power factors and efficiencies, the above ratios are increased by dividing by these two factors in decimal form.

Heating.

Difference current in the conductor is

$$I_{dcc} \left\{ \frac{4 \sin (\theta - \alpha - \phi)}{m \sin \pi/m . \, \eta \cos \phi} - 1 \right\}$$

I_{dcc} = D.C. current in the conductor

α = electrical angle that the conductor is from the mid-point between tapping points.

m = number of points in which convertor armature is tapped on A.C. side, per pole-pair.

$\cos \phi$ = power factor; η = efficiency

If W = loss in convertor armature at any given output

W_1 = loss in same armature running as D.C. generator with the same output,

then $\dfrac{W}{W_1} = \dfrac{8}{\{m\eta \sin (\pi/m) \cos \phi\}^2} - \dfrac{16}{\pi^2 \eta} + 1$

The output as a rotary compared with that as a D.C. generator for equal losses will be given by $1/\sqrt{\text{above ratio}}$ and is 133, 162, 193, and 219 per cent for 3, 4, 6, and 12-phase respectively, for $\cos \phi = 1$ and $\eta = 1$.

EXAMPLES 66

1. A 6-ring, 12-pole, lap-wound synchronous convertor with diametral tappings runs at 600 r.p.m. and supplies 2000 amperes D.C. There are 1200 armature conductors and the flux per pole is 5 megalines. The transformer is delta-connected to a 6600-volt, 3-phase supply. Assuming unity power factor and an armature efficiency of 96 per cent calculate (a) the turn-ratio of the transformer and the voltage between adjacent rings, (b) the current per ring and (c) the current in the armature connection between a slip-ring and a tapping point.
(C. & G., 1939.)

2. Draw a diagram of the main connections for a 750-kW., 500-volt, 50-cycle, 6-pole, 6-ring synchronous convertor using reactance control, fed from a high-voltage supply, and arranged for self-synchronizing and static balancing of 3-wire D.C. loads. Indicate the currents in all main connections for full-load with 200-ampere out-of-balance current on the positive side of the 3-wire system. Assume unity power factor at the 6600-volt input terminals, a power factor of 0·966 leading at the rings, and efficiencies of 98 per cent for the transformer and 96 per cent for the convertor. (I.E.E., May, 1938.)

3. Explain the advantages of using a large number of phases in a rotary convertor. If a 6-phase rotary is working at unity power factor, show that a coil close to a tapping point will be heated to about double the extent of a coil midway between tappings.

4. A 6-ring convertor with diametral tappings is supplied from a 33 kV., 3-phase supply. The transformer is delta-connected on the high-voltage side with a turn-ratio of 77 and an equivalent secondary reactance of 0·2 ohm. If the D.C. load remains constant at 500 amperes, find the change in commutator voltage when the power factor at the slip-rings increases from 0·8 leading to unity. Assume the efficiency to remain unaltered at 0·9. (C. & G., 1940.)

5. A dynamometer voltmeter and a permanent magnet moving-coil voltmeter were used simultaneously to measure the drop on the winding of the commutating poles of a rotary convertor. A considerable difference was observed between

the readings of the two instruments, although they read alike when connected together to a cell. Explain the probable reason for the difference in the readings and say which instrument should give the higher reading and why ?

(*C. & G., Final*, 1920.)

6. Connections are made to the negative brush on the D.C. side of a rotary convertor and to one of the brushes on the A.C. side. What will be the nature of the p.d. between them assuming a sine wave flux distribution, and what reading would be obtained on (*a*) a moving coil voltmeter, and (*b*) an electrostatic voltmeter, connected between these two brushes if the voltage on the D.C. side of the rotary convertor is 500 volts ?

(*Lond. Univ.*, 1925, *El. Tech.*)

7. Show how to calculate the equivalent heating due to resistance in the armature of a 6-phase rotary convertor, assuming unity power factor. Hence calculate the armature conductor losses in a 6-phase, 1000 kW. rotary convertor working at unity power factor, the D.C. voltage being 550 and the armature resistance as measured between neighbouring D.C. brushes being 0·005 ohm.

*8. A 6-ring, 8-pole, lap-wound rotary convertor has a D.C. output of 1600 amperes. Give a dimensioned graph, and determine the R.M.S. value of the wave shape of the current in an armature conductor midway between tapping points, at unity power-factor and efficiency. Why are six rings used in preference to three for such machines?

(*Lond. Univ.*, 1942, *El. Mach.*)

9. Explain how the D.C. voltage of synchronous convertors and of mercury arc rectifiers can be controlled. A reactance of 1 ohm is included in each lead of a 3-ring convertor which is supplied from a transformer giving a line voltage of 367 volts. Find the commutator brush voltage when the slip-ring current is 25 amperes at power factors of (*a*) unity, (*b*) 0·87 lagging, (*c*) 0·87 leading, at the transformer low-voltage terminals. Neglect any loss in the convertor. (*C. & G., Final*, 1933.)

10. A motor convertor, with equal numbers of poles on the two elements, works with the same output voltage and current as a 6-phase rotary convertor. The D.C. element has the same number of poles and phases as the rotary convertor. Determine the ratio of the R.M.S. currents in the mid-conductors of each phase for the rotary and for the D.C. element of the motor convertor. Losses may be neglected and unity power factor assumed. (*Lond. Univ.*, 1934, *El. Mach.*)

11. Determine the alternating-current (R.M.S.) voltage

corresponding to 100 volts direct current in the following rotary convertors: (a) single-phase, (b) 3-phase, (c) 6-phase. State for each case the alternating current per line corresponding to a direct current of 100 amperes, when the power factor is 0·9 and the efficiency 0·95. (*I.E.E.*, *Nov.*, 1932.)

12. A 6-ring, 800 kW. rotary convertor, with reactance control, having an efficiency of 95 per cent gives 565 volts on the D.C. side at full load. It is supplied across diametral tappings from a 1000 kVA. 3-phase transformer having a turn ratio of 6600 to 370. The high voltage supply is 6600 volts, the total reactance per phase 20 per cent and the transformer magnetizing current is 6 per cent. Calculate the current taken by the convertor at full load, and the reactive kVA. on the primary side of the transformer.

(*Lond. Univ.*, 1935, *El. Mach.*)

13. A motor convertor supplies 500 kW. at 600 volts on the D.C. side and takes 550 kW. at 6600 volts from the 3-phase supply mains. It is also used to supply a leading wattless current to the mains equal to 30 per cent of the power component of the full-load current. The magnetizing current is 25 per cent of the power component of the full-load current. Calculate the currents in the different windings of the convertor if there are 12 phases on the rotor and the number of poles on the A.C. and D.C. ends are the same.

(*Lond. Univ.*, 1936, *El. Mach.*)

*14. Draw a diagram of connections for a 1000-kW. motor-convertor to feed a 500-volt, 3-wire, D.C. system from 11-kV., 50-cycle, 3-phase supply. The A.C. rotor has 4 poles and 9 phases, and the D.C. end has 6 poles. Describe how the machine is started from the A.C. side. Calculate the rotor current per phase. (*I.E.E.*, *Nov.*, 1941.)

*15. A 6-ring, 500-kW. synchronous convertor with diametral connections supplies a balanced 3-wire, D.C. load with 550 volts between the outers. The transformer is delta-connected to 6600-volt, 3-phase lines. Draw the essential connections and calculate the voltage and current ratings of the transformer windings. Assume the convertor to be working on full load at a power-factor of 0·9 and an efficiency of 0·9. Neglect transformer losses. (*C. & G.*, *Final*, 1942.)

*16. If a 3-phase, 6-ring synchronous convertor has an efficiency of 92 per cent at full load and the power-factor is adjusted to unity, compare the heating of an armature conductor adjacent to one of the slip-ring tappings with the heating of the same conductor when the machine is run as a dynamo

with the same output. Sketch the wave shape of the current
in the two cases.   (*C. & G., Final*, 1945.)

*17. A 3-ring, synchronous convertor supplies a load of
550 kW. at 220 volts through a feeder of 0·01 ohm resistance.
Calculate the value of the reactance required to be inserted
in each slip-ring lead to maintain the voltage at the load
approximately constant at all loads. The convertor operates
at unity p.f., 0·95 efficiency, and the no-load slip-ring voltage
is that of the transformer.   (*C. & G., Final*, 1945.)

*18. A motor-convertor consists of an 8-pole induction motor
driving a 6-pole D.C. machine and is connected between
11,000-volt, 3-phase, 50-cycle mains and a 440-volt, D.C.
network. The output is 500 kW. Assuming unity power-
factor and neglecting losses, determine (*a*) the speed of the set,
(*b*) the power supplied electrically to the D.C. side, and (*c*) the
current in each of the twelve rotor phases.

(*C. & G., Final*, 1946.)

67. Rotary Convertor Design

References. C5; H3; S1, 2, 4.

EXAMPLES 67

1. What are the considerations which determine the number of ampere-turns to put on the commutating pole of a rotary convertor ? A 2000 kW., 525 volt, 6-ring, 50 cycle rotary convertor has 14 poles, 15 slots per pole, and 6 conductors per slot. How many ampere-turns are required on each interpole at full-load ? Assume suitable values for any quantities required in the calculation. The armature diameter is 150 cm. and the axial length of core and of interpole is 27 cm.

(Lond. Univ., 1923, *El. Mach.)*

2. A firm manufacturing a line of 6-pole, interpole D.C. machines wishes to build a rotary convertor to operate from a 6600 volt, 3-phase, 25 period circuit. What are the minimum alterations to the design of a standard 500 volt, 300 kW., 500 r.p.m. generator that will enable it to be used as such a rotary convertor, delivering power at 500 volts on the D.C. side ? Will the output remain the same ?

(I.E.E., April, 1923.)

3. What are the peculiarities of a rotary convertor in regard to commutation, and how is the design of the interpole affected thereby ? Explain why such machines are liable to flash-over, and how this danger may be minimized.

4. The speed of an " inverted " rotary convertor varies with the power factor of the A.C. load. Explain this effect and indicate how the speed variation may be reduced to a minimum.

5. What are the factors determining the number of poles and number of phases in a rotary convertor ? What values would you choose for these items in the case of the following convertors : (a) 2000 kW., 660 volt, 50 cycle, and (b) 500 kW., 110 volt, 50 cycle ?

6. Describe and criticize the methods of varying the voltage of rotary convertors in which the following apparatus is used : (a) reactance control, (b) booster control, (c) induction regulator control.   *(I.E.E., April,* 1921.)

7. A D.C. armature has 4 conductors in each of 162 slots, and is lap-wound for 6 poles. Show where you would tap this winding for connections to slip-rings for use as a rotary convertor for 3-phase supply.

68. A.C. Commutator Motors

References. O1; W2, 3; and *Journal I.E.E.*, Vol. 60, 1922. Papers by S. P. Smith (page 308) and F. J. Teago (page 328). *Journal I.E.E.*, Vol. 62, 1924. Paper by F. J. Teago (page 720). *Journal I.E.E.*, Vol. 64, 1926. Paper by A. H. M. Arnold (page 1139).

EXAMPLES 68

1. Explain the action of a simple series commutator motor. Show that the vector locus of the current with varying load is a circle. (*Lond. Univ.*, 1934, *El. Tech.*)

2. A 3-phase motor is required to have, approximately, a constant speed characteristic. The speed must, however, be capable of variation between the limits of 400 and 800 r.p.m. Explain the action, and give a diagram showing the circuits of a suitable motor. (*B.Sc.*, 1933, *El. Power.*)

3. Explain with connection and vector diagrams the working of the Schrage variable speed 3-phase commutator motor, showing how both speed and power factor are controlled.

(*I.E.E.*, *May*, 1935.)

*4. A 230-volt, 50-cycle, 4-pole A.C. series motor with neutralizing winding has a peak flux per pole of 1·2 megalines, and runs at 1500 r.p.m. when carrying 20 amperes. The field winding has 8 turns per pole. The resistance of the motor between terminals is 1·5 ohms and the leakage reactance is 1·0 ohm. Estimate the speed at which the motor would run if supplied at 230 volts (D.C.) and loaded to take 20 amperes. Show that the torque developed would be effectively the same in each case. (*I.E.E.*, *Nov.*, 1943.)

5. A single-phase series railway motor having an impedance $Z = 0·1 + 0·3j$ is started by a multi-tap transformer. The maximum current on each notch is 400 amperes, and notching up takes place when the current has fallen to 300 amperes. The flux at 300 amperes is 85 per cent of that at 400 amperes. Determine the voltage for the first tapping of the transformer, the back e.m.f. generated by the rotation of the armature when the current has fallen to 300 amperes on the first tapping, and the voltage for the second tapping of the transformer. Explain the method employed in your calculations.

(*Lond. Univ.*, 1933, *El. Power.*)

6. An industrial drive is required to be run by a 3-phase motor having a speed continuously variable and independent

of the torque over a range of from 500 r.p.m. to 1500 r.p.m. Describe and explain the construction and load characteristics of a motor suitable for this purpose.

(*C. & G., Final*, 1935.)

*7. A 2-pole closed circuit armature winding is connected to a commutator at one end by means of three equally spaced tappings to slip-rings at the other end. Three equally spaced brushes are placed on the commutator. Three-phase alternating currents having a constant R.M.S. value at 50 cycles are supplied to the brushes (*a*) on the slip-rings, (*b*) on the commutator. Explain what changes take place in the magnitude, frequency and phase of the voltages on the slip-ring and commutator brushes as the speed of the armature is varied from zero to above 3000 r.p.m. Show by a diagram of connections how a machine such as this may be used to improve the power factor of an induction motor.

(*Lond. Univ.*, 1945, *El. Mach.*)

*8. A series motor without compensating winding has a reactance of 4 ohms at 50 cycles and a resistance of 0·5 ohm. When operating on D.C. at 500 volts it takes 90 amperes at 780 r.p.m. Calculate the speed and the power-factor of the motor when operating on A.C. at 500 volts and taking 90 amperes (i) at 50 cycles and (ii) at 25 cycles. Neglect the effect of iron losses, of saturation and of short-circuit current under the brushes. (*Lond. Univ.*, 1946, *El. Power.*)

*9. Draw the vector diagram to scale and determine the applied voltage and power-factor for a 10 h.p., 25-cycle, 6-pole, A.C. compensated series motor running at 1000 r.p.m. and taking 60 amperes, given the following data: Armature wave connected 824 conductors; 2 turns per coil; useful flux per pole $0·77 \times 10^6$ lines; total flux per pole $0·8 \times 10^6$ lines; field winding 15 turns per pole, all poles in series; total ohmic resistance 0·3 ohm; total leakage reactance 0·53 ohm. The friction, windage and iron loss component of the current is 5 amperes and the component supplying the current in the short-circuited coils is 8 amperes. Determine also the transformer E.M.F. in the short-circuited coil.

(*Lond. Univ.*, 1947, *El. Mach.*)

69. Synchronous Induction Motors

References. C5; M7; S1, 4.

In Fig. 10, p. 187, giving the typical circle diagram of an induction motor, the best possible power factor is seen to be about 0·9 lagging. By injecting D.C. into the rotor, it becomes polarized, and can then run in synchronism with the rotating field produced by the stator. By over-excitation, the leading power factor properties of the synchronous motor can be obtained.

In Fig. 10, for the machine to give the same full-load output AT, but to be drawing a leading current from the mains, say 0·9 power factor, then the stator current would be OU and the corresponding rotor current AU. For the usual star-connected 3-phase rotor, a direct current passed into one phase to the star point, leaving by the other two phases in parallel, produces the same M.M.F. as an ordinary 3-phase alternating current according to the relation

$$I_{dc} = \sqrt{2} I_{ac}.$$

The length of AU in Fig. 10 is found to be $2·12'' = 21·2$ amperes stator $= 63·6$ amperes rotor (3/1 transformation ratio of turns) $= 90$ amperes D.C. Also, from the diagram, $AF = 1·54'' = 15·4$ amperes stator $= 46·2$ amperes, rotor.

Hence, when running as an ordinary induction motor, with rotor short-circuited, and delivering full-load horse-power, the rotor has an A.C. of 46·2 amperes in each leg of the 3-phase star. By injecting 90 amperes D.C. as explained above, the motor will run at full-load, 0·9 power factor leading, as a synchronous motor. If this D.C. excitation is maintained constant, with various loads, the locus of stator and equivalent rotor currents will be a circle with centre A, radius AU, as shown in Fig. 10. The maximum output from the machine under these conditions will be given by $AT'' = AU = 2·12'' = 538$ watts. This corresponds to 21·6 h.p. and a torque of 76 lb.-ft. This is the *pull-out* torque or horse-power of the motor, while JK in the circle diagram is the *stalling torque*. A load in excess of 21·6 h.p. will thus cause the motor to pull out of step, but it will then continue to run as an induction motor. If the exciter is still in the rotor circuit, there will be wide fluctuations of torque. It will revert to the ordinary induction motor when the rotor is short-circuited. The circle locus as a synchronous motor is considered to merge into the circle locus of the induction motor in the rather indefinite period between synchronous running and the slipping back of the rotor into induction motor state of running.

The vector diagram OAU can be used for calculations to determine requisite D.C. exciting currents.

EXAMPLES 69

*1. A 3-phase, 150-h.p., 400-volt synchronous induction motor takes, as an induction motor, a no-load current of 150 amperes at 0·05 power-factor. The stator current at full voltage on short-circuit is 1200 amperes at 0·2 power-factor, the rotor copper loss being half the stator copper loss. The D.C. excitation on the rotor is adjusted to give a leading power-factor of 0·9 on the stator when the motor is running synchronously on full load. Determine the reactive kVA. on no load and the maximum h.p. as a synchronous motor and as an induction motor. Explain how the power-factor may be maintained automatically constant over a wide range of speed.
(*Lond. Univ.*, 1947, *El. Mach.*)

2. A 40-h.p., 500-volt, 50-cycle, 3-phase, slip-ring induction motor has a short-circuit (line) current of 200 amperes at a power factor of 0·35, and a no-load current of 20 amperes at a power factor of 0·2. Running as a synchronous-induction motor, the full-load power factor is 0·95 leading. Draw the circle diagram for the machine and from it estimate in terms of full-load torque the synchronous pull-out torque and the stalling torque. Find also the power factor and the line current at half-load. Assume the stator and the equivalent rotor resistances to be equal, and the direct current excitation to be constant. (*Lond. Univ.*, 1931, *El. Mach.*)

3. An 80-h.p., 440-volt, 3-phase, slip-ring, star-connected induction motor with 64 stator and 85 rotor turns per phase is to be connected to a direct-current exciter to run as a synchronous motor at a leading power factor of 0·9. Operating as an induction motor with short-circuited slip-rings, the no-load current is 36 amperes at a power factor of 0·15, and the full-load current is 100 amperes at a power factor of 0·88. Estimate the requisite exciting current, and sketch the rotor circuit connections for starting and for synchronous running.
(*Lond. Univ.*, 1932, *El. Mach.*)

4. Explain the action of the synchronous induction motor as a phase-advancer, and compare the load characteristics of the machine with those of an ordinary induction motor. The exciter of a 500-volt., 40-h.p., synchronous-induction motor supplies the rotor with a current of 140 amperes, the current being led in by one slip-ring and out by the other two in parallel. As an induction motor the machine takes a no-load current of 15 amperes at a power factor of 0·15, and on full-load the efficiency is 90 per cent. The stator is star-connected, and has twice as many turns per phase as the rotor. Find the power factor at which the machine works on full-load as a synchronous motor. (*C. & G., Final*, 1933.)

5. Estimate the output rating of the exciter of a synchronous-induction motor from the following data: Name-plate rating, 40-h.p., 500 volts, 50 cycles, star connection; no-load current as induction motor, 18 amperes at power factor 0·1; short-circuit current 200 amperes at power factor 0·3; full-load power factor as synchronous motor, 0·9 leading; ratio of stator/rotor turns per phase, 2; rotor resistance per phase, 0·15 ohm; brush voltage drop, 2 volts.

(*I.E.E., Nov.*, 1932.)

6. Draw the current diagram of a 40-h.p., 500-volt, 6-pole, 3-phase star-connected, 50-cycle synchronous-induction motor having a ratio of stator to rotor turns per phase of 2. Use the following test data: (*a*) running as an induction motor; no-load current, 18 amperes at 500 volts, power factor 0·15; short-circuit current, 100 amperes at 250 volts, power factor 0·4. Find the rotor d.c. excitation to give a leading power factor of 0·9 when the machine is running on full load as a synchronous motor. Calculate the pull-out torque.

(*C. & G., Final*, 1932.)

7. From the following test figures on a 200-h.p., 3000-volt motor, find (*a*) the D.C. rotor excitation to give 0·9 leading power factor on full load, and (*b*) the pull-out torque in terms of full-load torque: no-load test as induction motor: 3000 volts, 17 amperes, power factor 0·09. The ratio of stator to rotor turns is 2·2 : 1. (*I.E.E., May*, 1935.)

*8. An 80-h.p., 440-volt, 3-phase, star-connected, slip-ring induction motor with 64 stator and 85 rotor turns per phase is connected to a D.C. exciter to run at synchronous speed with a power-factor of 0·9 leading. Draw a diagram of rotor connections, and estimate the rotor exciting current required. When the machine is operating as an induction motor with slip-rings short-circuited, the no-load current is 36 amperes at power-factor 0·15, and the full-load current is 100 amperes at power-factor 0·88. (*I.E.E., May*, 1942.)

*9. What are the relative merits of salient-pole synchronous motors and synchronous induction motors? Show how the rotor of the latter machine may be connected for D.C. excitation. Find the D.C. excitation needed to run a 40-h.p., 400-volt, 3-phase induction motor on full-load at synchronous speed at a power-factor of 0·9 leading, if its no-load current as an induction motor is 16 amperes at power-factor 0·2, and its full-load current is 60 amperes at power-factor 0·85. The ratio of stator to rotor turns per phase is 2·0. Find also the pull-out torque in synchronous kilowatts.

(*I.E.E., May*, 1943.)

*10. The input to a 3-phase, 50-h.p., 400-volt synchronous induction motor when running light as an induction motor at normal voltage was 40 amperes and 2500 watts. On short-circuit with reduced voltage (65 volts) the current and power were 54 amperes and 2100 watts respectively. The ratio of stator to rotor turns per phase is 2·5/1. Determine the exciting current when running at full-load as a synchronous motor with a power factor of 0·95 leading.

(*Lond. Univ.*, 1948, *El. Power.*)

70. Generating Stations

References. B4, 7 ; S5.

EXAMPLES 70

*1. Explain the reasons for the present tendency towards the use of higher steam pressures and temperatures in modern generating stations.   The relationship between the water evaporated (W lb.), coal consumed (C lb.) and kWh. generated per 8-hour shift for a generating station is as follows:

$$W = 60,000 + 10.5 \text{ kWh.}, \quad C = 11,000 + 1.75 \text{ kWh.}$$

To what limiting value does the water evaporated per lb. of coal consumed approach as the station output increases? How much coal per hour would be required to keep the station running at no-load (i.e. zero kWh. output)?

(*I.E.E.*, *May*, 1942.)

2. Each of the six units in a central station comprises one 3-phase, 6600-volt, 20,000-kVA. turbo-alternator and a bank of three 6600/20,000-volt single-phase transformers. Give a line diagram of a suitable scheme for the essential electrical connections, showing all bus-bars, protective reactors, oil switches, and current transformers. Describe fully a current-balance protective system for a generator and a transformer bank treated as one unit.   (*C. & G.*, *Final*, 1931.)

3. The coal burnt under a boiler has the following percentage analysis by weight—

Carbon	.	. 80	Hydrogen	.	. 3
Sulphur	.	. 0.5	Oxygen .	.	. 4
Ash	.	. 12.5			

If 17 lb. of air are supplied per lb. of coal, and combustion is complete, calculate the analysis by volume of the flue gas. Atomic weights: $H = 1$, $O = 16$, $C = 12$, $S = 32$, $N = 14$. Assume that 1 lb. of air consists of 23 per cent O_2 and 77 per cent N_2 by weight.   (*I.E.E.*, *May*, 1932.)

4. A generating station has a maximum demand of 20,000 kW., a load factor of 30 per cent, and a fuel consumption of 2.25 lb. of coal per unit. Assume the boiler efficiency to be 85 per cent, the turbo-alternator efficiency to be 90 per cent, and the calorific value of the fuel to be 11,500 B.Th.U. per lb. Determine the thermal efficiency of the station and the coal bill per annum if coal costs 15s. per ton. 1 kWh. = 3440 B.Th.U.   (*I.E.E.*, *Nov.*, 1937.)

*5. The annual working costs of a coal-fired turbine-driven electric generating station can be represented by the formula

$$\pounds(a + b \times \text{kW.} + c \times \text{kWh.})$$

where a, b, and c are constants for a particular station, kW. is the total power installed and kWh. is the energy produced per annum. Explain the significance of the constants a, b, c, and the factors upon which their numerical values depend. Determine their values for a 60-MW. station operating with an annual load factor of 50 per cent for which (i) the capital cost of the buildings and equipment is £500,000; (ii) the annual cost of fuel, oil, taxation, wages and salaries of the operating staff is £90,000; (iii) the interest and depreciation charges on the buildings and equipment are at the rate of 10 per cent per annum; and (iv) the annual costs of organization, interest on cost of site, etc., are £50,000. (*I.E.E.*, *Nov.*, 1942.)

6. A single-effect evaporator is supplied with live steam at 100 lb. per sq. in., the total heat per lb. of steam being 1186 B.Th.U. In the body of the evaporator the pressure is 20 lb. per sq. in., the total heat in saturated steam at this pressure being 1156 B.Th.U. per lb. Water is fed to the evaporator at 60° F., and the distillate leaves it at 90° F. The discharge from the live-steam side is taken through a steam trap direct to a tank, and contains 300 B.Th.U. per lb. The temperature rise in the cooling water is 60° F. Neglecting radiation losses and sludge, find the amount of gained water and the amount of cooling water per lb. of live steam. (*I.E.E. Nov.*, 1932.)

*7. A hydro-electric station operates with a mean head of 180 ft. and is supplied from a reservoir lake which drains a catchment area of 200 sq. miles, over which the average rainfall is 120 inches per annum. If 60 per cent of this rainfall can be utilized, calculate the power in kW. for which the station should be designed. Assume that 5 per cent of the head is lost in pipes, penstocks, etc.; the mechanical efficiency of the turbines is 85 per cent; and the efficiency of the generators is 95 per cent. (*I.E.E.*, *Nov.*, 1943.)

*8. Define load factor, diversity factor. Explain how each affects the operation and working costs of an electricity supply undertaking.

During a period of 24 hours the load on a station is as follows:

Period	12–7	7–9	9–11	11–1	1–4	4–10	10–12
Load, MW.	2	10	4·5	7	4	8·5	3

Calculate the daily load factor of the station. State the number and size of generators which should be installed to supply this load, and show graphically, on the load curve, how this plant should be operated.   (*I.E.E.*, *May*, 1944.)

*9. Define the terms "maximum continuous rating," "most economical rating," as applied to steam turbo-alternators. What is the usual ratio between these quantities for modern machines?

The steam consumption for two machines, *A* and *B*, is as follows:

Load, MW.		30	27	24	22	20	18	15
(*A*) Steam (lb./kWh.).	.	9·8	9·6	9·5	9·53	9·58	9·65	9·78
(*B*) Steam (lb./kWh.).	.	9·76	9·55	9·45	9·45	9·5	9·55	9·68

Determine the most economical rating of each machine. If the daily load-cycle on each machine is equivalent to 6 hours at 30 MW., 12 hours at 24 MW., 6 hours at 15 MW., determine (i) the daily steam consumption of each machine, (ii) the daily load factor.   (*I.E.E.*, *Nov.*, 1944.)

*10. Discuss the chief factors which affect the thermal efficiency of a power station equipped with steam-driven turbo-alternators. The maximum demand on a station is 80 MW., the annual load factor is 45 per cent, and the thermal efficiency is 23 per cent. Calculate the average daily coal consumption if the calorific value of the coal is 11,000 B.Th.U. per lb. Assume 1 kWh. to be equivalent to 3412 B.Th.U. What factors under the control of the station require careful consideration if a high thermal efficiency is to be obtained?

          (*I.E.E.*, *Nov.*, 1944.)

71. Mercury-Arc Rectifiers

References. R3; S5.

For general case without overlap

$$V_{d \cdot c \cdot} = \sqrt{2} \ V_{a \cdot c \cdot} \frac{p}{\pi} \sin \frac{\pi}{p} \ ,$$

where $p =$ number of phases, and $V_{d \cdot c \cdot}$ includes arc drop.

EXAMPLES 71

*1. A 6-anode mercury-arc rectifier giving 1200 kW. at 630 volts on the D.C. side is supplied from a transformer with its secondary windings connected in double star with an inter-phase transformer joining the two star points. Give a diagram of the connections of transformers and rectifier. Explain the action of the interphase transformer and calculate its rating. (*Lond. Univ.*, 1945, *El. Mach.*)

*2. A 3-phase grid-controlled mercury-arc rectifier is connected for charging a battery from A.C. mains. Explain any circuit changes to be made, and any other steps to be taken, to enable the rectifier to act as an inverter feeding power from the battery into the A.C. mains. State the exact sequence of operations when starting up the inverter. The R.M.S. phase voltage of the above rectifier is 150. Calculate the maximum battery voltage if the voltage drop in the arc and the battery is 24 volts. (*I.E.E.*, *May*, 1945.)

3. What is the meaning of "overlap" in a mercury arc rectifier, and upon what does it depend? In a 3-phase rectifier, the phase volts on the secondary side of the transformer are 1200 V. (r.m.s.). The arc drop is 24 volts and the full-load overlap is 30 degrees. Estimate the output voltage and the percentage regulation down.

4. A sub-station converting from 6600 volts, 3-phase, to 440 volts, 3-wire D.C., is equipped with 6-anode mercury-arc rectifiers. Give a connection diagram of one of the units and explain its operation. If the transformers have primary windings star-connected, find the turn-ratio, neglecting overlapping and assuming an arc-drop of 25 volts in the rectifier. (*C. & G.*, *Final*, 1934.)

5. Draw a diagram showing the essential internal connections of a 6-anode mercury-arc rectifier supplying a non-reactive resistance load of 2·0 ohms. The rectifier is to have an absorption reactor. Taking the peak voltage per transformer

secondary phase as 1000 volts, and choosing an instant 45° later than the peak voltage of anode 1, insert on the diagram the instantaneous currents and voltages in all parts of the system, draw the voltage half-waves for anodes 1, 2 and 3, and put in the output voltage wave. Arc drop, 25 volts.

(*I.E.E., May*, 1936.)

*6. Deduce the relation between the average D.C. voltage of a mercury arc rectifier and the phase voltage of each secondary winding of the star-connected transformer. A 3-anode rectifier supplies a load of 10 kW. at 220 volts, the arc drop being 20 volts. Find the kVA. rating of the transformer.

(*C. & G., Final*, 1943.)

7. A 6-anode mercury-arc rectifier may be supplied from a transformer having its secondary windings connected in (*a*) 6-phase star, (*b*) double 3-phase with interphase transformer, or (*c*) triple 3-phase or fork. Draw diagrams of all these showing how they would be connected to the rectifier and calculate for one of them the voltage and current rating of the transformer secondary in terms of the D.C. rating.

(*Lond. Univ.*, 1936, *El. Mach.*)

*8. A 50-cycle, 3-phase mercury arc rectifier has an effective inductance of 1 microhenry in each secondary phase connection, and the peak secondary phase voltage is 1000 volts. Plot curves to scale, showing (*a*) the voltage during overlap, (*b*) the voltage available to stop one anode current and start the next. Make an estimate of the shape of the anode current in the striking anode, and find the approximate overlap angle for an output current of 100 amperes. The load may be regarded as highly reactive. (*I.E.E., Nov.*, 1941.)

*9. A 3/6-phase, delta/star transformer supplies a mercury-arc rectifier. Assuming the current in each anode to be constant for one-sixth of a cycle and zero for the remainder, draw diagrams showing the current wave-form in the primary lines. Determine the rating of the transformer in terms of the D.C. output, neglecting losses. (*I.E.E., Nov.*, 1942.)

72. Three-Wire D.C. Systems

EXAMPLES 72

1. Give a diagram of connections and explain the action of *either* (*a*) a differential compound connected 3-wire balancer, *or* (*b*) a static balancer for connection to three slip-rings on a D.C. generator.   (*I.E.E., April*, 1921.)

2. A 400 volt, 3-core D.C. cable having cores of 0·5 sq. in., 0·25 sq. in., and 0·5 sq. in. is supplying a lamp load 1000 yd. away from the generating station. Between one side and the neutral there are 700 lamps of 16 c.p. each, and between the other side and the neutral there are 500 lamps of 16 c.p. each. Assume that the current per lamp is 0·3 amperes and that the resistance of 1 cub. in. of copper is equal to 0·66 microhm. If the neutral point of the system is earthed in the engine room, find the voltage which will have to be maintained there between each outer and the neutral.   (*I.E.E., Oct.*, 1926.)

3. A 3-wire D.C. system working at 460 volts between outers has the positive side more heavily loaded than the negative side to the extent of 150 kW., the positive outer carrying 2500 amperes. This out-of-balance load is carried by a balancer set in which the losses are 18 kW. Calculate the armature currents in the balancer and the total load on the generators.

4. Explain fully the reasons which forbid the inclusion of any circuit-breaking device on (*a*) the outer conductor of a single-phase concentric high-voltage cable, (*b*) the neutral conductor on a three-wire continuous-current system.

What would be the immediate consequence in the latter case if the neutral conductor were open-circuited when there was an out-of-balance load of 50 per cent of the power being supplied to the positive side of the system, the p.d. between the outer conductors being maintained at 500 volts?   (*C. & G.*, '28.)

*5. A 3-wire direct-current distributor, 400 yd. long, is fed at both ends at 235 volts between each outer and the neutral. Two loads, *P* and *Q*, are connected between the positive outer and the neutral, and two loads, *R* and *S*, are connected between the negative outer and the neutral. The loads and their distances from one end (*X*) of the distributor are as follows: Load *P*, 50 amperes, 100 yd. ; load *Q*, 70 amperes, 300 yd. ; load *R*, 60 amperes, 150 yd. ; load *S*, 60 amperes, 350 yd. Determine the voltage at each load point and the current at each feeding-point. The resistance of each outer is 0·25 ohm per 1000 yd., and that of the neutral is 0·5 ohm per 1000 yd.
                                            (*I.E.E., Nov.*, 1942.)

73. Comparisons of Systems of Supply

References. R2; S7; W6.

EXAMPLES 73

*1. Compare the relative weights of the line conductors for the following distribution systems: (i) 3-wire D.C., (ii) 3-wire single-phase, (iii) 4-wire 3-phase. In each case the distributor is 1 mile long; the total load (50 kW.) is at the end remote from the supply and is balanced; the efficiency is 90 per cent; the voltage (at the load) between the neutral and any outer is 230 volts; the neutral point is earthed; and the cross-section of the neutral conductor is one-half of that of an outer conductor. The power-factor of the A.C. systems is 0·95 (lagging). What advantages has the 4-wire, 3-phase system over the 3-wire, single-phase system? Explain how a single-phase, 3-wire system can be operated from a transformer without a mid-point tapping on the secondary winding. Draw a diagram of connections of the balancer, and describe any special features of its construction.   (*I.E.E.*, *May*, 1943.)

*2. Compare the relative advantages and disadvantages of single-phase 3-wire distribution and 3-phase 4-wire distribution for a network with lighting, heating and small-power loads. A distribution network requires 100 kW. at unity power-factor, and is to be supplied from a 3-phase system through a suitable transformer. Alternative schemes proposed for distribution are (i) the 3-phase, 4-wire, 400/230-volt system; (ii) the triple single-phase, 3-wire, 460/230-volt system. Determine the copper required for the distributors of each of these systems if the distributors are each 1000 yd. long and are uniformly loaded, the loads are balanced, the loss in the distributors is 8 per cent of the power distributed. Assume that the cross-section of any neutral conductor is one-half of that of a corresponding outer or phase-conductor and that the resistance of a copper conductor 1000 yd. long and 1 in.^{2} cross-section is 0·025 ohm.   (*I.E.E.*, *Nov.*, 1944.)

74. Tariffs and Economics

References. B4, 5; K2; R1; S5.

EXAMPLES 74

1. Find the best current density for a 3-phase overhead line if the line is in use for 2500 hours per annum, and if the material of the conductor costs £70 per ton, has a specific resistance of 0·67 microhms per in. cube and weighs 0·315 lb. per cub. in. Energy costs 0·6d. per unit, and interest and depreciation together amount to 12 per cent per annum of the capital cost of the conductor. (*I.E.E.*, *May*, 1934.)

2. A customer is offered power at £4 per annum per kVA. of maximum demand plus 1·05 pence per unit metered. He proposes to install a motor to carry his estimated maximum demand of 300 b.h.p. The motor available has a power factor of 0·85 at full-load. How many units will he require at 20 per cent load factor, and what will be his annual bill ?
(*I.E.E.*, *April*, 1925.)

3. If the capital cost including laying of a single-core cable, of section a sq. in. is £$(1000a + 100)$ per 1000 yds., find the most economical cross-section required to supply 200 amperes continuously for 4000 hours per annum. The combined rate of interest and depreciation is 10 per cent per annum, the cost of energy is 0·5d. per unit and the resistivity of the conductor is 0·7 microhm-inch. (*I.E.E.*, *Nov.*, 1935.)

4. You have the choice of two lamps, one costing 1s. and taking 100 watts and the other costing 5s. and taking 30 watts, and each giving the same candle-power and having the same life of 1000 hours. Which would you use with electrical energy at £4 per annum per kilowatt of maximum demand and 0·5d. per unit ? At what load factor would they be equally advantageous ? (*I.E.E.*, *April*, 1923.)

5. A single-phase load of 12,500 kW. at 66 kV. and a lagging power factor of 0·6 is received from a distribution centre 50 miles away. Each line conductor has a resistance of 0·44 ohm per mile. If the power factor were raised to 0·87 lagging by the installation of phase-advancing plant, calculate the annual saving effected. The cost of the additional plant is £10 per kVA, the additional loss entailed is 5 per cent of its kVA. rating, interest and depreciation charges 10 per cent and the cost of all energy wasted 0·5d. per kWh. The annual load factor is 40 per cent. (*C. & G.*, 1938.)

6. State the economic reasons in favour of 2-part tariffs.

A supply is offered on the basis of a fixed charge of £7 per annum plus 0·5 penny per unit, or, alternatively, at the rate of 4 pence per unit for the first 300 units per annum and 1 penny per unit for all additional units. Find the number of units taken per annum for which the costs under these two systems become the same. (*C. & G., Final*, 1932.)

7. The total installation of electrical appliances in an " all-electric " house of four apartments takes a maximum demand of 12 kW. The user has the alternative of paying either for 150 kW.-hours at 4½d. and all units in excess of this at 1d., or he can pay a fixed charge of £5 4s. per annum, plus a running charge of ½d. per kW.-hour. Draw graphs showing the cost per unit in each case for load factors up to 100 per cent.
(*I.E.E., April*, 1924.)

8. If the local gas supply undertaking advertised " Gas costs 9d. a therm, electricity for heating and cooking costs 2s. 5d. a therm," how would you suggest that the electricity supply undertaking should deal with the matter ? You should assume that the facts are correct and that the tariff cannot be reduced. To what price per unit does 2s. 5d. per therm correspond ? (*I.E.E., Oct.*, 1924.)

9. The owner of a new factory is comparing a private oil-engine generating station with public supply. Calculate the average price per unit his supply will cost him in each case, using the following data—

Maximum demand, 600 kW.; load factor 30 per cent; supply tariff £3 10s. per kW. of maximum demand + 0·35d. per unit; capital cost of plant required for public supply £5000; capital cost of plant required for private generating station £20,000; cost of fuel 80s. per ton; consumption of fuel oil, 0·65 lb. per unit generated. Other works costs for private plant are as follows : lubricating oil, stores and water = 0·035d. per unit generated; wages, 0·11d.; repairs and maintenance 0·03d. all per unit. (*I.E.E., May*, 1935.)

10. The capital cost of a power station of 50,000 kW. capacity is £15 per kW. on which the annual charges are 8 per cent. What are the total costs per unit on the basis of £ per kW. of maximum demand and pence per unit for the following cases ?

	(a)	(b)
Fuel, coal per unit	1·6 lb.	1·5 lb.
Max. demand	20,000 kW.	30,000 kW.
Load factor	20 %	30 %
Wages, salaries and repairs	£25,000	£27,000

, Include in the running charge 20 per cent of the wages, salaries and repairs. Take the cost of coal at 10s. per ton in both cases.   (*I.E.E.*, *May*, 1936.)

11. A factory has a total installed motor rating of 300 h.p. The maximum load is equal to this installed rating and the average load throughout the year is 25 per cent of this value. The average power-factor is 0·8 and the efficiency 0·85. Determine (*a*) the annual cost with the following alternative tariffs, (*b*) the annual cost under tariff (1) if a condenser was installed to raise the power-factor to 0·9 lagging. The cost of the condenser for this purpose is £250 and the interest on the cost 5 per cent per annum. *Tariff* 1. A quarterly maximum demand charge of £1 per kVA. based on the reading of the demand meter and 0·5d. per kWh. *Tariff* 2. A charge of 4d. per kWh. for the first 70 units taken per quarter for each installed horse-power plus 0·5d. for all other units.

                                        (*C. & G.*, *Final*, 1934.)

12. In a 3-phase transmission line the cost per mile of each conductor can be represented by a straight-line graph between £70 for zero cross-sectional area and £450 for a conductor of 0·5 sq. in. cross-section. The yearly load-factor for the copper loss in the line is 9 per cent. If interest and depreciation charges total 8 per cent of the capital cost and the cost of the energy wasted is 1d. per kWh., find the economical current density. Specific resistance of copper $0·68 \times 10^{-6}$ ohm per inch-cube.   (*C. & G.*, *Final*, 1934.)

13. A load of 500 kW. at 6600 volts is to be transmitted for 8 hours a day for 300 days a year. The total cost of the cable is £2·5 per yard for each square inch cross-section of copper plus £0·33 per yard independent of the size of conductor. The cost of energy wasted is 0·25d. per kWh. and interest and depreciation amount to 8 per cent per annum on the total capital cost. Find the most economical cross-section area of copper and criticize its use if the cable is 10 miles long. *R* per mile 1 sq. in. = 0·046 ohm.   (*C. & G.*, 1939.)

14. State and prove the law of economy as applicable to an insulated feeder cable. The cost of each of the copper conductors for a mile of an overhead transmission line is £100 plus £700 per square inch of cross-sectional area. The load factor of the main is 25 per cent and of the losses 11 per cent. The combined rate of interest and depreciation is 9 per cent per annum, and the cost of the energy wasted is 1d. per kWh. Calculate the economical maximum current density for the line. A mile of copper wire of 1 in.² cross-sectional area has a

resistance of 0·046 ohm. If the section of the conductor differed by 10 per cent from the most economical value, by what percentage would the total cost of running be increased?

(Lond. Univ., 1933, El. Power.)

15. Give the reasons for the use of maximum demand meters in connection with electric supplies. Describe such a meter and explain how it is employed on (i) A.C. systems, (ii) D.C. systems. An A.C. supply undertaking charges at the rate of £4 per annum per kVA. of maximum demand plus 0·2d. per B.O.T. unit. A consumer having an average load of 4000 kW. desires to limit his annual bill to £50,000. Assuming that his maximum kW. load is 10 per cent greater than his average load, what is the minimum power factor at which he can work?

(Lond. Univ., 1936, El. Tech.)

16. It is proposed to supply a consumer whose annual maximum demand is 1500 kW. and whose annual load factor is 40 per cent on one or other of the following tariffs—

Tariff A

kW. Charge							
For first 200 kW.	.	.	.	*.	£5	per kW.
,, second 200 kW.	.	.	.	.	£4 10s.	,,
,, next 200 kW.	.	.	.	.	£4	,,
,, all in excess .	.	.	.	.	£3 10s.	,,

Unit charge, 0·25d. per unit.

Tariff B

kW. Charge							
For first 300 kW.	.	.	.	.	£4 10s. per kW.
,, second 300 kW.	.	.	.	.	£4 5s.	,,
,, next 400 kW.	.	.	.	.	£4	,,
,, all in excess .	.	.	.	.	£3 15s.	,,

Unit charge, 0·25d. per unit.

Draw a graph showing the difference in total cost of supply under the two tariffs with variation in maximum demand at which the total cost of supply under each tariff is the same. Also determine the actual cost of the supply to the consumer mentioned above under each of the tariffs.

(I.E.E., Nov., 1935.)

17. The cost of a 2-core cable for a 500-volt circuit, together with all installation costs, is £10,000 per mile of cable for each sq. in. of conductor cross-section plus £2000 per mile of cable independent of the conductor size. The maximum current is 200 amperes and the yearly copper losses are such as would

be caused by a constant current of 100 amperes. Energy costs 0·5d. per kWh. and the yearly charge for interest on capital expenditure and depreciation is 10 per cent. Calculate the most economical cross-section and discuss this result as regards cable heating and voltage drop, if the cable were a mile long. The resistance of 1 mile of copper wire 1 in.^{2} cross-section is 0·046 ohm. (*C. & G., Final*, 1936.)

18. Give an account of the effect of the consumer's (*a*) load-factor, (*b*) diversity factor, (*c*) power-factor in determining an equitable tariff. A consumer has a yearly consumption of 200,000 units. The tariff is £5 p.a. per kW. of maximum demand and 0·75 penny per kWh. Find the total annual cost and the overall cost per unit if the load factor is 35 per cent. Find also the overall cost per unit if (*a*) the consumption were reduced by 25 per cent with the same load factor, (*b*) the consumption were 200,000 units per annum with the load factor 25 per cent. (*C. & G., Final*, 1935.)

19. An average load of 10,000 kW. is transmitted over a 3-phase overhead line to a point at which the line pressure is 33,000 volts and the power factor 0·8. If the load factor is 30 per cent, determine the most economical area of conductor taking interest and depreciation at 10 per cent per annum, cost of generation 0·5 pence per unit, and the cost of the complete line £(1050A + 950) per mile, where A is the area of each conductor in square inches. Take the specific resistance of the line at 0·7 microhm per inch cube.

(*Lond. Univ.*, 1926, *El. Power.*)

20. What considerations determine the cross-section of the conductor in a low-voltage system (*a*) for the feeder cables, (*b*) for the distributor cables ? Determine the most suitable cross-section for a 2-wire feeder cable 500 yd. long from the following considerations—

Cross-sectional area (sq. in.) .	0·1	0·15	0·20	0·25	0·30
Resistance in ohms per 1000 yd. .	0·245	0·167	0·126	0·10	0·081
10 per cent of cable cost in £ .	27·5	30·0	33·0	37·5	46·0
Maximum safe current (amperes) .	155	200	240	278	313

. Current, 175 amperes. Interest and depreciation, 10 per cent. Cost of energy wasted, 1d. per B.O.T. unit, the loss being such as would be produced by 175 amperes for 4 hours per day. (*C. & G., Final*, 1927.)

21. Assuming that all tariffs can be expressed in the general form $p = aC/B + bk$ where p is the price to be charged per

kW.-hour, C the fixed price per annum, k the cost of energy per kW.-hour, and B the hours of use per annum, show that p is a minimum when the ratio of the charge for energy to the fixed charge is inversely proportional to the square of the load factor expressed by B. Describe a meter in which a record is made of the essential factors in supply.

(Lond. Univ., 1927, El. Power.)

*22. The cost of an 11-kV., 3-core cable, including laying and trench work, is £$(2700 + 6300\ a)$ per mile, where a is the cross-sectional area of a core in sq. in. A load with a maximum demand of 5 MVA. is to be transmitted over a distance of 1 mile at 11 kV. Draw two graphs on the same sheet of paper relating to cable core sizes ranging from 0·1 to 0·3 sq. in., one showing the annual charges on the capital cost of the cable, and the other showing the annual value of the copper loss, assuming that the load factor of losses is 35 per cent. Deduce from these graphs which is the most economical size of core to use. The resistance of a 0·15 sq. in. core per mile is 0·29 ohm. The cost of energy is £2 10s. per kW. of maximum demand and 0·2d. per unit. The annual charges on capital cost are to be taken as 10 per cent. *(I.E.E., Nov., 1941.)*

*23. Determine the most economical section for a 3-phase line 5 miles long to supply a load at a constant voltage of 33 kV. During each 24-hour period the load is 3000 kVA. for 10 hours, 2000 kVA. for 6 hours and 1000 kVA. for 8 hours. The capital cost per mile of conductor is £$(500 + 2500a)$ where a is the area of each conductor in sq. in., interest and depreciation charges are 8 per cent and the cost of energy is 0·5 penny per unit. One mile of conductor 1 sq. in. in cross-sectional area has a resistance of 0·043 ohm.

(Lond. Univ., 1946, El. Power.)

75. Voltage Drops on Distributors

References. B4, 6; R1; S5; W1, 6.

The volt drop in a conductor due to a uniformly distri-buted load is given by

$$\tfrac{1}{2}irl^2$$

where i = current per unit length,

r = resistance per same unit length,

l = length of conductor in the same units,

or, what amounts to the same thing, considering the whole current concentrated at the centre of the conductor and therefore flowing through only half the conductor.

See Example No. 7 for alternative methods of solution. Only resistance is taken into account.

EXAMPLES 75

1. A dead-end distributor fed at 250 volts is loaded as follows—

Yards from feeder point .	150	200	280	320	390	450	500
Load in amperes . .	20	40	35	25	10	20	30

The resistance of the double run is 0·1 ohm. Find the p.d. of the last load.

2. If in the above problem the distributor had been extended another 150 yd. with the same sized cable, and there fed at the same voltage of 250 from another feeder, find the current entering from each feeder and the minimum p.d. on the cable.

3. A 3-wire D.C. distributor 300 yd. long is fed at 230 volts at each end, and is loaded as follows—

Positive Side.

Yards from left feeder point . .	30	100	140	160	210	240
Load in amperes	20	40	50	10	25	30

Negative Side.

Yards from left feeder point . . .	60	80	120	180	274
Load in amperes	30	25	35	60	25

The outers each have a resistance of 0·15 ohm, while the neutral has a cross-section of half the outers. Find the lowest p.d.'s on each side, and the supply currents in each of the feeders.

4. A sub-station supplies two consumers A and B, who take 250 and 150 amperes respectively. A cable is used to carry the total current to a point C which is one mile from the sub-station, and the cables which run from C to A and B are one-half mile and one-quarter mile long respectively. If the maximum allowable voltage drop is 40 volts, and all three cables are worked at the same current density, calculate the cross-sections of the cables. *(I.E.E., Nov., 1934.)*

5. A D.C. ring main $ABCDE$ is fed at the point A from a 220-volt supply, and the resistances (including both lead and return) of the various sections are as follows (in ohms): $AB = 0\cdot1$; $BC = 0\cdot05$; $CD = 0\cdot01$; $DE = 0\cdot025$; and $EA = 0\cdot075$. The main supplies loads of: 10 amperes at B, 20 amperes at C, 30 amperes at D, and 10 amperes at E. Find the magnitude and direction of the current flowing in each section and the voltage at each load point. If the points C and E are further linked together by a conductor of $0\cdot05$ ohm resistance, and the output currents from the main remain unchanged, find the new distribution of the currents and voltages in the network. *(Lond. Univ., 1935, El. Tech.)*

6. A section of 2-wire distributor network is 1200 yards long and carries a uniformly distributed load of $0\cdot5$ ampere per yard. The section is supplied at each end by a feeder from a distribution centre at which the voltage is maintained constant. One feeder is 900 and the other 600 yards long, and each has a cross-sectional area 50 per cent greater than that of the distributor. Find the current in each feeder cable, and the distance from one end of the distributor at which the p.d. is a minimum. *(Lond. Univ., 1932, El. Power.)*

7. A 2-wire distributor is fed at both ends with a 480 volt, direct-current supply. The resistances and loads are as follows—

	·004		·0085		·005		·005		·0025 ohm	
A		40		20		30		50 amperes		B
	·004		·0085		·005		·005		·0025 ohm	

Determine the position and value of the maximum drop in volts and the magnitudes and the directions of the currents in the various parts of the distributor. If the voltage at the feeding point A happens to be $480\cdot5$ volts, while that at B is held constant at 480 volts, determine the redistribution of currents in the distributor on the assumption that the load currents remain unaltered. *(Lond. Univ., 1923, Trans.)*

8. A 2-core distributor cable is required to supply the

lighting load in a thoroughfare 600 yd. long. The maximum load is estimated to be 0·3 ampere per yard and the maximum voltage drop must not exceed 5 volts. Calculate the minimum cross-sectional area of the core if the distributor is supplied (*a*) from one end, (*b*) at a point half-way along its length. One mile of copper wire 1 sq. in. cross-sectional area has a resistance of 0·0415 ohm. (*C. & G., Final*, 1934.)

9. A 2-wire D.C. distributor *PQ* is 500 yds. long. It is supplied by 3 feeders entering at *P*, *Q* and *R*, where *R* is midway between *P* and *Q*. Resistance of distributor (go and return) = 0·05 ohm per 100 yds. The distributor is loaded as follows: at *a*, 100 yds. from *P*, 30 amperes and at *b*, 350 yds. from *P*, 40 amperes. In addition, a distributed load of ½ ampere per yd. exists from *b* to *Q*. Calculate: (*a*) the current supplied by each feeder if, at *P* and *R* the feeder potential difference is 220 volts while at *Q* it is 215 volts. (*b*) the voltage at a point between *b* and *Q* and 50 yds. from *b*.
(*B.Sc.*, 1940, *El. Power.*)

10. Three consumers, *A*, *B*, and *C*, each taking a current of 50 amperes, are connected to a feeding point maintained at 250 volts by separate cables of total resistance 0·05 ohm, 0·1 ohm and 0·02 ohm respectively. An interconnector cable connecting the points *A*, *B*, and *C* together has a resistance of 0·1 ohm between *A* and *B*, and 0·15 ohm between *B* and *C*. Calculate the voltage at each load point. Mark on a diagram the magnitude and direction of current in each section of the mains. (*C. & G.*, 1939.)

11. Four power loads, *B*, *C*, *D*, and *E*, are connected in this order to a 2-core distributor cable arranged as a ring main, and take currents of 20, 30, 25, and 30*A* respectively. The ring is supplied from a sub-station at the point *A* between *B* and *E*. An interconnector cable joins the points *C* and *E*, and from a point *F* on this interconnector cable a current of 20*A* is taken.

The total resistances of the cable between the load points are: *AB* = 0·04 ohm, *BC* = 0·03 ohm, *CD* = 0·02 ohm, *DE* = 0·03 ohm, *EA* = 0·04 ohm, *CF* = 0·02 ohm, and *FE* = 0·01 ohm. Calculate the current in each section of the ring and interconnector. (*Lond. Univ.*, 1933, *El. Power.*)

12. A pair of distributing mains of uniform section, 1000 yd. in length, having a resistance of 0·15 ohm each, are loaded with currents of 50, 100, 57·5, 10, and 75 amperes at distances measured from one end, where the voltage between the mains is 211·6, of 100, 300, 540, 740 and 850 yd. respectively. If the voltage at the other end is maintained at 210, calculate the

total current entering the system at each end of the mains, and the position of the point of minimum potential.

(I.E.E., May, 1934.)

13. A 2-core distributor cable AB, 400 yd. long, supplies a uniformly distributed lighting load of 1 ampere per yard. There are concentrated loads of 120, 72, 48 and 120 amperes at 40, 120, 200 and 320 yd. respectively from the end A. The cable has a resistance of 0·15 ohm per 1000 yd. run. Calculate the voltage at, and the position of the lowest-run lamp when the cable is fed at 250 volts (*a*) from both ends A and B, (*b*) from end A only.   *(Lond. Univ., 1934, El. Power.)*

14. A 2-core ring feeder cable $ABCDEA$ is connected to a sub-station at A and supplies feeding points to a distribution network at B, C, D and E. The points C and E are connected by an interconnector CFE and a load is taken at F. The total resistance in ohms of both conductors in the several sections is AB 0·05, BC 0·04, CD 0·03, DE 0·04, EA 0·05, CF 0·02, FE 0·01. The currents taken at the load points are B, 12 amperes; C, 15 amperes; D, 12 amperes; E, 15 amperes; and F, 10 amperes. Calculate the current in each section of the cable and the p.d. at each load point, if the p.d. at A is maintained constant at 250 volts.   *(C. & G., Final, 1936.)*

*15. A distributor is fed from both ends. At feeding point A the voltage is maintained at 236 volts and at B at 235 volts. The total length of the feeder is 200 yd., and loads are tapped off as follows: 20 amperes at 50 yd. from A, 40 amperes at 75 yd., 25 amperes at 100 yd., 30 amperes at 150 yd. The resistance per 1000 yd. of one conductor is 0·4 ohm. Calculate the current in the various sections of the feeder, the minimum voltage and the point at which it occurs.

(Lond. Univ., 1944, Ap. El.)

*16. A 2-wire D.C. distributor AB is 500 yards long and is fed at end A. The resistance of the distributor (go and return) per 100 yd. is 0·01 ohm. The distributor supplies concentrated loads as follows: At C, 100 yd. from A, 50 amperes; at D, 200 yd. from A, 100 amperes. Between C and D it is desired to establish a uniform load of $\frac{1}{2}$ ampere per yard, starting from C and extending towards D. The permissible drop to any consumer is 3 volts. Calculate to what distance from C the uniform load may extend. When this distance is reached, the distributor is fed at B also at a voltage which is 2 volts higher than that at A. Calculate the voltage drop from A to a point in the uniform load 50 yards from C.

(Lond. Univ., 1942, El. Power.)

*17. State and discuss Thévénin's Theorem. A D.C. ring main $ABCDEA$ is fed at A and is loaded as follows: 20 amperes at B, 25 amperes at D, 10 amperes at E. The resistance (go and return) of each section is AB 0·1 ohm, BC 0·15 ohm, CD 0·05 ohm, DE 0·1 ohm, EA 0·075 ohm. Calculate the current in each section, If C and E are joined by a conductor of 0·1 ohm resistance, the loads remaining unchanged, calculate now the current in each section; a solution employing Thévénin's Theorem will be preferred.

(Lond. Univ., 1942, El. Power.)

*18. A two-core distributor AB, 600 yards long, has concentrated loads of 50, 100, 70 and 150 amperes at 80, 200, 300, and 360 yards respectively from the end A. Each core has a resistance of 0·1 ohm per 1000 yards, and a voltage of 240 volts is maintained at A and 230 volts at B. Determine the voltage at each of the loads, and also the uniform load in amperes per yard to produce the same maximum voltage drop. *(Lond. Univ., 1948, El. Power.)*

*19. A 2-wire distribution network $ABCDEA$ is fed at the point A with 240 volts. The point E is directly connected to B by a cable of the same size as that used in the network. At B, C, D and at E the respective loads are 20 A., 15 A., 60 A., and 30 A. The lengths of the sections are $AB = 50$ yd., $BC = 100$ yd., $CD = 50$ yd., $DE = 150$ yd., $EB = 250$ yd. and $EA = 100$ yd. Calculate the resistance per 1000 yards of each conductor if the lowest voltage at any load point is 230 volts. *(C. & G., Final, 1948.)*

76. Capacities of Lines, Cables, etc.

References. B3, 6; D6; G2; R1; S5, 7; T1; W1, 6.

See also Volume I, Examples 15, page 22 (Seventh Edition).

Units.

1 C.G.S. electrostatic volt = 300 practical volts

3×10^9 C.G.S. electrostatic units of quantity = 1 practical coulomb

∴ 9×10^{11} C.G.S. electrostatic units of capacity = 1 practical farad

The C.G.S. unit of capacity = 1 " cm."

Hence capacity in " cm." $\times 1\cdot11$ = capacity in $\mu\mu$ farads (i.e. micro-micro-farads, or 10^{-12} farads, or picafarads).

Parallel Plate Condenser.

$$C = \frac{A \varepsilon\, n}{4\pi d} \text{ " cm " } = \frac{0\cdot0885\varepsilon A\, n}{d} \mu\mu\text{F, or pF.}$$

where A = area of one unit of dielectric under strain, in cm.^{2}

n = number of such units of dielectric (generally 1 less than the number of plates).

d = distance between plates, cm.

ε = permittivity or dielectric constant

Note. $A\, n$ above = total cross-section of dielectric under strain.

Co-axial Cylinders (such as a cable).

$$C = \frac{\varepsilon}{2 \log_e R/r} \text{ " cm." per cm. length} = \frac{0\cdot039\varepsilon}{\log R/r}$$

microfarads per mile

where R = outer radius of dielectric

r = inner radius of dielectric

Parallel wires far apart, in comparison with radius of wire (as in an overhead transmission line).

Single-phase.

$$C = \frac{\varepsilon}{2 \log_e s/r} \text{ " cm." per cm. length of single conductor}$$

$$= \frac{0 \cdot 0388\varepsilon}{\log s/r} \text{ microfarads per mile of single conductor}$$

and half this value per mile of loop,

where s = spacing apart of wires $\left.\right\}$ both in the same units; \
r = radius of wire $\left.\right\}$ e.g. ins. or cms.

ε = permittivity = 1 for air

Three-phase. With the three conductors symmetrically placed at the corners of an equilateral triangle, of side s, each conductor will have a capacity given by the above formula for single-phase. Each wire will individually have this capacity with respect to the others. Hence in 3-phase, capacity per conductor is given by

$$C = \frac{0 \cdot 0388}{\log s/r} \, \mu\text{F per mile.}$$

Each condenser draws a charging current to impart to the conductors the necessary potentials with respect to "neutral," or the star-point of the supply, so that each conductor condenser is charged to phase volts, the three condensers being regarded as though connected in star. Hence the capacity of each conductor given by the above formula is often referred to as the "capacity to neutral," but it must be realized that the capacity is calculated up to a distance s from the conductor, i.e. the spacing apart of the wires.

Charging Current.
$$I_c = \omega C. \, V$$

where $\omega = 2\pi \times$ frequency

C = capacity in farads

V = charging p.d. in volts

EXAMPLES 76

1. A concentric cable 10 miles long, when connected to a 5000 volt supply of 50 frequency, is found to take a charging current of 5 amperes. Calculate the capacity per mile of the cable.

2. An air condenser consists of five plates, each 100 cm. by 50 cm., spaced 0·5 mm. apart. Find its capacity in microfarads.

3. Establish the formula for the capacity of a tubular condenser, and specify the C.G.S. unit and show the conversion to microfarads. Calculate the capacity of the tubular condenser, having the following data : length, 20 cm. ; diameters, 35 mm. and 42 mm, of dielectric, having a constant (S.I.C.) of 3·5.

4. Explain one method of adjusting the voltage distribution over a suspension insulator consisting of a number of units. A suspension insulator is made up of two units. The capacitance of the link pin to earth is 20 per cent of the self-capacity of each unit. Find the line voltage to earth for which the insulator is suitable if the working voltage on each unit is not to exceed 20 kV. The capacitance between the line conductor and the pin may be neglected.

(*C. & G., Final*, 1930.)

5. Develop the expression of the capacity of 1-phase overhead transmission line L km. in length with conductors of r cm. radius a cm. apart. Ignoring capacity to earth, find the charging current when $L = 25$ km., $a = 100$ cm., and $r = 0·5$ cm., the applied pressure being 20,000 volts at 50 cycles per second.

(*C. & G., Final*, 1923.)

6. Find the potential difference across each unit of an overhead line suspension insulator consisting of four similar units. The pressure between the line conductor and earth is 60 kilovolts and the ratio of capacity of each unit insulator to the capacity, relative to earth, of each intermediate section of the connecting metalwork is five to one. It is assumed that no leakage takes place. (*I.E.E., May*, 1936.)

7. A single-phase concentric cable, 1 mile long, when connected to 50 cycle, 10,000 volt busbars, takes a charging current of 1 ampere. The inner conductor has a diameter of 12 mm. and the radial thickness of the insulation is 10 mm. Calculate the value of the specific inductive capacity of the material forming the dielectric. (*C. & G., Final*, 1925.)

8. Explain what is meant by the string efficiency of a suspension insulator consisting of a number of units. Describe

one method of adjusting the voltage distribution over such a string. Find the voltage distribution and the string efficiency of a three-unit suspension insulator if the capacitance of the link pins to earth and to the line are respectively 20 per cent and 10 per cent of the self-capacitance of each unit.

(*Lond. Univ.*, 1930, *El. Power.*)

9. A parallel plate condenser with plates 2 mm. apart is charged to a surface density of 6×10^{-10} coulombs per sq. cm. If the dielectric has a capacity constant of 3·2, find (*a*) the flux density in the dielectric, and (*b*) the electric potential across the dielectric.

10. Obtain an expression for the capacity of a parallel plate condenser. The plates of a condenser consist of 101 parallel square plates of 40 cm. side. If the plates are 0·2 mm. apart, and the dielectric has a permittivity (specific inductive capacity) of 4, calculate the kVA. rating of the condenser when used on a 2000 volt, 50 frequency circuit. (*C. & G., Final*, 1926.)

11. Sketch the form of construction of a suspension-type insulator. Show how the voltage distribution over a string of insulators can be improved and explain what is meant by string efficiency. A string of suspension insulators consists of (*a*) two units, (*b*) three units. The capacitance between each link-pin and earth is one-eighth of the self-capacitance of the unit. If the maximum peak voltage per unit is not to exceed 20 kV., find the greatest working voltage in each case. Find also the string efficiency in each case.

(*Lond. Univ.*, 1934, *El. Power.*)

*12. If the voltage across the units in a 2-unit suspension insulator is 60 per cent and 40 per cent respectively of the line voltage, find the ratio of the capacitance of the insulator to that of its capacitance to earth. (*C. & G., Final*, 1944.)

*13. The string insulators in a h.-v. transmission line are made up of (*a*) 3, (*b*) 9, similar units. The capacitance between the metal interlinks is ten times the capacitance between each interlink and earth. The flashover voltage of one insulator is 100 kV. Calculate the voltages at which the three-string and the nine-string assemblies respectively will flash over.

(*C. & G., Final*, 1946.)

77. Capacities of Three-Phase Lines and Cables

References. B3, 6; D2; G2; R1; S5, 7; T1; W1, 6.

Cables.

C_s = capacity between a core and the earthed sheath

C_c = capacity between cores

C_l = capacity as measured between a pair of lines (it being immaterial whether the third line is earthed or insulated)

then $2C_l = C_s + 3C_c$

If V_l = line volts

V_p = phase volts = $V_l/\sqrt{3}$

then charging current $I_c = V_p \left(C_s + 3C_c\right) \omega = \dfrac{2}{\sqrt{3}} V_l C_l \omega$

Overhead Lines. Here C_s becomes the capacity to ground, which is negligible in comparison with C_c, the capacity between a pair of lines, calculated as for single-phase,

C_l = capacity as measured between lines

$\quad = \dfrac{3}{2} C_c$

Charging current per line

$$I_c = V_l C_l \omega = \dfrac{3}{2} \omega C_c V_l$$

Three-phase Cable Tests for Capacity.

Test A. Bunch all three cores and measure the capacity of the bunch to earthed sheath. This gives $3C_s$.

Test B. Join two cores to sheath, and then measure the capacity between these and the third core. This gives $2C_c + C_s$. Thence both C_s and C_c are known.

Test C. Capacity measured between a pair of cores with third core free or shorted to sheath. This gives C_l as above, this single measurement sufficing for calculation of the capacity current per core, as above.

EXAMPLES 77

1. A mile of 3-phase cable measured as in test A gave a capacity of $0\cdot7\mu$F. and in test B of $0\cdot37\mu$F. Find (a) the capacity that should be obtained when tested as in test C, (b) the capacity that should be obtained in a test wherein two cores are connected together, but not to the sheath, and tested to the third core, also insulated, (c) the capacity current per core per mile when fed at 6600 volts at 50 frequency ?

2. A 3300 volt, 3-phase cable was found to have a capacity per mile of $0\cdot3\mu$F. between lines. Find the charging current at 50 frequency for a length of 9 miles of this cable.

3. Calculate the charging current taken by a 3-core, 3-phase cable working at a line voltage of 22,000 volts, having given the following capacities : (a) three cores bunched and sheath, 3·5 microfarads, (b) one conductor and other two joined to sheath, 2·9 microfarads ; frequency 50.

4. A 3-core, 3-phase cable tested for core capacity between a pair of cores with the third insulated from sheath gave a capacity of 0·4 microfarad per mile. Calculate the charging current for 25 miles of this cable when working at 33,000 volts and 50 frequency.

5. The capacitances per mile of a 3-phase cable are 0·63 μF. between the three cores bunched and the sheath, and 0·37 μF. between one core and the other two connected to the sheath. Calculate the charging current taken by eight miles of this cable when connected to a 3-phase, 50-cycle, 6600-volt supply.

(I.E.E., May, 1934.)

6. Show diagrammatically the distribution of electrostatic capacity in a three-core, three-phase, lead-sheathed cable.

The capacity of such a cable measured between any two of the conductors, the sheathing being earthed, is 0·3 microfarad per mile. Find the equivalent star-connected capacity and the kVA. required to keep 10 miles of the cable charged when connected to 20,000-volt, 50-frequency busbars.

(C. & G. Final, 1928.)

78. Transmission Line Surges
References. D2; G2; R1; S5; T1; W1, 6.

EXAMPLES 78

1. Deduce a simple expression for the natural impedance of a transmission line. A transmission line has a capacity of 0·0125 microfarad per mile and an inductance of 1·5 millihenrys per mile. This overhead line is continued by an underground cable with a capacity of 0·3 microfarad per mile and an inductance of 0·25 millihenry per mile. Calculate the rise of voltage produced at the junction of the line and cable by a wave with a crest value of 50 kV. travelling along the cable.
(*Lond. Univ.*, 1931, *El. Power.*)

2. What do you understand by " surge impedance " of an overhead transmission line, and show how to calculate approximately the voltage rise to be expected on the rupturing of a short-circuit current. Describe any form of " surge absorber " or " surge arrester," explaining how it functions.

An overhead line is carried to a sub-station transformer through a length of underground cable. For the line, $L = 1·5$ mH. per mile and $C = 0·012$ μF. per mile. For the cable, $L = 0·3$ mH. per mile and $C = 0·4$ μF. per mile. If a surge of 10-kV. travels along the line towards the sub-station, estimate the voltage of the surge which will reach the transformer. Had the 10-kV. surge originated in the cable, what voltage would have been transmitted along the line?

*3. An overhead transmission line 186 miles long, having a surge impedance of 500 ohms, is short-circuited at one end and a steady voltage of 3000 volts is suddenly applied at the other end. Neglecting the resistance, explain, with diagrams, how the current and voltage change at different parts of the line and calculate the current at the sending end of the line 0·004 second after the voltage is applied. (*Lond. Univ.*, 1945, *El. Power.*)

*4. Explain what is meant by a surge in a transmission system, and enumerate the different methods by which surges are produced. Two stations are connected together by an underground cable having a characteristic or surge impedance of 60 ohms joined to an overhead line with a surge impedance of 400 ohms. If a surge having a maximum value of 100 kV. travels along the cable towards the junction with the overhead line, determine the values of the reflected and transmitted waves of voltage and current at the junction. State any assumptions made in your calculations. (*Lond. Univ.*, 1944, *El. Power.*)

79. Inductance of Overhead Transmission Lines

References. B4, 6; D2; G2; R1; S1, 5; T1; W1, 6.

Single-phase. Coefficient of self-induction

$$L = 2 \log_e s/r \text{ C.G.S. units per cm. of conductor}$$
$$= 7 \cdot 4 \times 10^{-4} \log s/r \text{ henrys per mile of conductor}$$

and double this value per mile of loop

where s = spacing apart of the conductors

r = radius of a conductor

$\left.\right\}$ in any units, since ratio s/r is used

Three-phase. Calculate the inductance of the line across to either of the others (assuming symmetrical triangular spacing) as above for single-phase, and treat the drop caused by this inductance as a "phase" drop; i.e. each line has its own drop, 120° apart. This value is often called the "inductance to neutral."

Alternatively, an equivalent single-phase may be taken, carrying half the power. (See Section 80, Question 4.)

EXAMPLES 79

1. An overhead transmission line is comprised of two conductors 0·36 in. in diameter spaced 3 ft. apart. Find the inductance of a 20 mile run of this line.

2. An overhead line 30 miles in length is to be constructed of conductors 0·4 in. in diameter, for a single-phase transmission. The inductance must not exceed 0·1 henry. Find the maximum permissible spacing.

3. Find the inductive drop on a single-phase line 25 miles in length carrying 50 amperes at 50 frequency, if the conductors are 1 cm. in diameter and are spaced 1 metre apart.

80. Transmission Line Regulation

References. B4, 6; D2; R1; S5; T1; W1, 6.

Single-phase.

Resistance drop, RI, in phase with current.

Reactance drop, ωLI, at 90° lag with current.

Capacity drop, $\frac{1}{2}I_c R = \frac{1}{2}\omega CVR$, at 90° lead with voltage, the value of same at the middle of the line usually being taken, and the drop considered at 90° lead with the load volts,

where R = total resistance of the double run

L = inductance of the loop line

I = load current

I_c = charging current

C = capacity of the pair of lines

$\omega = 2\pi \times$ frequency

To find the sending-end volts, take current as axis of reference, resolve load volts in-phase and in quadrature, adding RI to former and ωLI to latter. Thence find closing vector.

Approximate formula for drop = $RI \cos \phi \pm \omega LI \sin \phi$ where ϕ is the angle of lag $(+)$, or lead $(-)$ of the load.

Three-phase. To find the drop due to resistance and inductance, find that for a single-phase line comprising conductors of the same size and spacing and carrying one-half the power conveyed by the 3-phase line. The charging current per line can be found as in Section 77, and the drop due to this current flowing through a resistance equal to that of one line gives the capacity drop. This is at right-angles to voltage, and is moreover generally small, so that its effect can usually be neglected.

Aliter. As for single-phase above, using phase volts.

EXAMPLES 80

*1. Explain how the voltage variation along a transmission line is influenced by the power-factor of the load at the receiving end. A three-phase overhead transmission line 100 miles long operates at 110 kV. between lines at the sending end. The line conductors have a diameter of 0·7 inch and are symmetrically spaced at a distance of 11 feet apart. Neglecting line losses, calculate the value of the receiving end load having a power-factor of unity for which the voltage at the receiving end will be the same as that at the sending end.

(*Lond. Univ.*, 1946, *El. Power*.)

*2. A 3-phase transmission line has a resistance of 10 ohms per phase and reactance of 25 ohms per phase. Determine the maximum power that can be delivered at the receiving end if the line voltage at each end is 33 kV. Sketch a diagram showing the relation between the power delivered and the angle between the voltages at the two ends if these voltages are maintained constant. Show how this diagram could be used to find the maximum load that can be switched on suddenly without loss of stability. (*Lond. Univ.*, 1946, *El. Power*.)

3. A short 3-phase transmission line supplies a load of 2000 kW., power factor 0·71 lagging, at a voltage of 11,500 volts. Each line conductor has a resistance of 3 ohms and the conductors are arranged symmetrically at the corners of an equilateral triangle, the reactance of a loop formed by two conductors being 12·56 ohms. A condenser-bank rated at 840 kVA. is connected across the load. Calculate the voltages at the sending end with and without the condensers in circuit. Give vector diagrams to illustrate these conditions.

(*C. & G.*, 1939.)

4. A 50-frequency, 3-phase line 100 km. long delivers a load of 40,000 kVA. at 110 kV. and a lagging power factor of 0·7. The line constants (line to neutral values) are : resistance 11 ohms, inductive reactance 38 ohms, capacitive susceptance 3×10^{-4} mhos (half at each end) leakage negligible. Find the sending-end voltage, current, power-factor and power input.

(*C. & G.*, 1937.)

5. A 3-phase transmission line delivers 10,000 kW. at 132,000 volts, 50 frequency, 0·8 power-factor (lagging). Each conductor has a resistance of 40 ohms and a reactance of 60 ohms. Assume that the capacitance of the line may be represented by a star-connected system of condensers connected at the middle of the line, each phase having a capacitance

of 0·5 microfarad. Calculate the voltage at the generator end of the line. (*Lond. Univ.*, 1941, *El. Power.*)

6. A 3-phase load of 10,000 kW. at 10 kV. with a power-factor of 0·71 lagging is received over a 50-cycle transmission line 10 miles long. The resistance of each conductor is 0·022 ohm per mile. The conductors are disposed at the corners of an equilateral triangle and the inductance of the loop formed by a pair of conductors is 0·5 millihenry per mile. Find the voltage at the sending end. If a bank of condensers be used at the receiving end to raise the resultant power-factor to 0·87 lagging, calculate the leading kVA. required and the p.d. at the sending end to maintain 10 kV. across the load when the phase-advancing apparatus is in circuit.

(*C. & G., Final*, 1935.)

7. An air-core reactance coil (of $X = 5$ ohms) is included on each side of a single-phase feeder. A current of 200 amperes is taken from the feeder at (*a*) unity power factor, and (*b*) at 0·8 lagging. Calculate the voltage on the load side in each case, if the supply voltage is 11,000 volts.

8. A 3-phase transmission line delivers current at 33,000 volts to a balanced load having an equivalent impedance "to neutral" of $(240 + j320)$ ohms. The line is 50 miles long and has a resistance per mile per conductor of 0·4 ohm and a reactance per mile per conductor of 0·6 ohm. Calculate the voltage at the generator end. If the load is made $(280 + j370)$ ohms, calculate the receiving-end voltage if the voltage at the generator end is unchanged.

(*Lond. Univ.*, 1940, *El. Power.*)

9. A 2-wire feeder 1500 yards long supplies a load of 120 amperes at 0·8 power factor at its far end and a load of 80 amperes at 0·9 power factor at its mid-point. Both power factors are lagging and refer to the voltages at the respective load points. The resistance and reactance of the feeder per mile (go and return) are 0·1 ohm and 0·15 ohm respectively. If the voltage at the far end is to be maintained at 230 volts, calculate the voltage at the sending end and the phase angle between the voltages at the two ends.

(*I.E.E.*, Nov., 1932.)

10. A 3-phase transmission line has an impedance, phase to neutral, of $1·5 + j3·5$ ohm. It supplies a load with a constant voltage of 11,500. Connected in parallel with the load is a synchronous condenser, so adjusted that with a useful load of 2500 kW. at 0·8 power factor, lagging, the voltage at the sending-end is also 11·5 kV. Determine approximately (i) the

rating of the condenser if its losses are 130 kW., (ii) the voltage at the sending-end when the useful load is 5000 kW. at 0·8 power factor lagging.   (*Lond. Univ.*, 1936, *El. Power.*)

11. A 3-phase, 50-frequency transmission line has condensers connected to it at the load end and also at a point one-third of the way along the line from the load end. In both cases the condensers constitute a 3-phase, star-connected load, each phase of which has a capacitance of $10\mu F$. The total resistance per conductor of the transmission line is 13·5 ohms and the total reactance per conductor is 18 ohms. The voltage at the load end is 10 kV. and the current delivered to the load (excluding the condenser at the load end) is 100 amperes at 0·8 power factor (lagging). Calculate the current in the line at the load end and also at the generator end.

     (*Lond. Univ.*, 1940, *El. Power.*)

12. A single-phase line has an impedance of $5/\underline{60°}$ and supplies a load of 120 amperes, 3300 volts at 0·8 lagging power factor. Calculate the sending-end voltage and draw a vector diagram approximately to scale.   (*C. & G.*, 1940.)

13. Each of the three conductors of the "National Grid" network has a resistance of 0·0479 ohm per 1000 ft. The effective diameter of the wire is 0·77 in., the mean equilateral spacing is 15 ft., and the inductance 2·06 millihenrys per mile, line to neutral. Determine, analytically or graphically, the voltage at the sending end of a 50-mile length of Grid single-circuit line delivering 50,000 kVA. at 132 kV., power factor 0·8 lagging.   (*C. & G., Final*, 1932.)

*14. A 3-phase overhead transmission line, having a resistance of 5 ohms per phase and reactance of 20 ohms per phase, has a load of 25,000 kW., 33 kV., 0·8 power-factor lagging at the receiving end. Determine the voltage at the sending end. If a synchronous phase modifier is connected at the receiving end and the voltages at the two ends kept constant at 33 kV., determine the kVAR. of the synchronous phase modifier when the load at the receiving end is 25,000 kW. at 0·8 power-factor lagging and also the maximum load which can be transmitted over the line.

     (*Lond. Univ.*, 1945, *El. Power.*)

81. Dip, Span, and Tension of Overhead Lines

References. B4, 6; D2; R1; S5; T1; W1, 6.

If w = weight of conductor per foot run

l = length of span, in feet

T = tension in lb.

then, assuming the conductor to hang in a parabola, instead of a catenary, and for supports at the same level, the dip in feet is given by

$$d = \frac{wl^2}{8T}$$

If one support is h feet higher than the other, the distance the lowest point is from the lower support is given by

$$x_1 = \frac{l}{2} - \frac{hT}{wl}$$

and the dip below the lower support is

$$d_1 = \frac{w}{2T} x_1^2$$

Factor of Safety is usually 5, i.e. working stress $\times 5$ = breaking stress.

Temperature Allowance. The minimum temperature for the British Isles is usually taken as 22° F. At this temperature the dip should be such that the stress is within the maximum permissible. At a higher temperature $t°$ F., the dip will increase to

$$d_t = \sqrt{d^2 + al^2 (t - 22)}$$

where a = ·375 times the temperature coefficient of expansion of the conductor material, i e. for copper 0·00000354, and for aluminium 0·0000048.

Ice Coating. This has the effect of increasing the weight per foot run used in the above formulae.

Wind Pressure. It is usual to consider that the surface acted upon normally by the wind is 0·6 of the projected area of the conductor. If the wind pressure is p lb. per sq. ft. (maximum usually taken as 30 lb.), and diameter of the conductor is d' in feet, the wind pressure per foot run will be $0·6pd'$ lb. This must be regarded as acting in a horizontal direction, and the resultant " weight per foot run " must be obtained by vectorially combining the ice-loaded weight (acting vertically) with the wind pressure found above (acting horizontally).

EXAMPLES 81

1. Obtain an expression for the relation between sag, span, and tension in an overhead conductor of a given weight per unit length on a level run. Assume a parabolic curve. How is the presence of ice on the conductor taken into account ? Apply the expression obtained to calculate the sag under the following conditions : length of span, 500 ft. ; cross-sectional area of conductor, 0·196 sq. in. ; breaking strength, 60,000 lb. per sq. in. ; factor of safety, 5 ; weight of conductor, 0·76 lb. per ft. ; maximum wind pressure, 30 lb. per sq. ft.

(C. & G., Final, 1924.)

2. A transmission line has a span of 600 ft. between level supports. The conductor has a cross-sectional area of 0·2 in.^{2}, weighs 2360 lb. per 1000 yd. and has a breaking stress of 60,000 lb./in.^{2} Calculate the sag for a factor of safety of 5, allowing a maximum wind pressure of 25 lb./ft.^{2} of projected surface. Show how to allow for the presence of ice on the wire.

(C. & G., Final, 1936.)

3. The 600-ft. spans in an overhead transmission line are calculated to have a vertical sag of 20 ft. The conductor has a cross-sectional area of 0·2 sq. in. and weighs 2·3 lb. per yd. If the hard-drawn copper has a breaking stress of 60,000 lb. per sq. in. find the working factor of safety when the wind pressure at right angles to the length of the conductor is 25 lb. per sq. ft. Establish any formulae used in the calculation.

(C. & G., Final, 1929.)

4. The standard line conductor for the "National Grid" Transmission Scheme weighs 571 pounds per 1000 ft., has an overall diameter of 0·77 in., and an ultimate breaking strength of 17,732 pounds. If the factor of safety is to be 2 when the conductor has an ice load of 2 pounds per yard and a horizontal wind pressure of 3 pounds per yard, find, approximately, the

amount of vertical sag which corresponds to this loading in a 900-ft. span between level supports. Give a roughly dimensioned sketch of the form of clamp adopted for jointing this conductor. (*C. & G., Final*, 1931.)

5. Two electric tramway trolley wires are supported 8 ft. apart by a span wire attached to two points on the level 40 ft. apart. The span wire weighs 10 lb. and each trolley wire with its fittings weighs 70 lb. If the dip in the span wire is 1 ft., calculate the tension. (*C. & G., Final*, 1935.)

*6. When determining the sag and stress of a steel-cored aluminium overhead conductor the "virtual coefficient of expansion" and "virtual modulus of elasticity" are used. Justify the use of these and calculate their values for a conductor comprising one strand of steel and six strands of aluminium, all strands of the same diameter. The coefficients of expansion of aluminium and steel per °C. are respectively $22 \cdot 7 \times 10^{-6}$ and $11 \cdot 5 \times 10^{-6}$ and their moduli are $9 \cdot 5 \times 10^{6}$ and 30×10^{6} lb. per in.^{2} Under what conditions do the virtual values not apply for a steel-cored aluminium conductor?

(*Lond. Univ.*, 1945, *El. Power.*)

82. Properties of Insulations

References. B3, 4; D6; G2; R1; S1, 5; W1, 6.

The stress in the dielectric of a cable (if homogeneous) is given by

$$\text{Stress} = \frac{V}{x \log_e R/r} \text{ volts per cm.}$$

where V = volts across dielectric

x = distance in cm. from centre of core

R = outer radius of dielectric

r = inner radius of dielectric

This becomes a maximum at the inner radius, of value

$$\text{Max. stress} = \frac{V}{r \log_e R/r}$$

The gradient will be in max. volts or R.M.S. volts, according to whether V is expressed in max. or R.M.S. value. The highest value for impregnated paper is about 50 kV. (R.M.S.) per cm.

Graded Insulations. Potentials other than those given by the above expression for a simple dielectric can be given to any desired point in the dielectric in two ways—

(a) The dielectric is divided into layers of different nature and thickness, and the whole insulation thereby split up into a number of condensers in series. The capacity of a condenser can be expressed as

$$C = k \cdot \frac{\varepsilon A}{t}$$

where k is a constant

ε = dielectric constant or permittivity

A = cross-section area of dielectric normal to flux

t = thickness of dielectric

It thus follows that the capacities of these condensers can be adjusted by variation of these various factors, e.g. the constant, ε, can be varied by the degree of vulcanization of the rubber, or by use of impregnated paper; the area is largely controlled by the distance from the centre, increasing with the outer layers ; while t is a balancing factor to give the desired capacity. Then, since with condensers in series the total voltage across the group is subdivided across each unit in accordance with the individual capacities, it follows that definite voltages can be given to definite points in the cable dielectric by this use of graded insulation, and better stress gradients obtained in consequence.

(b) By the use of intersheaths. Layers of copper strip are inserted in the dielectric, and are charged to some definite voltage by connections to tappings on the transformer feeding the cable. These intersheaths may carry definite power currents.

Specific Resistivity of a Dielectric. If two transverse planes in a single-core cable are taken 1 cm. apart, the insulation resistance between core and sheath of this unit length of cable is given by

$$R = \frac{\rho \log_e R/r}{2\pi} \text{ ohms}$$

where ρ is the specific resistivity of the dielectric. For a greater length, the value of R is correspondingly *less*.

EXAMPLES 82

1. Describe a method of assessing the electrical suitability of sheet insulating materials without testing to destruction. An imperfect condenser is represented by a capacitance C and a shunt resistance R. Find an expression in terms of C and R for the tangent of the angle δ by which the current of the combination departs from $90°$ lead on the applied voltage.

(I.E.E., Nov., 1935.)

2. Describe briefly, with the aid of a diagram, apparatus for the D.C. testing of cables at high voltage. What precautions should be taken at the conclusion of such a test? What advantage has the use of D.C. over A.C. in the pressure-testing of lengths of high-voltage cable during and after laying?

(Lond. Univ., 1936, El. Tech.)

3. The leading-in conductor to a sub-station has a diameter of 1 cm. and passes centrally through a porcelain cylinder of internal diameter 2 cm. and external diameter 7 cm. The cylinder is surrounded by a tightly fitting metal sheath. The permittivity of porcelain is 5, and the peak voltage gradient

in air must not exceed 34 kV. per cm. Find the maximum safe working voltage.   (*Lond. Univ.*, 1933, *El. Power.*)

4. Sketch approximately to scale and describe the form of a terminal bushing suitable for a 132 kV. installation. A high-voltage bushing comprises a central conductor of 2·5 cm. diameter wound with bakelized paper to an overall diameter of 4·5 cm. The assembly is immersed centrally in oil, which is contained in a porcelain cylinder with walls 1 cm. thick and an outside diameter of 8 cm. The cylinder is enclosed in a tight-fitting earth metal sheath. The permittivities of paper, oil, and porcelain are 6, 2·5, and 5 respectively, and the corresponding maximum allowable electrical stresses are 80, 160, and 60 kV. (r.m.s.) per cm. Find the greatest voltage that the bushing could withstand and the maximum gradient in each part of the bushing when this voltage is applied.

(*I.E.E.*, *May*, 1942.)

5. A 66-kV. concentric cable with two intersheaths has a core diameter 1·8 cm. Dielectric material 3·5 mm. thick constitutes the three zones of insulation. Find the maximum stress in each of the three layers if 20 kV. is maintained across each of the inner two.   (*C. & G.*, *Final*, 1938.)

6. A single-core 0·1 sq. in. paper insulated cable, lead covered and armoured, is buried in the ground at a mean depth of 2 ft. The core radius is 5·2 mm., dielectric thickness 2 mm., lead sheath thickness 1·8 mm., and the final covering, including the armouring, is 8 mm. If the thermal resistivities of the dielectric, covering and soil are respectively 850, 300 and 200° C. per watt per cm., find the permissible current loading for a temperature rise of the core of 50° C. Take the resistivity of the hot copper as 2·16 microhm-cms. (See ref. R1, S5.)

*7. A single-core cable, 1 km. in length, has a core diameter of 1·0 cm. and a diameter under the sheath of 3·0 cm. The permittivity is 3·5. The power-factor on open circuit is 0·04. Calculate (*a*) the capacitance of the cable; (*b*) the equivalent insulation resistance; (*c*) the charging current; (*d*) the dielectric loss, when the cable is connected to 11-kV., 50-cycle bus-bars.   (*C. & G.*, *Final*, 1946.)

*8. The inner conductor of a concentric cable has a diameter of 3 cm., the diameter over the insulation being 8·5 cm. The cable is insulated with two materials having permittivities of 5 and 3 respectively with corresponding safe working stresses of 38 kV. per cm. and 26 kV. per cm. Calculate the radial thickness of each insulating layer and the safe working voltage of the cable.   (*C. & G.*, *Final*, 1943.)

*9. A 66-kV., single-core, lead-covered cable laid 3 feet below ground level has the following dimensions: Conductor, 37/0·093 in.; dielectric thickness, 0·65 in.; lead sheath thickness 0·15 in.; serving thickness 0·15 in. Calculate the current the cable can carry continuously if the thermal resistivity in °C. per watt per cm. cube of the dielectric is 550, of the outer covering 300, and of the earth 160. The maximum temperature rise is not to exceed 50° C., and the specific resistance of the conductor is 0·8 microhm-in.

(*Lond. Univ.*, 1947, *El. Power.*)

*10. Each core of a 3-core cable for a 33-kV., 3-phase system is lead covered and the conductor, 0·65 in. in diameter, is insulated with impregnated paper to a radial thickness of 0·175 in. Calculate the maximum electric stress on the insulation at normal working voltage, assuming the dielectric constant to be 3·2. (*Lond. Univ.*, 1947, *El. Power.*)

11. Explain the principle of grading the insulation of a cable by the use of intersheaths, and show how the potentials of the intersheaths can be fixed. A cable with homogeneous dielectric has an inner radius of 1 cm., a voltage of 66,000 volts core to earth, and the dielectric stress reaching 30 kV. (r.m.s.) per cm. at the core. If two intersheaths had been introduced so that the dielectric was divided into three zones, and potentials of 44,000 and 22,000 volts applied thereto, and the gradient restored to the maximum of 30 kilovolts per cm. against each intersheath, to what extent could the total thickness of dielectric have been reduced? Ignore thickness of intersheaths themselves.

12. A single-core cable having a core diameter of 7 mm. and diameter over insulation of 30 mm., is found to have an insulation resistance of 80,000 ohms per mile. Calculate the specific resistivity of the dielectric.

13. Explain the principles of intersheath grading and capacitance grading of cables for alternating voltages. What are the practical difficulties and chief disadvantages involved in these methods of grading? A single-core cable for a working voltage of 90 kV. is insulated with a material which can be worked at 60 kV. per cm. Calculate the diameter of the intersheath and the voltage at which it must be maintained to obtain the minimum overall cable diameter. (See ref. R1.)

(*C. & G., Final*, 1936.)

14. In a test on a bakelite sample at 20 kV. 50-frequency, by a Schering bridge having a standard condenser of 106 μF., balance was obtained with a capacitance of 0·35 μF. in parallel

with a non-reactive resistance of 318 ohms, the non-reactive resistance in the remaining arm of the bridge being 130 ohms. Calculate the capacitance and the power factor of the specimen and its equivalent series resistance. Deduce any formula employed and draw the vector diagram for the balanced bridge. (Ref. H1.) (C. & G., Final, 1937.)

15. Obtain an expression for the electric gradient at a point midway between a cylindrical rod which is maintained at a voltage V and an outer concentric earthed cylinder, the space between being occupied by two concentric layers of media of the same thickness but of different specific inductive capacities.

The core of a transformer is a cylinder 13 cm. in diameter. The low-tension winding surrounds a solid insulating barrier 3·2 mm. thick which is arranged concentric with the core, but with an oil-duct 3·2 mm. wide between core and barrier. Calculate the maximum voltage gradient in the solid barrier when a test voltage of 10,000 is applied between low-tension winding and core. The S.I.C. of oil is 2, and that of the solid barrier 3. (Lond. Univ., 1926, El. Mach.)

16. A single-core high voltage cable has a conductor diameter of 0·15 in., the diameter of the cable over the insulation being 1 in. Calculate the insulation resistance per mile of cable, given that the insulating material has a specific resistance of 5×10^{10} ohms per cm. cube. (C. & G., Final, 1927.)

17. An insulated cable consists of a conductor of 4 mm. diameter, surrounded by a dielectric 4 mm. thick, having a dielectric constant of 3, and by a lead sheath. Calculate its capacity in microfarads per mile. Assuming a dielectric strength for the insulation, show how to calculate the highest voltage that could be applied between conductor and sheath without breakdown. In what respect is the design of high-tension cables affected by consideration of dielectric strength, assuming that the relation between breakdown thickness t and voltage can be expressed by $t = AV + BV^2$, where A and B are constants. (Lond. Univ., 1927, El. Power.)

18. What is a condenser bushing? Upon what principle is it based? What is the advantage of filling the bushing with oil? A condenser bushing consists of 10 layers, the central conductor being 1 cm. in diameter, and the outer layer 5 cm. in diameter. If this outer layer has an axial length of 10 cm., give a table of the lengths of the other layers to give equal voltage distribution. The bushing is oil-filled, and the permittivity of oil-impregnated paper is 4.

83. Insulation Resistance and Fault Localization

References. B4, 6; D2, 6; G2; R2; S5; T1.

Fault Resistances. Equating the algebraic sum of the leakage currents to zero with varying potentials given to the mains by means of auxiliary faults to earth of known magnitude will enable the fault resistances to be determined.

Mains Potentials. These can be obtained from the same principles as employed above.

Loss of Charge Method. The insulation resistance of a cable, condenser, etc., can be ascertained as follows —

Let v = voltage across condenser at any instant

R = the insulation resistance

i = v/R = current flowing at that instant

C = capacity of the condenser

q = C.v. = charge on condenser

hence $i = \dfrac{dq}{dt} = - C \dfrac{dv}{dt} = \dfrac{v}{R}$ and $\dfrac{dv}{v} = - \dfrac{dt}{CR}.$

If the voltage falls from V_0 to V_1 in time t seconds, then

$$t = CR \log_e V_0/V_1 \text{ and } R = \frac{t}{C \log_e V_0/V_1}$$

The insulation resistance of another body can be ascertained by placing it in parallel with the condenser of known capacity and resistance, and noting the new " loss of charge." If the capacity of the condenser or the combination is unknown, a third test can be applied with a known high resistance (free from capacity) acting as a leak. (See Example 5.)

In the above, an electrostatic voltmeter is employed to read the various voltages. The instrument not being dead-beat, the voltage at any instant is often doubtful, especially if the charge is being lost at a fairly rapid rate. To overcome this difficulty, the charged condenser can be discharged through a ballistic galvanometer, and thence the charge present at any given time ascertained. If the charge falls from Q_0 to Q_1 in time t seconds, then

$$R = \frac{t}{C \log_e Q_0/Q_1}$$

As above, C can be eliminated by the use of a known leak. (See Example 6.)

EXAMPLES 83

1. The voltage between the neutral point and earth of a 2×230-volt D.C. 3-wire insulated system was measured by an electrostatic voltmeter and found to be 40 volts. When an ammeter in series with a resistance was connected between the neutral point and earth the current was $0 \cdot 05$ ampere and the voltage 8 volts. Develop an expression for the fault resistance in the above test and use it to calculate the value with the figures given. (*Lond. Univ.*, 1936, *El. Power.*)

2. The middle wire of a 3-wire D.C. distribution system is earthed through a resistance of 10 ohms in series with an ammeter. On the positive side there is a fault to earth of 15 ohms, and on the negative side of 12 ohms. If the balancer maintains 230 volts between the mid-wire and each of the outers, calculate the potentials of the positive, negative, and middle wires at the balancer terminals and the ammeter reading. (*C. & G., Final*, 1940.)

3. Deduce expressions for the insulation resistance to earth of each conductor of a pair of live mains in terms of the volt-meter readings between each main and earth, the p.d. between mains and the resistance of the voltmeter.

What is the insulation resistance of each main when the respective voltages to earth measured on a voltmeter having a resistance of 80,000 ohms are 80 volts and 30 volts? P.d. between mains 250 volts. (*C. & G., Final*, 1936.)

4. Describe the " loss of charge " method of measuring the insulation resistance of a cable, showing how unknown constants of the apparatus can be eliminated. If a cable and electrostatic voltmeter connected thereto have a joint capacity of $0 \cdot 0005$ microfarad, and it is found that the combination will fall in voltage from 120 to 100 volts in 25 seconds, estimate the insulation resistance of the cable, assuming that of the voltmeter to be infinite.

5. A cable immersed in a testing tank is charged to a voltage of 200, an electrostatic voltmeter being connected between core and tank. After one minute's electrification, the cable and

voltmeter are isolated, and it is found that in 20 seconds the voltage falls to 150 volts. The test is repeated with a resistance of 20 megohms between core and tank, and the voltage is then found to fall to 100 volts in the same time. Find the insulation resistance of the cable, that of the voltmeter being given as 50 megohms.

6. A cable under test for insulation resistance was charged to 100 volts between core and sheath and, after one minute's electrification, was immediately discharged through a ballistic galvanometer, giving a deflection of 120 scale divisions. It was recharged for one minute, then isolated for 20 seconds, and then again discharged through the ballistic, giving a scale deflection of 80 divisions. A resistance of 25 megohms was then connected from core to sheath, the cable recharged, isolated for the same time, and again discharged through the ballistic, giving a deflection of 60 divisions. Find the insulation resistance of the cable.

7. The insulation resistance of a porcelain terminal bushing is to be measured by the "loss of charge" method. For this purpose the bushing is connected in parallel with a condenser of 0·1 microfarad capacity, and the combination is charged through a ballistic galvanometer which gives a throw of 160 scale divisions. The condenser with the bushing still in parallel is now isolated for 150 seconds, at the end of which time the throw on recharge was 10 scale divisions. Assuming that the insulation of the condenser alone is perfect, calculate the insulation resistance of the bushing.

(I.E.E., Nov., 1935.)

8. Explain how to determine the insulation resistance of a low or medium voltage network without interrupting the supply to the consumers. Distinguish carefully between A.C. and D.C. networks. One point of a D.C. network is connected to earth through a voltmeter having a resistance of r ohms. Show that the resistance x it is necessary to connect across the voltmeter in order to halve the reading so obtained, is given by

$$x = Rr/(R + r)$$

where $R =$ the insulation resistance of the network.

(I.E.E., May, 1934.)

9. The insulation resistance of an isolated feeder is tested by means of a voltmeter having a resistance of 50,000 ohms. It is used in conjunction with a two-wire d.c. system in which the negative main is earthed. When the voltmeter is connected from the positive main to earth it records 460 volts, and when

it is connected between the positive main and the core of the feeder it records 23 volts. Calculate the insulation resistance of the feeder.

10. Explain with diagrams the tests to be carried out to locate the position of an earth fault in a low-voltage distribution network. Each conductor in a section of a distributor cable 300 yards long has a resistance of 0·01 ohm per yard. When the section is isolated from the supply, the resistance between the conductor and earth with the distant end insulated is 11·5 ohms and when earthed is 2·88 ohms. Calculate the distance of the earth fault from the testing end and the resistance of the fault.   (*Lond. Univ.*, 1931, *El. Power.*)

11. A fault to earth on one core of a two-core cable is to be located by the Murray loop and slide wire method. A metre wire with galvanometer in parallel is connected across the test end of the cable, the two cores at the far end being shorted. The battery with one pole earthed gave balance with the jockey reading 35 cm. on the wire. If the cable is 150 yards long, how far down the one core is the fault?

84. Power Factor Improvement

References. B4, 5; C3; D2, 3; K2; R1; S5; T1; W1, 6.

EXAMPLES 84

1. State concisely the more important methods in use for improving the power factor at the receiving end of a transmission line. A 3-phase, 50-cycle, 3,000-volt motor develops 600 horse-power, the power factor being 0·75 lagging, and the efficiency 0·93. A bank of condensers is connected in delta across the supply terminals, and the power factor raised to 0·95 lagging. Each of the capacitance units is built up of five similar 600-volt condensers. Determine the capacitance of each condenser. (*Lond. Univ.*, 1933, *El. Power*.)

2. A sub-station, which is fed by a single feeder cable, supplies the following loads: 1000 kW. at 0·85 lagging, 1500 kW. at 0·8 lagging, 2000 kW. at 0·75 lagging, 500 kW. at 0·9 leading. Find the power factor of the supply to the sub-station and the load the feeder cable could carry at unity power factor with the same cable heating. (*I.E.E.*, *Nov.*, 1935.)

3. A factory sub-station requires 2 MW. at 0·8 power factor (lagging), but the thermal rating of the transmission line from the power station is 2·4 MVA. What is the kVA. capacity of the synchronous motor required to allow the load to be supplied without exceeding the rating of the transmission system? If the factory needs an additional drive of 150 kW., calculate the rating of the synchronous motor required so that it can be used for power factor correction as well as driving. (*I.E.E.*, 1940.)

4. What are the effects of low power factor? Where in a distribution network should corrective apparatus be installed?

A 3-phase synchronous motor is connected in parallel with a load of 200 kW. at 0·8 power factor (lagging) and its excitation is adjusted until it raises the total power factor to 0·9 (lagging). If the mechanical load on the motor, including losses, takes 50 kW., calculate the kVA. input to the motor.

(*I.E.E.*, *May*, 1934.)

5. An industrial load of 4000 kW. has a bulk supply at 11,000 volts, the power factor being 0·8. A synchronous motor is required to meet an additional load of 1500 h.p., and at the same time raise the resultant power factor of the installation to 0·95 lagging. Find the kVA. rating of the motor and the power-factor at which it must be operated. Motor efficiency 0·92. Give a diagram to illustrate these conditions and an

explanation of the control of power factor by the synchronous machine. *(C. & G., Final, 1934.)*

6. A single-phase induction motor running from a 230-volt, 50-cycle A.C. supply takes a current of 40 amperes at a power factor of 0·866 lagging. If a condenser is placed in parallel with the motor, find the capacity and kVA. rating required to make the total supply current a minimum for the same motor load. *(Lond. Univ., 1935, El. Tech.)*

7. Show that the economical limit to which the power factor of a lagging load can be raised is independent of the original value of the power factor when the tariff consists of a fixed charge per kVA. plus a flat rate per unit. A consumer is charged £3 per annum per kVA. maximum demand, plus a flat rate per kWh. Phase advancing plant can be purchased for £3 per kVA., the cost for depreciation, housing, and interest on capital being 12 per cent. Find the most economical angle of lag to which the load can be improved under these conditions. *(Lond. Univ., 1932, El. Power.)*

8. The following figures give the load on a sub-station working on a 3-phase supply at 3300 volts : (i) balanced incandescent lighting load of 40 kW. ; (ii) induction motor taking 25 kW. at a power factor of 0·85 lagging ; (iii) induction motor taking 55 kW. at a power factor of 0·89 lagging ; (iv) synchronous motor taking 50 kW. At what power factor must the synchronous motor be worked in order to raise the power factor of the whole station to unity, and what will it be rated at in kVA. at this load ?

9. A 3-phase, 3000-volt, 50-frequency motor develops 375 h.p., the power factor being 0·75 lagging, and the efficiency 92 per cent. A bank of condensers is star-connected in parallel with the motor and the total power-factor raised to 0·9 lagging. Each phase of the condenser bank is made up of three condensers joined in series. Determine the capacitance of each. *(Lond. Univ., 1939, El. Power.)*

10. An industrial load has an average value of 300 kW. at a power factor of 0·71 lagging for 2000 hours in the year. The recorded maximum demand is 25 per cent above the average load. Energy costs £5 per annum per kVA. maximum demand plus 0·5 penny per unit. Find the annual saving in cost due to installing phase-advancing plant, which costs £3 per kVA. and which raises the average power factor to 0·9 lagging. Allow 10 per cent for interest and depreciation on the capital cost of the phase-advancer and neglect additional losses. *(C. & G., Final, 1932.)*

11. What factors determine the economical limit of power factor correction ? A system is working at its maximum kVA. capacity with a lagging power factor of 0·71. An anticipated increase of load could be met by (a) raising the power factor of the system to 0·87 by the installation of phase advancers, (b) by installing extra generating plant, cables, etc., to meet the increased power demand. The total cost for the latter method is £8 per kVA. Estimate the limiting cost per kVA. of phase advancing plant which would justify its installation.

(*I.E.E.*, *Nov.*, 1939.)

*12. A load had a maximum-demand of 400 kVA. at a power-factor of 0·8 (lagging) and the tariff is £5 per kVA. of maximum-demand plus 0·5 pence per kWh. Calculate the saving in the maximum-demand charge if the power-factor is "corrected" to 0·9 (lagging). Calculate also the total saving if an annual charge of 10s. per kVA. is allowed for the correcting apparatus. (*Lond. Univ.*, 1943, *El. Power.*)

*13. Compare the synchronous induction motor and the static condenser as means of improving the power-factor of a load. The load at a factory is 1000 kW., 0·75 power-factor lagging. A motor of 250 h.p. and 92 per cent efficiency is installed raising the power-factor of the whole load to 0·87 lagging. Determine the power-factor of this motor.

(*Lond. Univ.*, 1946, *El. Power.*)

*14. A consumer takes a steady load of 2000 kW. at a lagging power-factor of 0·707 for 3500 hours a year. The tariff is £3 per kVA. demand plus 0·5d. per kWh. The annual cost of phase-advancing plant is £0·3 per kVA. Determine the kVA. capacity of such phase-advancing plant which would result in minimum total annual expenditure.

(*C. & G.*, *Final*, 1944.)

85. Protective Systems and Gear

References. B4; D2; G1; M4; R1, 2; S5, 6; T1; W4.

EXAMPLES 85

1. Describe the construction of an air-core reactance such as is used for current-limiting purposes of large capacity and state how the capacity is usually expressed. What would be a suitable value for an external reactance to an alternator having 5 per cent internal reactance, so that the short-circuit current cannot exceed the full load of 1000 amperes at 11,000 volts, 3-phase, 50 periods?   (*I.E.E.*, *May*, 1936.)

2. Give an account of the characteristics, the requirements and the limitations of reactors in the control of large amounts of power, and a diagram showing the positions in which such reactors are desirable in a large generating station. Explain how these reactors are rated. Each of two 10,000-volt sectional bus-bars have a normal full-load rating of 20,000 kW. at unity power factor and are connected by a reactor with a voltage drop of 40 per cent, for a transfer rate of 20,000 kW. The feeder loads connected to the respective sectional bus-bars are 10,000 and 30,000 kW. at unity power factor, while the generator capacity connected to each sectional bus-bar is 20,000 kW. If the two groups of generators are equally loaded, find the phase-angle between the bus-bar sections.

(*Lond. Univ.*, 1934, *El. Power.*)

3. Explain with a diagram the application of the Merz-Price circulating current system to the protection of alternators. What precautions must be taken in installing this system? A 6600-volt, 3-phase turbo-alternator has a maximum continuous rating of 2000 kW. at 0·8 power factor and its reactance is 12·5 per cent. It is equipped with Merz-Price circulating current protection which is set to operate at fault currents not less than 200 amp. Find what value of neutral earthing resistance leaves 10 per cent of the windings unprotected.   (*I.E.E.*, *Nov.*, 1934.)

4. Give a description of a thermal type of overload protective relay. Explain why this type when used to protect a motor from dangerous overheating is more fundamentally correct than other types.   (*I.E.E.*, *April*, 1924.)

5. Describe the Merz-Price circulating current system for the protection of transformers. Show how this type of protective gear can be made to operate on over-loads, and how the operation of the relays by transient magnetizing currents

can be avoided. Give a diagram of connections of this system applied to the protection of a 1000-kVA., 11,000/400-volt, delta-star, 3-phase transformer, and mark on the diagram the turn-ratios of the current transformers for a nominal 5-ampere secondary current. (*Lond. Univ.*, 1932, *El. Power.*)

6. A 3-phase, star-connected, 50 frequency generator, rated at 1000 kVA. and 6600 volts line pressure, has a short-circuit current of 220 amperes per phase when excited so that on open circuit the line pressure would be 2200 volts. Calculate the inductance of the reactor necessary in each line between the terminals of the machine and the busbars in order to limit the current per phase to 350 amperes on short-circuit at the busbars with normal excitation. The effective resistance per phase of the alternator is 1·5 ohms, and the resistance of each reactor is to be 0·5 ohm. (*Lond. Univ.*, 1924, *El. Power.*)

7. Power is transmitted from a generating station to a distribution centre and thence to a number of sub-stations through a system of branched duplicate feeders. Explain how a defective line can be selected and isolated by a combination of graded and reverse-power relays. Describe the construction and action of the relays employed and the characteristics required in the relays to give discrimination.
(*C. & G., Final*, 1935.)

8. Explain simply what is meant by "positive," "negative," and "zero" phase sequence. Illustrate, with circuit diagrams, a system of protection making use of zero-sequence currents for the operation of relays. (*I.E.E., May*, 1939.)

9. What is the object of a Petersen Coil? Describe, with the aid of sketches, how it functions. Calculate the reactance of a coil suitable for a 33-kV., 3-phase transmission system of which the capacitance to earth of each conductor is 4·5 μF.
(*I.E.E., May*, 1940.)

10. Six high-voltage sub-stations are supplied through an overhead ring-main system. The distance between stations is 5 miles. What form of non-pilot protection should be used? Comment on the selectivity to be obtained and the limitations of the form of protection suggested. (*I.E.E., May*, 1936.)

11. Give the principles of the horn-arrester spark-gap, and show how resistance can be inserted in the earth path to limit the current following an arcing ground, and yet to be capable of being by-passed by a high-frequency surge of high power.

12. Explain with connection diagram one system of automatic protection for the high-voltage generators in a large

central station. How does the system described act in the event of a failure of (a) the steam supply, (b) the exciting current of the alternator?   (*Lond. Univ.*, 1934, *El. Power.*)

13. Make a sketch showing in sectional elevation an outdoor-type liquid earthing resistance of 800 amperes rating and suitable for service on a 33-kV. system. Give the approximate dimensions and comment on the size and type of electrode, the nature of the electrolyte, the usual basis of the current and the time rating, and what precautions are taken to prevent freezing of the electrolyte.   (*I.E.E.*, *May*, 1936.)

14. Describe one type of reverse power relay suitable for use on a high-voltage circuit. Explain two alternative methods by means of which compensation may be obtained for a possible fall of busbar voltage before the relay comes into action.

(*C. & G.*, *Final*, 1924.)

15. What do you understand by the percentage rating of a current limiting reactance used in sectionalizing the busbars in a large generating station?

A total load of 50,000 kilowatts is supplied from two busbars which are connected together through a 30 per cent reactance coil. The capacity of the generator plant connected to each sectional busbar is 25,000 kilowatts and the alternators are all similarly loaded. Calculate the phase angle between the voltages of the section busbars if the voltage of both of these busbars is 20,000 volts and the respective feeder loads on the section busbars are in the ratio 2 to 3.

(*Lond. Univ.*, 1929, *El. Power.*)

16. Mercury rectifiers are installed in a sub-station converting energy from a three-phase 6600-volt system to a three-wire direct-current network with 500 volts between the outers. The high-voltage supply is by duplicate feeders. Give a suitable connection diagram showing main oil switches, discriminating protective gear for the duplicate high-voltage mains, the transformer connections, and the external connections of the rectifiers. Describe briefly the system of protection adopted for the high-voltage feeders.   (*Lond. Univ.*, 1929, *El. Power.*)

86. Electric Furnaces

References. B3; M3, 5; P2.

EXAMPLES 86

1. Describe, with sketches, a modern form of high-frequency electric furnace of the induction type. Explain the mode of operation and state the advantages of this type of electric furnace compared with the earlier type of "cored" induction furnace. (*C. & G., Final*, 1932.)

2. Describe, with a roughly dimensioned sketch, a 3-phase electric furnace suitable for melting a 10-ton charge of iron, specifying the methods adopted to maintain balance between the phases. Explain why reactance is often introduced into the transformers feeding electric furnaces, and how the reactance of the leads can be kept down to a minimum.

3. 1000 kg. of brass are to be raised to melting point (910° C.) from 20° C. The supply voltage and current are 100 volts and 2250 amperes respectively, and the thermal efficiency is 0·7. How long does the operation take? The specific heat of brass is 0·093. (*I.E.E., May*, 1939.)

4. Describe with sketches the construction of an electric furnace with the leads and transformers for the production of iron alloys on a large scale. When the total power supplied is 2000 kW. at a power factor of 0·8, the generated line voltage 5500, and the transformation ratio 40 to 1, find the current per phase on both primary and secondary sides. Is there any reason why the power factor should not be improved ?
(*Lond. Univ.*, 1925, *El. Power.*)

5. Describe, with sketches, one form of electric furnace, and state some of the processes for which it would be suitable.

The melting point of copper being taken as 1080° C., its specific heat 0·094, and the latent heat of fusion 43 calories per gramme, calculate the electrical energy required to fuse 1 cwt. of this metal in an electric crucible. The efficiency of the apparatus may be taken to be 30 per cent and the initial temperature 15° C. (*C. & G., Final*, 1926.)

87. Bulk Supply and Interconnectors

References. B4, 6; R1, 2; S5; T1; W1, 6.

EXAMPLES 87

1. Two 3-phase feeders A and B, connected in parallel, supply a transformer which delivers 2500 kW. at 6600 volts, 0·8 power factor (lagging) on its secondary side. Particulars of the feeders are: A, $R = 20$ ohms, $X = 30$ ohms; B, $R = 40$ ohms, $X = 50$ ohms per conductor. The equivalent impedance of the transformer "to neutral" referred to the secondary side is $(0·1 + j1)$ ohms. Calculate the power factor at the primary terminals of the transformer. Calculate also the current carried by each feeder and its phase relationship to the primary voltage of the transformer. Transformer primary has 5 times as many turns as its secondary.

(Lond. Univ., 1940, El. Power.)

2. Three towns, A, B, and C, are situated at the corners of an equilateral triangle whose sides are 20 miles long. It is proposed to supply electric power to the amount of 5000 kW., 7000 kW., and 1000 kW. respectively to A, B, and C from one central station. In the absence of any other considerations where should the central station be placed? Discuss any considerations which might affect the selection of the site.

(Lond. Univ., 1922, El. Power.)

3. A 3-phase load at 0·8 power factor (lagging) is supplied at 10,000 volts through a transmission line A fed by two other lines B and C which are connected in parallel. Calculate the voltage at the generator end of B and C when the current in B is 100 amperes. Calculate also its phase-relationship to the voltage at the load. The following particulars hold: $A, R = 1$, $X = 2$; $B, R = 2$, $X = 4$; $C, R = 2$, $X = 6$ ohms.

(Lond. Univ. 1937, El. Power.)

4. Two 3-phase systems are linked by a 20,000-volt interconnector cable, which is connected to the respective systems by a transformer at each end. The total resistance and reactance per phase of the line and the transformers (referred to the high-voltage side) are 4 and 40 ohms respectively. Calculate the power factor of the load at the sending end of the interconnector and the boosting voltage required when at the other end there is taken a load of 6000 kVA. at unity power factor. *(Lond. Univ., 1931, El. Power.)*

5. Discuss from the aspect of (a) reliability, (b) operating

characteristics, (c) power factor control, the relative merits of synchronous motor-generator sets and induction motor-generator sets for linking up two power areas, the frequencies of which are 50 and 25 respectively. What factors determine the kW. and kVA. loadings of the interconnector cables ?

(C. & G., Final, 1926.)

6. A total load of 12,000 kW. at a power factor of 0·8 lagging is transmitted to a substation by two overhead 3-phase lines connected in parallel. One line has a conductor resistance of 2 ohms per conductor and a reactance (line to neutral) of 1·5 ohm, the corresponding values for the other line being 1·5 and 1·2 ohm. Calculate by an exact method the power transmitted by each overhead line. (Lond. U., 1933, El. Power.)

7. The 3-phase output from a hydro-electric station is transmitted to a distributing centre by two overhead lines connected in parallel but following different routes. Describe with connection diagrams (a) the system of protection you would adopt to ensure continuity of supply, (b) the method of compensating for line drop and control of reactive current.

Find how a total load of 5000 kW. at a power-factor of 0·8 lagging would divide between the two routes if the respective line resistances are 1·5 and 1·0 ohm, and their reactances at 25 frequency are 1·25 and 1·2 ohms. (C. & G., 1929.)

8. The 3-phase 11-kV. busbars of two generating stations are tied together through an interconnector having an equivalent resistance and reactance per phase of 0·4 ohm and 0·8 ohm respectively. When station A, at which the busbar voltage is 11,250 volts, is receiving 25 MW. at 0·9 power factor lagging from B, determine the busbar voltage at B and its phase displacement relative to the busbar voltage at A.

(I.E.E., May, 1940.)

9. What factors govern the rating of a frequency-changer linking two central stations? The turbines in a 50-frequency station have a uniform speed drop of 2·5 per cent between no-load and full-load, and the rated capacity of the generators connected to the busbars is 60,000 kW. This station is linked through a 10,000-kW. induction motor-generator set having a full-load slip of 3·0 per cent, with a station which has generators totalling 35,000 kW. on the busbars and a similar uniform speed regulation of 3·5 per cent. Consumers connected to these two stations take loads of 32,000 kW. and 24,500 kW. respectively. Find the load on the interconnector cable under these conditions. (C. & G., Final, 1932.)

10. Two 3-phase cables connected in parallel supply a

6600-volt, 1000-kW. load at a lagging power factor of 0·8. The current in one of the cables is 70 amperes, and it delivers 600 kW. Calculate its reactance and resistance, given that the other cable has a reactance of 2·6 ohms and a resistance of 2 ohms. (*Lond. Univ.*, 1932, *El. Power.*)

*11. A 6600-volt substation taking a total 3-phase load of 5000 kW. at a lagging power-factor of 0·8 is supplied through two feeder cables A and B in parallel which have impedances of $Z_A = 0·5 + j0·8$ ohm and $Z_B = 1·0 + j0·4$ ohm per phase. Calculate the kW. and kVA. carried by each cable.

(*C. & G.*, *Final*, 1945.)

*12. A 3-phase generating station A, with a line voltage of 6600 volts, supplies two substations B and C, through two independent feeders, the substations being also connected by another feeder. The impedances of the feeders, per phase, are: A to $B = 1 + j2·5$ ohms; A to $C = 2 + j1·2$ ohms; and B to $C = 1·5 + j2$ ohms. The load at B is 150 amperes per phase at 0·7 power-factor (lagging) and at C 100 amperes at 0·9 power-factor (lagging), both power-factors being referred to the voltage at A. Calculate the current flowing in each feeder. Determine also the voltage difference between the two substations if the feeder BC is removed, the loads being maintained at the above values. (*Lond. Univ.*, 1947, *El. Power.*)

*13. A 3-phase transmission line is to be erected to operate in parallel with an existing line. The total load to be supplied is 8000 kW., 31 kV., 0·8 power-factor lagging. The completed transmission scheme is to have an efficiency of 95 per cent, the generating station voltage being 33 kV. The existing line has a resistance of 6·45 ohms and reactance of 7·82 ohms. Find the corresponding values for the new line.

(*C. & G.*, *Final*, 1946.)

88. Corona

References. P1; R1; S5; W6.

The *Disruptive Critical Voltage* is that which establishes a gradient of about 30 kV./cm. adjacent to a smooth round wire, and is given by $V_n = 30\delta r \log_e s/r$

where V_n =max. p.d. to neutral in k.-volts

r = radius of conductor in cm.

s = spacing of conductors in cm.

$\delta = 3 \cdot 92 b/(273 + T)$

b = barometric height in cm.

T = temperature in °C., i.e.

$\delta = 1$ at 76 cm. and 25° C.

The *Visual Critical Voltage* is greater than this, given when the stress becomes

$$30\delta(1 + 0 \cdot 3/\sqrt{r\delta}) \text{ kV./cm. max.}$$

and the voltage to neutral to start visual corona is

$$V_o = 30m\delta r (1 + 0 \cdot 3/\sqrt{r\delta}) \log_e s/r$$

Here m is a surface factor, to allow for stranding and weathering. It is about $0 \cdot 72$ for local discharge, and about $0 \cdot 82$ for decided discharge.

When the voltage exceeds this critical value, there is a loss of energy, depending upon the square of the excess voltage, the frequency (f), and the size and spacing, and is given by

loss $= (V - V_0)^2 \times 2 \cdot 4 (f + 25) \sqrt{r/s}$ watts per kilometre of conductor

where V = max. k.-volts to neutral of the conductor.

EXAMPLES 88

1. How does corona effect limit the voltage at which an overhead line can be operated, and what is the influence of size of conductor ? What part does corona play in the breakdown of high-tension switchgear ?

2. In a 3-phase overhead line, the conductors have each a diameter of 1·25 in. and are arranged in delta formation. Assuming a critical voltage of 230 kV., the air density factor 0·95 and the irregularity factor 0·95, find the minimum spacing distance between conductors, assuming fair weather conditions, and a breakdown strength of 30 kV./cm. for smooth conductors. (*C. & G.*, 1937.)

3. Explain the phenomenon of corona discharge on high-voltage lines. What factors determine the voltage at which the discharge may begin? Taking the dielectric strength of air to be 3×10^4 volts per cm., find the voltage at which corona discharge will begin on a 3-phase line with smooth circular conductors symmetrically placed 2 metres apart, the diameter of each conductor being 1 cm.

(*C. & G., Final*, 1933.)

89. Short-Circuit kVA., etc.

References. G1; W1, 4, 6.

EXAMPLES 89

1. Distinguish between "star" and "ring" systems of connection of current-limiting reactors in a generating station. Give a connection diagram of each of these methods showing the position of selector oil switches and isolating plugs for feeder and generator circuits. In a large generating station, the busbars are divided into four sections, each section being connected to a tie bar through a reactor rated at 10 per cent. The generating plant associated with each section has a capacity of 25,000 kVA. and a short-circuit reactance of 20 per cent. Find the kVA. developed should a short-circuit occur between the busbars of one section when the reactors are (a) in circuit, (b) short-circuited.   (C. & G., Final, 1930.)

2. The running plant in a station consists of three 11,000-volt, 2,500-kVA., 3-phase generators, each having a short-circuit reactance of 30 per cent. The output is transmitted over two transmission lines connected in parallel, each with a reactance of 0·6 ohm, line to neutral, to a substation containing a 3,000-kVA. transformer in parallel with a 2000-kVA. transformer, each having a reactance of 6 per cent. Calculate the short-circuit current in each generator armature when a short-circuit occurs (a) between bus-bars at the generating station, (b) between the low-voltage bus-bars in the substation.

(C. & G., Final, 1932.)

3. A power station supplying 3-phase current at 6,600 volts, 50-cycles per second, contains one 10,000-kVA. generator (reactance to its rating 12 per cent), and two 5,000-kVA. generators (reactance of each to its rating 8 per cent). A substation C on the distribution system is fed from the power station via two other substations, A and B, by the following system of cables. From power station to A: Two cables in parallel, each 2·3 miles long. From power station to B: Two cables in parallel, each 3·1 miles long. From A to C: Two cables in parallel, each 5·1 miles long. From B to C: One cable 3·7 miles long. Each cable has a reactance of 0·15 ohm per phase per mile at 50 cycles per second. Calculate the maximum fault kVA. at C when all the cables are switched in and all three generators are running. The resistance in the cables, the decrement in the generators, and the doubling effect, are to be neglected.   (I.E.E., Nov., 1932.)

4. A 3-phase, 6600-volt, 10,000-kVA. alternator with a reactance of 15 per cent is connected to a 33,000-volt feeder 25 miles long through two transformers in parallel. One transformer is rated at 5000 kVA. and has a short-circuit reactance of 5 per cent, and the other rated at 4000 kVA. has a reactance of 4 per cent. The feeder has a reactance (line to neutral) of 0·5 ohm per mile. Calculate the generator current in the event of a short-circuit between lines at the distant end of the feeder cable. (*C. & G., Final*, 1933.)

5. What are the features in the design of switchgear which determine its rupturing capacity? Two generators, one of 20,000 kW. capacity and the other of 30,000 kW. capacity, have reactances of 12·5 and 15 per cent respectively. They supply a load over a 15-mile line, the reactance of which may be expressed as 1 per cent per mile on a load of 100,000 kVA. Determine the minimum rupturing capacity necessary for (*a*) the generator switches; (*b*) the switches at the far end of the line. (*I.E.E., May*, 1934.)

6. Two 3-phase A.C. generators *A* and *B* of 8000 kVA. and 10,000 kVA. capacity respectively, are supplying, in parallel, the 11-kV. bus-bars of a power station. The 11-kV. bus-bars are coupled through two 15,000-kVA. transformers in parallel to the 66-kV. bus-bars. From the 66-kV. bus-bars an overhead transmission line is taken to a distant sub-station *S* where the voltage is stepped down from 66 kV. to 6·6 kV. by a 10,000-kVA. transformer. Calculate the initial fault current if a fault occurs on the 6·6-kV. bus-bars at *S*. The following additional data should be used—

Percentage reactances of generator *A* = 10, of *B* = 8, of each transformer = 5, and the reactance of each conductor of the transmission line = 5 ohms. (*I.E.E., May*, 1935.)

7. A 3-phase, 50-cycle, 6600-volt power station contains two generators *A* and *B* coupled to one set of bus-bars, and two generators *C* and *D* coupled to another set of bus-bars. The capacity and reactance of the generators are as follows—

A = 5000 kVA., 10 per cent; *B* = 10,000 kVA., 8 per cent; *C* = 7500 kVA., 8 per cent; *D* = 7500 kVA., 8 per cent. It is proposed to connect the two sets of bus-bars through a reactor, through which the maximum normal transfer is to be 7500 kVA.

Out-going feeder switchgear of 250,000 kVA. rupturing capacity is connected to each set of bus-bars. Determine the percentage reactance of the reactor in order that on the occurrence of a 3-phase short-circuit on any feeder, the switchgear shall not be called upon to rupture more than its rated capacity. Feed into the station from the out-going feeders may be neglected. (*I.E.E.*, *Nov.*, 1935.)

8. Give an account of the use of reactance for the control of large powers in generating stations and interconnected systems. Explain precisely what is meant by the percentage rating of a reactor. The estimated short-circuit kVA. at the bus-bars of a generating station is 1 million kVA., and of another station 666,000 kVA. The generated voltage at each station is 11,000 volts. Calculate the possible short-circuit kVA. at each station when they are linked by an interconnector cable having a reactance of 0·4 ohm. (*C. & G., Final*, 1936.)

*9. A 33-kV., 3-phase transmission line of resistance 3 ohms and reactance 10 ohms is connected at each end to a 1000-kVA., 33/6·6-kV., 3-phase, mesh-star connected transformer. The resistance and reactance voltage drops of each transformer are 1 per cent and 4 per cent respectively. If a dead short-circuit occurs across the three phases at the low-voltage side of the step-down transformer, calculate (*a*) the fault current supplied by the generators, (*b*) the current in the line.

(*C. & G., Final*, 1944.)

*10. Solve the following problem (*a*) by first calculating the resistances and reactances of the various parts, (*b*) by referring to an arbitrary kVA. base.

Two 3-phase alternators running in parallel, each of 5000-kVA. capacity and having each a reactance of 20 per cent, feed directly 11-kV. station bus-bars. These bus-bars feed 33-kV. bus-bars through two transformers in parallel, each of 5000-kVA. capacity and 5 per cent reactance. Two overhead transmission lines in parallel are connected to the 33-kV. bus-bars, the resistance of each conductor being 3 ohms and its reactance 6 ohms. If a symmetrical 3-phase fault occurs at the end of the transmission lines, calculate the fault kVA. Justify the procedure followed when referring to an arbitrary kVA. base. (*Lond. Univ.*, 1943, *El. Power*.)

*11. The bus-bars of a generating station are divided into two sections, *A* and *B*, connected by a reactor. A 40-MVA. generator of 20 per cent reactance is connected to *A*, and two generators—one of 20 MVA. with 15 per cent reactance and one of 15 MVA. with 14 per cent reactance—are connected to *B*. If all feeder switchgear has a rupturing capacity of 350 MVA., determine the rating of the reactor in order that a short-circuit on any feeder with all machines running may be interrupted by a feeder circuit-breaker. (*I.E.E.*, *April*, 1946.)

90. Traction—General

References for all Traction Sections. B6; D4, 5, 6; R3; S4.

EXAMPLES 90

1. Give an account of the advantages of series-parallel control for traction motors. Descr:be with diagrams the bridge method of transition from series to parallel connection in the starting of two D.C. traction motors. What further economy can be effected by field control? (*C. & G., Final*, 1934.)

2. Two 600-volt motors are started with series-parallel control. Each motor has a resistance of 0·1 ohm and the time of starting is 20 seconds. The current in each motor during starting is maintained constant at 400 amp. Calculate in kWh. the energy dissipated in the starting rheostats.

(*C. & G., Final*, 1935.)

3. Describe briefly with sketches (*a*) the single catenary, (*b*) the double catenary, and (*c*) the slewed catenary types of overhead-line construction.

In a single-catenary system the cross sections of the wires are copper catenary 0·2 sq. in., trolley wire 0·1 sq. in. The line is single track only, and the starting current of a locomotive is 2000 amp.; what is the voltage drop in the overhead-line when the locomotive starts up between two substations 8 miles apart, the distance from the locomotive to the nearest substation being 2 miles? The resistance of copper is 0·75 microhm per inch cube. (*I.E.E., Oct.*, 1927.)

4. A D.C. railway is supplied from rectifier substations spaced at 5-mile intervals along the track. A train running on the track takes a constant current of 1000 amp. from the conductor rails. Calculate and draw a curve showing how the voltage at the train will vary during the 5-mile run from one substation (*A*) to the next (*B*). The voltage/current characteristic of each substation is a straight line falling from 700 volts at no-load to 680 volts at a load of 1000 amp. The resistance per mile of the conductor rail is 0·03 ohm, and that of the cross-bonded track rails (which act as the return) is 0·016 ohm. Each substation feeds the track at one point only, which is directly adjacent to the substation concerned, and the feeders are of negligible resistance. Assume that during the run from substation (*A*) to substation (*B*) the train receives energy from these substations only. (*I.E.E., May*, 1935.)

5. A 400-ton train descending a steady gradient of 1 in 70 has its speed reduced from 50 m.p.h. to 30 m.p.h. in two

minutes, by regenerative braking. Determine the kWh. returned to the line. The retardation may be assumed constant, train resistance to have a mean value of 12 lb. per ton, the allowance for rotational inertia to be 10 per cent and the efficiency to be 80 per cent. (*Lond. Univ.*, 1940, *El. Power.*)

6. A 3-mile section AB of a tramway rail system is earthed at one end A, and tapped by a negative feeder at a point X, 2 miles from A. The loading is 400 amperes per mile and may be assumed uniformly distributed. The total resistance of the rails is 0·03 ohm per mile, and leakage is negligible. Calculate and plot graphs showing how (*a*) the current in the rails and (*b*) the potential of the rails, vary from A to B, if the potential of X is 2 volts above A. (*Lond. Univ.*, 1939, *El. Power.*)

7. Explain with connection diagrams the function of (*a*) feeder boosters, (*b*) negative boosters, in an electric tramway system. A section of a tramway track 3 miles long has a resistance of 0·0145 ohm per mile, and a uniformly distributed load of 320 amp. per mile. A negative feeder having a conductor resistance of 0·046 ohm per mile is connected to the track at a point 2 miles from the station, and a negative booster is included in the circuit. If the potential of the track is reduced to zero at the point of connection to the booster, calculate the rating of the booster required and the maximum potential of the rails above earth. (*L. U.*, 1931, *El. Power.*)

8. Give a diagram of connections and explain the action of a negative booster. A section ABC of an uninsulated rail return system is 3 miles long. A is earthed, and B is 2 miles from A. A negative feeder, with booster in circuit, is tapped to the rail at B. The loading is 400 amp. per mile and may be assumed to be uniformly distributed. Determine the maximum p.d. between any two points on the rail system, assuming no leakage, if the potential of B is 2·5 volts below earth. Determine also the output of the booster. The resistance of the rail system is 0·035 ohm per mile. The resistance of the negative feeder is 0·03 ohm. (*Lond. Univ.*, 1936, *El. Power.*)

9. How can the rail voltage drop be reduced in (*a*) a tramway system, (*b*) a heavily loaded single-phase railway? Give connection diagrams in explanation. In a section of a tramway system the track resistance is 0·08 ohm and the total current which may be considered to be taken uniformly along the length of the section, is 300 amp. Calculate the current to be carried by a negative feeder connected to the distant end of the section to reduce the voltage drop between the ends of the section to 6 volts. (*C. & G., Final*, 1936.)

10. A locomotive is required to start and haul a 500-ton goods train up a gradient of 1 per cent with an acceleration of 0·75 m.p.h.p.s. The coefficient of adhesion is 0·25, the tractive resistance 12 lb. per ton and the allowance for the effect of the rotating masses 10 per cent of the dead weight. Find approximately the minimum adhesive weight of the locomotive.

(*C. & G.*, 1938.)

11. A 1500-volt electric locomotive is required to start a train weighing 350 tons (inclusive of the locomotive) on an up-grade of 1 in 200, and to accelerate the train at the rate of 0·5 m.p.h.p.s. up to a speed of 30 m.p.h. What must be the minimum adhesive weight of the locomotive? Find the number of driving axles required and the approximate size and the number of motors. Describe the method of mounting the motors and a suitable system of power transmission. The train resistance is 12 lb. per ton, the effective weight of the train 10 per cent greater than the dead weight and the coefficient of adhesion is 20 per cent. (*C. & G., Final*, 1935.)

12. Sketch a magnetic brake for a tramcar, showing particularly the shape of the pole pieces and the arrangement of the magnetic circuit. Show how such a brake is suspended from the truck and how the thrust is transmitted. The cross-section of each of the pole faces of a magnetic track brake is 12 in. × ⅝ in., and the flux density at the pole faces is 16,000 gauss. Calculate the vertical force between the pole faces and the rail.

(*I.E.E., May*, 1935.)

13. Explain how regenerative braking can be carried out with D.C. railway motors. A 300-ton train, in travelling down a uniform gradient of 1 in 75, has its speed reduced, by regenerative braking, from its initial value of 36 miles per hour to 22 miles per hour, between which values it has travelled 8000 ft. down the gradient. Calculate the kWh. returned to the line. Take tractive resistance as 10 lb. per ton, the allowance for rotary inertia as 7·5 per cent, and the overall efficiency as 72 per cent. (*Lond. Univ.*, 1933, *El. Power.*)

14. The speed of a 350-ton train is reduced from 38 to 20 m.p.h. by regenerative braking on a gradient of 1 in 76 which is 1·5 miles long. If the tractive resistance is 12 lb. per ton, the allowance for rotational inertia 10 per cent, the overall efficiency 75 per cent, calculate the energy in kWh. returned to the line during the descent. (*C. & G., Final*, 1936.)

91. Traction—Speed Time Curves

EXAMPLES 91

1. A train has a total weight of 308 tons, and is equipped with 8 motors each of 300 h.p. The characteristics of the motors are—

Current (amp.) . . .	100	200	300	400	500
Speed (m.p.h.) . . .	65	36·5	29·8	26·5	24·7
Tractive effort (lb.) . .	330	1450	2740	4100	5450

The ratio of effective weight to the dead weight of the train is 1·1 : 1.

The mean accelerating current is 415 amp. per motor. The braking retardation is 1·75 m.p.h. per sec. and the train resistance can be assumed as 10 lb. per ton throughout the run.

Draw the speed-time curve for a run on the level of 1·1 miles to be made in 152 sec.

Calculate the R.M.S. current per motor for the run.

(I.E.E., April, 1927.)

2. What is meant by the schedule speed of a train? A schedule speed of 26 m.p.h. is required on a section of an electrified system with 1·2 miles between stations. Find the maximum speed that must be attained, allowing station stops of 20 seconds, an acceleration of 1·6 m.p.h.p.s. and a retardation of 2·2 m.p.h.p.s. Assume a simplified speed-time curve and derive any formula employed.

(Lond. Univ., 1930, El. Power.)

3. The stations on an electric railway are half a mile apart and the running time between stations is 1·5 minutes. The braking rate is 2 miles per hour per second. If the maximum speed is 20 per cent higher than the average running speed, find (a) the acceleration required, (b) the horse-power of the motors, to give this service with a 300-ton train. Assume a rectilinear speed-time curve with free running at the maximum speed, a track resistance of 10 lb. per ton, and allow 12 per cent for rotational inertia. *(C. & G., Final, 1932.)*

4. The schedule speed with a 200-ton train on an electric railway with stations 850 yd. apart is 17 miles per hour, and the maximum speed is 20 per cent higher than the average running speed. The braking rate is 2 m.p.h.p.s., and the duration of stop is 20 sec. Find the acceleration required. Assume a simplified speed-time curve with free running at the maximum speed. *(C. & G., Final, 1934.)*

5. An electric train is accelerated uniformly from rest to a speed of 30 m.p.h., the period of acceleration being 24 sec. It then coasts for 69 sec. against a constant resistance of 13 lb. per ton, and is brought to rest in a further period of 11 sec. by braking at a uniform rate of 2 m.p.h.p.s. Calculate (a) the acceleration, (b) the coasting retardation, (c) the schedule speed, if the station stops are of 20 sec. duration. What would be the effect on the schedule speed of reducing the station stops to 10 sec., other conditions remaining the same? Allow 10 per cent for rotational inertia. (*I.E.E., May*, 1934.)

6. The speed/time and speed/current curves of an electric train running on level track are as follows—

Time (sec.) .	0	12·15	25·3	30	35	40	48*	151†	167
Speed (m.p.h.)	0	12·15	25·3	28·3	31·7	33·9	37·5	27·7	0
Current (amp.)	700	1500	1500	1140	960	876	768	0	0

* Power off.   † Brakes applied.

Calculate (a) the schedule speed, allowing a stop of 20 sec. at the stations, (b) the R.M.S. current for the train.

(*I.E.E., Nov.*, 1934.)

7. A 125-ton motor-coach train makes the run between two stations on level track according to the following speed-time curve—

Time (sec.) . .	0	11·5	23	29·3	41	58*	124†	140
Speed (m.p.h.) . .	0	12·5	25	30	35	39	32	0

* Power off.   † Brakes applied.

Calculate the schedule speed if the station stop is 20 sec. Calculate and draw the tractive-effort/time curve for the portion of the run from start to cut off. Allow 10 per cent for rotational inertia and assume train resistance at 10 lb. per ton at all speeds. (*I.E.E., May*, 1935.)

8. Assuming that the retardation during the period of drift is very small, estimate the installed h.p. on an electric motor-coach train weighing 200 tons, for which the following particulars hold: length of run = 1·25 miles; time of run = 200 sec.; acceleration = 1·0 m.p.h.p.s.; retardation = 2·0 m.p.h. p.s. What maximum crest speed could be reached on this service? (*I.E.E., May*, 1936.)

9. A train starting from rest is accelerated uniformly for 22 sec. until a speed of 26 m.p.h. is reached. The train then coasts for 42 sec. at a uniform retardation of 0·11 m.p.h.p.s.

before the brakes are applied, and the train is brought to rest in 1·25 min. from the start of the run. Assuming a simple speed-time diagram, calculate the average speed from start to stop. (*C. & G., Final*, 1936.)

10. An electric railway is constructed with graded track between the stations. The gradients, in the direction of running, are: 1 in 33 ("down") on the leaving side of the station and 1 in 100 ("up") on the entering side. A 130-ton train completes the run from one station *A* to the next *B* in 103 sec. It starts with uniform acceleration of 1·25 m.p.h.p.s., which is maintained until the speed reaches 27·5 m.p.h. Power is then cut off and the train coasts for 10 sec. down the remaining portion of the 1 in 33 gradient. The coasting is continued for a further period of 65 sec. up the 1 in 100 gradient (at the summit of which station *B* is situated) and the brakes are then applied so as to bring the train to rest with uniform retardation. Draw the speed-time curve and determine the points on the route at which power must be cut off and the brakes applied. Determine also the schedule speed if the duration of the stop at station *B* is 20 sec. Assume the train resistance during coasting to be 12 lb. per ton, and allow 10 per cent for rotational inertia. (*I.E.E., Nov.*, 1935.)

*11. Draw the speed/time and speed/distance curves for an electric train travelling on level track between two stations 1200 yd. apart; the train weighs 200 tons and starts from rest at one station and is brought to rest at the other by braking with a retardation of 1 m.p.h. per sec. The motors may be assumed to take a constant total current of 500 amperes at 600 volts and to produce a tractive effort of 17,000 lb. until a speed of 30 m.p.h. is reached; power is then cut off and the train coasts until the brakes are applied. Friction and windage resistance may be assumed constant at 2000 lb. at all speeds, and the effect of rotational inertia may be neglected. Determine also the average speed and the energy consumption in watt-hours per ton-mile. (*I.E.E., May*, 1942.)

*12. On an electric railway the stations are 2560 feet apart and the trains operate to a schedule speed of 16 m.p.h. The duration of station stops is 20 seconds, the maximum speed is 22 per cent higher than the average running speed, and the rate of braking retardation is 2 m.p.h.p.s. Calculate the rate of acceleration required to operate this service. State the necessary assumptions made. (*C. & G., Final*, 1946.)

*13. A 200-ton train starts on a uniform down grade of 1 in 100 between two stations, the speed-time curve being

rectilinear. Power is cut off 20 seconds after the start when the
speed is 30 m.p.h., the brakes are applied 110 seconds after
the start at a speed of 38 m.p.h., and the train brought to rest
130 seconds after the start. Calculate for this run (a) the
schedule speed allowing for a 20-second station stop, (b) the
coasting retardation on a level track assuming the train
resistance to be unchanged, (c) the specific output in Wh. per
ton-mile from the driving axles. Take 12 per cent for the
effects of rotational inertia.   (C. & G., Final, 1942.)

92. Traction—Motor Characteristics

EXAMPLES 92

1. A direct-current series motor is to be used for rheostatic braking on a tramcar. With the field separately excited on test, the open circuit voltage across the armature at a speed corresponding to 15 m.p.h. was—

Field amperes . . .	10	20	40	60	80
Armature volts . . .	145	280	500	630	700

When the machine is being used for braking on the tramcar, what external resistance would have to be put in the motor circuit to obtain a current of 70 amp. at a speed of 10 m.p.h.? The resistance of the motor armature and fields can be neglected.

What would you expect to happen if a resistance of 25 ohms were put in the motor circuit when the car was running at 15 m.p.h.?   (*I.E.E.*, *April*, 1927.)

2. A motor has the following characteristics—

Current (amp.) . . .	50	100	150	200	250
Speed (m.p.h.) . . .	46	30	25·7	23·3	22
Tractive effort (lb.) . .	300	1050	1860	2670	3500

The size of the car wheel is 40 in. and the gear ratio is 72 : 23. The car wheel is changed to 42 in.; the gear ratio to 75 : 20. Give the new characteristic.   (*I.E.E.*, *Oct.*, 1927.)

3. In a direct-current traction system two motors are connected in permanent series. Draw a diagram showing the minimum number of switches which can be used to tap the field of both motors.

A motor has the following characteristics—

Current (amp.) . . .	50	100	150	200	250
Speed (m.p.h.) . . .	46	30	25·7	23·3	22
Tractive effort (lb.) . .	300	1050	1860	2670	3500

Give the approximate speeds and tractive efforts for the same currents when 47 per cent of the main field windings are cut out.   (*I.E.E.*, *April*, 1927.)

4 The following motor characteristic is based on a wheel diameter of 36 in.—

Current (amp.) . . .	80	160	240	320	400
Tractive effort at wheel tread (lb.)	400	1350	2470	3700	4950
Speed (m.p h.) . . .	53	34·5	28·8	25·5	23·2

A motor bogie is fitted with two of these motors, one pair of wheels being 36 in. diameter and the other pair 35 in. diameter. The motors are operated in series-parallel. Suppose the tractive effort at the 36-in. wheels is 3000 lb., what will be the current and tractive effort of the other motor (a) in full series, and (b) in full parallel? (*I.E.E.. Nov.* 1928.)

5. Under what conditions is field weakening adopted for controlling the speed of a direct-current series traction motor? From the following table, giving the tractive-effort-current and the speed-current characteristics, derive the corresponding curves for the machine working with two-thirds of the normal field-turns in circuit—

Current in amperes .	40	60	80	100	120	160	200
Speed in m.p.h.	36·3	29·6	25·2	22·4	21·2	18·8	17·8
Draw-bar pull in lb.	370	880	1400	1940	2490	3600	4720

(*Lond. Univ.*, 1930, *El. Power.*)

6. What are the conditions under which field weakening is advantageous for controlling the speed of D.C. traction motors? A tramcar motor has the following tractive-effort and speed-current characteristics—

Current (amp.) .	45	67·5	90	1125	135	180	225
Speed (m.p.h.) .	41	33·3	284	25·2	238	211	20
Tract. effort (lb.) .	415	990	1585	2190	2790	4050	5300

Calculate and plot the corresponding curves when the machine is working with the field obtained by cutting out one-third of the field turns. (*C. & G., Final,* 1931.)

7. A train is hauled by two locomotives equipped with similar 3-phase induction motors. The locomotives are each rated at 1000 h.p., at which output the slip of the motor is 4 per cent. The locomotives have driving wheels of 1·5 metres and 1·47 metres respectively. Calculate the distribution of the load between the locomotives when (a) running up a gradient which demands a total output of 2000 h.p., (b) running on the level when the total output is 100 h.p. (*C. & G., Final,* 1932.)

8. A motor bogie is fitted with two D.C. series-wound motors, each of which has nominal characteristics, at 575 volts and 43 in. wheels, as follows—

Current (amp.)	200	300	400
Speed (m.p.h.)	36·5	27·4	23·8
Tractive effort (lb.)	1450	2750	4200

If the pair of wheels driven by one motor are 43 in. in diameter and the other pair are 41 in. in diameter, what will be the speed of the train and the total tractive effort of the bogie when the motors are in full series and the current is 350 amperes, the line voltage being 575? The resistance of each motor is 0·1 ohm. (*I.E.E., Nov.*, 1934.)

9. The following data refer to a motor for a locomotive : 4 poles; wave (2-circuit) armature winding with 686 conductors; resistance of armature winding and brushes 0·1 ohm ; resistance of field windings, 0·13 ohm; normal operating voltage, 1500 volts; full-load current, 250 amp.; flux per pole at full-load current, 13×10^6 lines; core, friction and gear losses at full-load, 29 kW. A locomotive is equipped with four of these motors, each being geared to 52-in. wheels by gearing of ratio 4·56 : 1. Calculate the tractive effort and speed of the locomotive when the motors are operating in parallel at 1500 volts and each motor is taking a current of 250 amp. (*I.E.E., May*, 1935.)

10. The following figures refer to the speed-current and tractive-effort-current characteristics of a direct-current series traction motor

Current (amp.) .	100	150	200	250	300	400
Speed (m.p.h.) .	32	25·5	22·5	20·5	19	18
Tractive effort (lb.) .	1050	2100	3200	4250	5350	7500

Derive corresponding approximate characteristic curves when the field is weakened by the field current being halved. Discuss the advantages of control by field weakening in electric traction. (*C. & G., Final*, 1936.)

*11. A D.C. electric locomotive has driving wheels of 52 in. diameter, a gear ratio of 4·56 : 1, and is driven by four 1500-volt electric motors, each of which has a total resistance of 0·3 ohm and a 4-pole wave-connected armature with 686 conductors. The following table gives the relation between field current and flux per pole (in megalines) :

Amperes.	50	100	150	200	250	300
Flux	5·75	8·73	10·3	11·22	12·0	12·64

If the total iron, friction and gear loss is assumed constant at 8 per cent, determine the relation between locomotive speed in miles per hour and tractive effort in lb. at the wheel tread over the above range of current. (*I.E.E., Nov.*, 1943.)

*12. Two railway series motors are operated in parallel from a 660-volt supply. Each motor is geared through a 5·4 : 1 reduction gear to 28-in. diameter wheels. The resistance of each motor is 0·4 ohm and the mechanical efficiency including friction, windage and iron losses is 80 per cent at all speeds. Find (a) the speed at which the tractive effort of the motors totals 3000 lb., (b) the corresponding tractive effort of each motor. The magnetization curve for the two machines when running at 700 r.p.m. is given by:

I . . .	20	40	60	80	100
E_A . .	300	550	610	650	680
E_B .	300	500	575	640	675

(C. & G., Final, 1941.)

*13. The characteristics of a certain traction motor at 525 volts are as follows—

Current (amps.) . . .	50	70	80	90
Speed (m.p.h.). . .	21	16·7	15·6	14·75
Gross torque (lb.-ft.) . .	210	260	312	370

Determine the gross braking torque at a speed of 16 m.p.h. when operating as a self-excited series generator and loaded with an external resistance of 6 ohms. Resistance of motor = 0·5 ohm. (Lond. Univ., 1948, El. Power.)

*14. What are the more important investigations necessary to determine the type and size of motors for intermittent loads? In a haulage system the load is accelerated uniformly during a period of 25 seconds, increasing from zero to a maximum of 2200 h.p. The full-speed period lasts for 40 seconds, during which the load delivered is steady at 1000 h.p. Regenerative braking is employed to bring the motor to rest in 10 seconds, during which time the power returned to the supply falls uniformly from 350 h.p. to zero. Reloading occupies 20 seconds before the cycle of operations is repeated. Calculate approximately the continuous rating of a suitable motor. What other information respecting the motor selected would be required? (C. & G., Final, 1945.)

*15. A 400-ton train is driven by two 3300-volt, three-phase induction motors, working in parallel. Determine the power input and current when running at steady speed (a) up, and (b) down a gradient of 1 in 80. Synchronous speed is 40 m.p.h.;

tractive resistance is 10 lb. per ton. Test data for each motor are:

No-load: 3300 volts, 45 amperes, 0·1 power-factor.
Short-circuit: 3300 volts, 500 amperes, 0·2 power-factor.

On short-circuit, 45 per cent of the losses are stator copper loss. (*Lond. Univ.*, 1944, *El. Power.*)

*16. The magnetization curve of a D.C. series railway motor when running at 400 r.p.m. is as follows:

Field amperes	.	.	.	.	44	66	110	155	200
Armature e.m.f.	.	.	.	.	392	567	800	960	1040

The total resistance of the motor is 0·6 ohm. The motor drives the 43 in. diameter train wheels through a 59/25 reduction gear. Plot curves of train speed in miles per hour and tractive effort in pounds at the wheel rim on a base of current when operating from a 1200 volts supply. Assume that 5 per cent of the total torque is lost in motor and gear. Determine also the change in line current if, when the train is running at 25 miles per hour, the field is suddenly shunted with a resistance which takes 30 per cent of the total current. Neglect the change in the resistance of the circuit.

(*Lond. Univ.*, 1945, *El. Mach.*)

*17. Explain briefly how regenerative braking is obtained with D.C. locomotives. A 300-ton train has its speed reduced from 50 to 30 m.p.h. in travelling 5000 ft. down a uniform gradient of 1 in 90. If regenerative braking is used, determine the kWh. returned to the line. Take 10 per cent allowance for rotary inertia, 12 lb. per ton for tractive resistance, and neglect motor losses.

(*Lond. Univ.*, 1945, *El. Power.*)

*18. Grade the resistors on the series notches for a pair of D.C. series railway motors, working with series-parallel control. Line voltage, 600, number of series notches, 5, maximum current on each notch, 300 amperes, resistance of each motor 0·12 ohm. Magnetization data for motors:

Current (amp.)	.	.	.	.	300	250	230	220	200
Flux (megalines)	.	.	.	.	7·25	6·75	6·5	6·35	6·0

(*Lond. Univ.*, 1945, *El. Power.*)

*19. The characteristics of a compound trolleybus motor at 525 volts with the shunt field fully excited are as follows:

Armature current (amp.) . . .	25	100	150	200
Speed (m.p.h.)	12·8	11·3	10·6	10·1
Tractive effort (lb.)	440	1950	3100	4240

When operating with the series field-winding alone the characteristics are:

Armature current (amp.) . . .	100	150	200
Speed (m.p.h.)	26	19·2	15·8
Tractive effort (lb.)	850	1680	2540

Calculate the speed and approximate tractive effort when braking regeneratively (differentially compounded) at armature currents of 100, 150, 200 amperes; the line voltage being constant at 525 volts. Resistance of armature and series windings, 0·15 ohm; resistance of shunt winding, 175 ohms; number of turns in each shunt field coil, 1200; number of turns in each series field coil, 12.

(*Lond. Univ.*, 1947, *El. Mach.*)

*20. In the above question, if 350 ohms are added to the shunt field when braking regeneratively (differentially compounded), re-calculate the speeds and tractive efforts.

(*Lond. Univ.*, 1948, *El. Mach.*)

93. Traction—Specific Energy Consumption

EXAMPLES 93

1. A motor-coach train has an overall efficiency of 72 per cent, and operates on a section in which the stops are 1200 yd. apart. The sections between the stations are uniformly graded so that the latter are at the summits of 1 per cent gradients. The resistance to motion is 15 lb. per ton, and the maximum speed 36 m.p.h. The maximum speed is attained by a uniform acceleration of 1 m.p.h. per sec., after which the power is switched off. Calculate the specific energy consumption in watt-hours per ton-mile required to operate this service.

(Lond. Univ., 1929, El. Power.)

2. A multiple-unit train weighs 350 tons, and is equipped with 12 motors, each of which develops an effective accelerating tractive effort of 3200 lb. The average current per motor during acceleration is 380 amp. Series-parallel control is employed and the full line voltage of 600 volts is applied to each motor when a speed of 26 m.p.h. is reached. Calculate the useful energy input to each motor during the starting period, and the speed at which the connections are changed from series to parallel. The resistance of each motor is 0·158 ohm. Allow 10 per cent for rotational inertia.

(Lond. Univ., 1931, El. Power.)

3. On a suburban electric railway the distance between stops on the level is 0·5 mile and the mean speed from start to stop is 24 miles per hour. Assuming a rectilinear speed-time curve with an acceleration and a braking retardation of 1·5 and 2·5 m.p.h.p.s. respectively, estimate the specific energy consumption in watt-hours per ton-mile. The tractive resistance is 10 lb. per ton and the average efficiency of the motors and gearing 70 per cent. Allow an addition of 10 per cent for rotational inertia.

(C. & G., Final, 1931.)

4. A 450-ton train starting on an up-grade of 1 in 75 has a uniform acceleration of 1 m.p.h.p.s. The tractive resistance is 20 lb. per ton and 10 per cent allowance must be made for rotational inertia. Calculate (a) the energy in kWh. usefully employed in attaining a speed of 30 m.p.h. from rest, (b) the specific energy consumption in watt-hours per ton-mile when running at a steady speed of 35 m.p.h. up this gradient if the overall efficiency of the equipment is 72 per cent.

(C. & G., Final, 1932.)

5. An electric train maintains a schedule speed of 28 m.p.h.

between stations situated 3 miles apart with station stops of 30 seconds. The acceleration is 1·5 m.p.h.p.s. and the braking retardation is 2 m.p.h.p.s. Assuming a simplified rectilinear speed-time curve, calculate (a) the maximum speed of the train (b) the energy output of the motors in watt-hours per ton, if the tractive resistance is 10 lb. per ton.

(*Lond. Univ.*, 1932, *El. Power.*)

6. The following data relate to the speed-time curve of a 127-ton train working off a 1375-volt D.C. system—

Speed (m.p.h.) .	0	13·25	26·5	30	32·5	35	37·5	40
Time (sec.) .	0	9·3	18·6	21·6	24·8	29	34·5	41·2
Current (amp.) .		450	900	650	530	460	405	370

The motor current may be assumed constant until 26·5 m.p.h., all resistance being then cut out. At 40 m.p.h. power is cut off, and the train allowed to coast until 30 m.p.h. is reached, when the brakes are applied. Determine the watt-hours consumed per ton-mile. Take retardation during coasting as 0·12 m.p.h.p.s., and retardation during braking as 2 m.p.h.p.s.

(*Lond. Univ.*, 1934, *El. Power.*)

7. The average speed of a 300-ton electric train between stations situated on the level 1·3 miles apart is 30 m.p.h. The acceleration and retardation are 1·3 and 2·4 m.p.h.p.s. respectively. The free-running speed is 30 per cent higher than the average speed. The train resistance is 12 lb. per ton and the allowance for rotational inertia 10 per cent. Find (a) the specific energy output of the motors in watt-hours per ton-mile, (b) the power in kilowatts usefully employed at the end of the acceleration period and during free-running.

(*C. & G.*, *Final*, 1934.)

8. A motor coach train makes a run of 1·3 miles, on level track, according to the following speed-time curve, the voltage at the train throughout the run being 600 volts—

Time (sec.) .	0	25·3	30	35	40	45	48	151	169
Speed (m.p.h.)	0	25·3	28·3	31·7	33·9	35·8	37·5	28·9	0

The train is equipped with four motors, each of which has characteristics, at 600 volts, as follows—

Current (amp.) .	100	200	300	350	400	500
Speed (m.p.h.) .	63	36·5	27·4	25·3	23·8	22

Each pair of motors is controlled on the series-parallel system, and the current per motor during starting is maintained constant at 350 amp. Calculate (a) the energy consumption in kWh. per train mile, for the run, (b) the R.M.S. current per motor, (c) the schedule speed, allowing a station stop of 20 seconds duration. (*I.E.E., May*, 1935.)

9. Two stations on a suburban railway are 1·1 miles apart and are situated on a uniform gradient of 1 in 80. The train service in the direction down the gradient is scheduled at an average speed (excluding stops) of 28 m.p.h. Draw to scale the speed/time diagram and estimate the energy consumption, basing the calculations on a rectilinear speed/time diagram and the following data: weight of train, 200 tons; mean tractive effort of motors during acceleration, 30,000 lb.; mean braking effort due to the brakes 45,000 lb.; train resistance 11 lb. per ton; allowance for rotational inertia, 10 per cent.

(*I.E.E., Nov.*, 1934.)

10. The speed-time graph for an electric train operating on a uniform up-gradient of 1 in 150 comprises—

(i) Uniform acceleration, from rest, at 0·75 m.p.h.p.s. for 50 sec.
(ii) Steady speed, with power on, for 50 sec.
(iii) Coasting, with power off, for 60 sec.
(iv) Braking at 2 m.p.h.p.s. to standstill.

Determine the watt-hours consumed per ton-mile. Take tractive resistance to be constant at 10 lb. per ton, allowance for rotary inertia as 8 per cent, overall efficiency as 0·75. Neglect the motor losses during coasting.

(*Lond. Univ.*, 1935, *El. Power.*)

11. An electric train reaches a speed of 28 m.p.h. starting on an upgrade of 1 in 240 and runs on the level at this speed until the brakes are applied. On the level the rated acceleration is 1·2 m.p.h.p.s. and the retardation 2·3 m.p.h.p.s. The time taken for the run is 3 min. 40 sec. Calculate the specific energy consumption in watt-hours per ton-mile. Assume a train resistance of 10 lb. per ton, an overall efficiency of 70 per cent and allow 12 per cent for rotational inertia.

(*C. & G., Final*, 1935.)

12. A 300-ton train has 8 motors and is started with series-parallel control, the average current in each motor during the starting period being 425 amperes. The train resistance is 10 lb. per ton at all speeds. The direct-current motors have the following characteristics at 600 volts—

Amperes per motor	200	300	400	500
Tractive effort per motor in lb. . .	1455	2745	4110	5460
Train speed, m.p.h.	37	30	26·5	25

Estimate the energy input to the train and draw the speed-time graph for a run on the level from the start until a speed of 35 m.p.h. is attained. Allow 10 per cent for rotational inertia. (*C. & G., Final*, 1936.)

*13. A 250-ton train is started from rest up a steady gradient of 1 in 80. Power is cut off after travelling 5000 ft., the speed then being 35 m.p.h., and the energy consumed 37 kWh. Coasting continues until the speed has fallen to 20 m.p.h., when the brakes are applied giving a retardation—to standstill —of 2 m.p.h. per sec. Determine the energy consumption in watt-hours per ton mile, and the efficiency of the run.

(*Lond. Univ.*, 1943, *El. Power.*)

*14. A motor-coach train accelerates uniformly from rest to a maximum speed of 30 m.p.h. which is maintained until the brakes are applied. The distance covered during braking is 200 ft. Estimate the approximate specific energy consumption in Wh. per ton-mile if the stations are (*a*) ½ mile apart, (*b*) ¾ mile apart. Assume a tractive resistance of 10 lb. per ton, an additional 12 per cent of the dead weight for rotational inertia and an overall efficiency of 70 per cent.

(*C. & G., Final*, 1941.)

*15. A 300-ton train is equipped with 8 motors. The characteristic of each motor at 600 volts is as follows:

Current (A.)	200	300	400	500
Speed (m.p.h.)	36·5	29·8	26·5	24·7

A run of 1·1 miles is made in accordance with the following schedule:

Time (secs.) . .	0	29·3	32·3	38·9	47·3	52	136	152
Speed (m.p.h.) .	0	26·2	28·5	32·0	35·0	36·3	27·5	0

The full voltage is applied to the motors at 26·2 m.p.h. and power is cut off at 36·3 m.p.h. The mean value of the current during starting is 415 amperes per motor, the supply voltage is constant at 600 volts and the train is started on the series-parallel system. Calculate the specific energy consumption in Wh. per ton-mile for the run. (*C. & G., Final*, 1944.)

BIBLIOGRAPHY AND REFERENCES

A1. Archibald—*Polyphase Induction Motors.* (Chapman & Hall.)
A2. Aston—*Design of Alternating Current Machines.* (Oxford University Press.)
B1. Barr and Archibald—*Design of Alternating Current Machinery.* (Pitman.)
B2. Beauchamp—*Industrial Electric Heating.* (Pitman.)
B3. Beaver—*Insulated Electric Cables.* (Benn Bros.)
B4. Beckett—*Generation and Transmission.* (Blackie.)
B5. Bolton—*Electrical Engineering Economics.* (Chapman & Hall.)
B6. Bradfield and John—*Telephone and Power Transmission.* (Chapman & Hall.)
B7. Bruce—*Power Station Efficiency Control.* (Pitman.)
C1. Chapman—*A Study of the Induction Motor.* (Chapman & Hall.)
C2. Clayton—*Alternating Currents.* (Longmans, Green.)
C3. Clayton—*Power Factor Correction.* (Pitman.)
C4. Cotton—*Electrical Technology.* (Pitman.)
C5. Cotton—*Design of Electrical Machinery.* (Pitman.)
C6. Creedy—*Theory and Design of Electrical Machinery.* (Pitman.)
D1. Dance—*The Induction Motor.* (Oxford University Press.)
D2. Dannatt and Dalgleish—*Electrical Power Transmission and Intercommunication.* (Pitman.)
D3. Dover—*Alternating Currents.* (Pitman.)
D4. Dover—*Electric Traction.* (Pitman.)
D5. Dover—*Traction Motor Control.* (Pitman.)
D6. Dunsheath—*High Voltage Cables.* (Pitman.)
F1. Fleming and Johnson—*Insulation and Design of Electric Windings.* (Longmans, Green.)
G1. Garrard—*Electric Switch and Control Gear.* (Benn Bros.)
G2. Golding—*Electrical Measurements and Measuring Instruments.* (Pitman.)
H1. Hague—*A.C. Bridge Methods.* (Pitman.)
H2. Hawkins—*The Dynamo.* (Pitman.)
H3. Hill—*Rotary Convertors.* (Chapman & Hall.)
H4. Hobart—*Electric Motors—Vol. II—Polyphase.* (Pitman.)
J1. James—*Controllers for Electric Motors.* (Chapman & Hall.)
K1. Kapp—*Transformers.* (Pitman.)
K2. Kemp—*Alternating Current Electrical Engineering.* (Macmillan.)
M1. Maccall—*Electrical Engineering.* (University Tutorial Press.)
M2. Mallett—*Vectors for Electrical Engineers.* (Chapman & Hall.)
M3. Marquand—*Electric Welding.* (Benn Bros.)
M4. Marshall and Henderson—*Alternating Current Protective Systems and Gear.* (Pitman.)
M5. Moffett—*The Electric Furnace.* (Pitman.)

167

M6. Monk—*Electrical Transformer Theory*. (Pitman.)

M7. Monk—*Induction Motors*. (Blackie.)

O1. Olliver—*A. C. Commutator Motor*. (Chapman & Hall.)

P1. Peek—*Dielectric Phenomena in High Voltage Engineering*. (McGraw-Hill.)

P2. Pring—*The Electric Furnace*. (Longmans, Green.)

R1. Rapson—*Electrical Transmission and Distribution*. (Oxford University Press.)

R2. Reed—*Essentials of Transformer Practice*. (Chapman & Hall.)

R3. Rissik—*Mercury-arc Current Convertors*. (Pitman.)

S1. Say and Pink—*Performance and Design of Alternating Current Machines*. (Pitman.)

S2. Smith, E. F.—*Rotary and Motor Convertors*. (Lockwood.)

S3. Smith, S. P.—*Papers on the Design of A.C. Machinery*. (Pitman.)

S4. Smith and Say—*Electrical Engineering Design-class Manual*. (Oxford University Press.)

S5. Starr—*Generation, Transmission and Utilization of Electric Power*. (Pitman.)

S6. Stigant and Lacey—*J. & P. Transformer Book*. (Johnson & Phillips, Ltd.)

S7. Stubbings—*Underground Cable Systems*. (Chapman & Hall.)

S8. Stubbings—*Automatic Protection of A.C. Circuits*. (Chapman & Hall.)

T1. Taylor and Neale—*Electrical Design of Overhead Power Transmission Lines*. (Chapman & Hall.)

V1. Vickers—*The Induction Motor*. (Pitman.)

W1. Waddicor—*Principles of Electrical Power Transmission*. (Chapman & Hall.)

W2. Walker—*Specification and Design of Electrical Machinery*. (Longmans, Green.)

W3. Walker—*Control of Speed and Power Factor of Induction Motors*. (Benn Bros.)

W4. Wedmore and Trencham—*Switchgear for Electric Power Control*. (Oxford University Press.)

W5. Wilson—*Calculation and Design of Electrical Apparatus*. (Pitman.)

W6. Woodruff—*Electrical Power Transmission and Distribution* (Wiley.)

ANSWERS TO QUESTIONS
VOLUME II

EXAMPLES 36

1. $1 \cdot 192 - j0 \cdot 54$. **2.** $1501 \cdot 7$ volts; 1492 volts. This being very near resonance, great accuracy is desirable in the calculations. Use 5-figure logs and $\pi = 3 \cdot 1416$. **3.** (a) 38 watts; (b) $88 \cdot 35$ volts; (c) $50 \cdot 5$. **4.** $6 \cdot 7$ amp.; 844 volts. **5.** $C = 4780$; 5000; 5200 $\mu\mu$F. $I = 0 \cdot 0956$; $0 \cdot 2$; $0 \cdot 109$ amp. **6.** 1130 mts.; 265 kilo-cycles. **7.** 8 ohms. **8.** (a) $0 \cdot 75$; 375 watts; (b) $0 \cdot 562$; 225 watts. **9.** $0 \cdot 836$ cm. **10.** $R = 8 \cdot 95$ ohms; $L = 0 \cdot 01425$ henry. **11.** $31 \cdot 25$ watts. **12.** 5kW.; $70 \cdot 7$ amp. at $0 \cdot 707$ p.f.; $R = 1$ ohm. **13.** $3 \cdot 52$ volts. **14.** 20 amp.; $31 \cdot 6$ amp.; $0 \cdot 6$ and $0 \cdot 95$. **15.** (a) $13 \cdot 7 - j3 \cdot 2$ (capacitative); (b) $2 \cdot 25$ kW.; (c) $13° 8'$. **16.** $3 \cdot 94$ and $1 \cdot 79$ joules. **17.** *Out:* $0 \cdot 27$H; $0 \cdot 427 \times 10^8$ linkages. *In:* $0 \cdot 736$H; $0 \cdot 447 \times 10^8$ linkages. **18.** (a) $17 \cdot 6$ amp.; (b) 445 volts; (c) 349 volts. **19.** $4 \cdot 7\%$. **21.** $7 \cdot 85$ ohms.

EXAMPLES 37

1 (a) $5 \cdot 05$ amp. at $0 \cdot 303$ p.f.; (b) $20 \cdot 88$ amp. at $0 \cdot 4$ p.f.

2. $13 \cdot 62$, $7 \cdot 59$, $1 \cdot 97$ and $2 \cdot 68$, $7 \cdot 59$, $2 \cdot 27$ amp.

3. $I_1 = \dfrac{200}{10 + j30} = \dfrac{20}{1 + j3} \times \dfrac{1 - j3}{1 - j3} = \dfrac{20 \, (1 - j3)}{1^2 + 3^2}$

$= \dfrac{20 \, (1 - j3)}{10} = 2 - j6$

$I_2 = \dfrac{200}{20} = 10$

$I_3 = \dfrac{200}{1 - j20} \times \dfrac{1 + j20}{1 + j20} = \dfrac{200 \, (1 + j20)}{1^2 + 20^2}$

$= \dfrac{200 \, (1 + j20)}{401} = 0 \cdot 49 + j9 \cdot 97$

Total $I = 2 + 10 + 0 \cdot 49 + j(9 \cdot 97 - 6) = 12 \cdot 49 + j3 \cdot 97$ of value $\sqrt{12 \cdot 49^2 + 3 \cdot 97^2} = 13$ amperes at a leading power factor of $12 \cdot 49/13 = 0 \cdot 96$.

4. 394 ohms.

5. $3 \cdot 16 + j5 \cdot 48$; $38 \cdot 32\%$.

6. $15 \cdot 9$ μF.; 100 ohms; 100 ohms.

7. $13 \cdot 15$ μF.; $4 \cdot 08$ amp.; $0 \cdot 878$ amp.

8. (a) Y's = $0 \cdot 1562$; $0 \cdot 078$; $0 \cdot 2343$ mhos. G's = $0 \cdot 0976$; $0 \cdot 0488$; $0 \cdot 1464$ mhos. B's = $0 \cdot 122$; $0 \cdot 061$; $0 \cdot 183$ mhos. (b) $46 \cdot 86$ amp. at $0 \cdot 624$ p.f.; 583 μF.

9. Simplify A and B in parallel by product/sum, i.e.—

$$\frac{(3 + j4)\,(5 - j12)}{8(1 - j1)} \times \frac{1 + j1}{1 + j1}$$

$$\frac{\{15 + 48 + j(20 - 36)\}\,(1 + j1)}{8 \times 2}$$

$$\frac{(63 - j16)\,(1 + j1)}{16} = \frac{63 + 16 + j(63 - 16)}{16}$$

$$\frac{79 + j47}{16} = 4{\cdot}94 + j2{\cdot}94.$$

Adding this equivalent impedance to C, the total impedance is $7{\cdot}94 + j7{\cdot}94$ indicating a 45° impedance, with current consequently lagging 45° on volts.

$$I = \frac{100}{7{\cdot}94(1 + j1)} \times \frac{(1 - j1)}{(1 - j1)} = \frac{100(1 - j1)}{7{\cdot}94 \times 2}$$

$$= 6{\cdot}3 - j6{\cdot}3 \text{ or } 6{\cdot}3\,\sqrt{2} = 8{\cdot}9 \text{ amperes.}$$

The common voltage across the AB pair

$$= 6{\cdot}3\,(1 - j1)(4{\cdot}94 + j2{\cdot}94)$$
$$= 6{\cdot}3\,\{4{\cdot}94 + 2{\cdot}94 + j(2{\cdot}94 - j4{\cdot}94)\}$$
$$= 6{\cdot}3\,(7{\cdot}88 - j2) = 49{\cdot}6 - j12{\cdot}6 = 51{\cdot}18 \text{ volts.}$$

The voltage across C is

$$= 6{\cdot}3\,(1 - j1)(3 + j5)$$
$$= 6{\cdot}3\,\{3 + 5 + j(5 - 3)\}$$
$$= 6{\cdot}3\,(8 + j2) = 50{\cdot}4 + j12{\cdot}6 = 51{\cdot}95 \text{ volts.}$$

Note that the sum of these two voltages must be the $(100 + j0)$ volts applied.

The total current has the two components in A and B given respectively by

$$\frac{6{\cdot}3(7{\cdot}88 - j2)}{3 + j4} \times \frac{3 - j4}{3 - j4} = \frac{6{\cdot}3(23{\cdot}64 - 8 - j6 - j31{\cdot}52)}{25}$$

$$= \frac{6{\cdot}3(15{\cdot}64 - j37{\cdot}52)}{25} = 3{\cdot}94 - j9{\cdot}45 = 10{\cdot}24 \text{ amp.}$$

and

$$\frac{6{\cdot}3(7{\cdot}88 - j2)}{5 - j12} \times \frac{5 + j12}{5 + j12}$$

$$= \frac{6{\cdot}3(39{\cdot}4 + 24 + j)(94{\cdot}56 - 10)}{169}$$

$$= \frac{6{\cdot}3(63{\cdot}4 + j84{\cdot}56)}{169} = 2{\cdot}36 + j3{\cdot}15 = 3{\cdot}936 \text{ amp.}$$

Note that the sum of these two currents gives $6{\cdot}3 - j6{\cdot}3$.

The components of all these voltages and currents enable the vector diagram to be drawn at once, as shown in Fig. 4A, taking the 100 volts as the axis of reference.

10. 32·1; 10; 42·1 amp.
11. R's, $A = 7.5$, $B = 7.14$, $Eq = 4$ ohms; X's, $A = 3.63$, $B = 9.3$, $Eq = 3$ ohms; B takes 8·53 amp. at 0·61 p.f.
12. 1·58, 1·86, 2·24, 2·78, 3·54 ohms.
13. 20 ohms; 125 μF.
14. 0·195 henry; 34·3 μF.

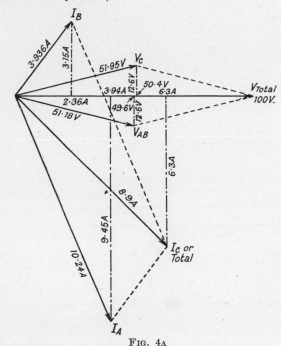

FIG. 4A

15. 1437 kVA. at 0·915 leading.
16. $L = 0.0478$H, $C = 53\mu$F.,
  $Y = 0.0347 - j0.0078$;
  12° 25′ lagging.
17. 103 c/s.
18. 53° and 73°.

EXAMPLES 38

2. 6·32 amp.; 10 amp.   **3.** 5×10^{-8}; 0° 3′ 14·5″.
4. 3 mins. 9 sec.   **5.** 125 ohms.   **6.** 6·816 amp.
7. 1500 amp., $f = 796$ cycles.

8. 0·952 amp.; 0·69 secs.

9. Let C = capacity of condenser (farads)

R = resistance of circuit (ohms)

E = battery E.M.F. (volts)

Then, after time t secs., q = condenser charge.

v = condenser volts = q/C,

and $\quad i$ = current = $\dfrac{dq}{dt} = \dfrac{E - q/C}{R}$

Then $dt = \dfrac{R}{E - q/C}\, dq = \dfrac{RC}{EC - q}\, dq$

Thus $t\quad = -RC \log_e (EC - q) +$ constant k

When $t\ = 0, q = 0$, and $k = RC \log_e EC$

Thus $t\quad = RC \log_e EC - RC \log_e (EC - q) = RC \log_e \dfrac{EC}{EC - q}$

whence $e^{t/RC} = \dfrac{EC}{EC - q}$ or $q = EC\left(1 - e^{-\frac{t}{RC}}\right)$

Applying this, we have

$$0·99 \times 3 \times 10^{-6} \times E = 3 \times 10^{-6} \times E\left(1 - e^{-\frac{t}{10^{6} \times 3 \times 10^{-6}}}\right)$$

i.e. $\quad 0·99 = 1 - e^{-t/3}$, or $e^{-t/3} = 0·01$, or $-t/3 = 2·3 \log 0·01 = -4·6$.

whence $\quad t = 3 \times 4·6 = 13·8$ sec. *Ans.*

10. (a) 3·75 sec.; (b) 8·62 sec.

11. 2·72 megohms.

EXAMPLES 39

1. 0·707 kWh.   **5.** 4·7 mA.

6. Moving-coil 0·3; hot-wire 0·746; power from mains **133·33** watts; power wasted in device 77·77 watts.

EXAMPLES 40

1. 151 volts and 68 volts.   **2.** 22,500, 2258, and 341·3 volts.

3. 18·85μF. and 4600 volts.   **4.** 147·9 amp. and 3892·5 volts.

5. 72 amp. and 0·0027 henry.

6. $Z_1 = \sqrt{[25 + (10 - 254·5)^2]} = 245$ ohms

$I_{1max} = 100\sqrt{2}/245 = 0·5775$ amp.

$Z_3 = \sqrt{[25 + (30 - 84·8)^2]} = 55$ ohms

$I_{3max} = 20\sqrt{2}/55 = 0·515$ amp.

$I = \sqrt{[\frac{1}{2}(0·5775^2 + 0·515^2)]} = 0·547$ amp.

Power = $I^2R = 0·547^2 \times 5 = 1·5$ watts.

8. (a) 0·041 henry; (b) 1444 volts and 31·6 amp.

9. 3·81 amp.; 0·535.

EXAMPLES 41

1. 19·5; 14·7; 4·8 amp.

2. 0·886 and 0·189 lagging and leading.

3. 100 amp.; 44 and 22·3 kW.; $r = 0·506$.

4. 0·064.

5. ACB (if R fed from A), 451 volts.

6. 405 amp., 234 amp.

7. 1·15 amp.

8. 8·03 amp.; p.f. $= 0·317$.

9. 36 amp.

EXAMPLES 42

1. 510, 587, 699, neutral 174 amp.

2. 12·7; 10; 10·16 amp; 2·58; 1·41; 2·57 kW.

3. 64·2 amp., 380·7 amp., 406 amp.   **4.** 100, 51·8, 51·8 volts.

5. 21·75; 21·75 and 37·66 amp.

6. (a) 15·1 amp.; (b) 234·4 volts. **7.** 229·1 volts. **8.** (a) 237 volts; (b) 408 volts.

9. 90·6; 36·7 and 111·6 amp.; 39·86 and 16·14 kW.

10. 0·89 p.f.; 1237, 1303, 1765 amp. in phase lines, 555 amp. in neutral.

11. Taking V_{12} as axis of reference,

then $V_{23} = a^2 V_{12}$ and $V_{31} = a V_{12}$

Current from $V_{12} = 151$ amp at 0·7 p.f. leading
$= 105·7 + j107·8$

Current from $V_{23} = 232·5$ amp. at 1 p.f. $= 232·5 + j0$

Current from $V_{31} = 174$ amp. at 0·6 p.f. lagging
$= 104·4 - j139·2$

Then $i_a = 105·7 + j107·8 = i_{a1} + i_{a2} + i_{ao}$

$i_b = a^2\, 232·5 = -116·25 - j201·5$
$= i_{b1} + i_{b2} + i_{b0} = a^2 i_{a1} + a i_{a2} + i_{ao}$

$i_c = a(104·4 - j139·2) = 68·4 + j160$
$= i_{c1} + i_{c2} + i_{c0} = a\, i_a + a^2 i_{a2} + i_{ao}$

For positive sequence components—

$3i_{a1} = i_a + a i_b + a^2 i_c$
$= 105·7 + j107·8 + a^3 232·5 + a^3(104·4 - j139·2)$
$= 442·6 - j31·4$ (since $a^3 = 1$)

$\therefore\ i_{a1} = 147·533 - j10·466$ *Ans.*

For negative sequence components—

$3i_{a2} = i_a + a^2 i_b + a i_c$
$= 105·7 + j107·8 + a^4 232·5 + a^2(104·4 - j139·2)$
$= -183·35 + j288·5$ (since $a^4 = a$)

$\therefore\ i_{a2} = -61·166 + j96·166$ *Ans.*

For zero sequence components—

$$3i_{a0} = i_a + i_b + i_c$$
$$= 57 \cdot 85 + j66 \cdot 3$$
$$\therefore \quad i_{a0} = 19 \cdot 3 + j22 \cdot 1 \quad Ans.$$

To find the line currents of question 3, find the value of $i_b - i_a$; $i_c - i_b$ and $i_a - i_c$, noting that $i_b - i_a = i_{a1}(a^2 - 1) + i_{a2}(a - 1)$, etc.

EXAMPLES 43

1. 1,700; 2940 volts.   **2.** 19·2 volts.   **4.** 795 volts.
5. 1365 volts.   **6.** (a) 750 volts; (b) 1842 volts.
7. 230 volts at 0°; 230 volts at 60°; 400 volts at 210°.
8. 7920 volts.

EXAMPLES 44

1. 9·85 cub. metres per sec.
2. 94·8%.
3. 35·4 cub. mt. per sec. intake.

4. Watts loss $\quad = \dfrac{1 \cdot 2}{98 \cdot 8} \times 5,000,000 = 60,700$

Loss per minute $\quad = 60,700 \times 60$ joules
$\qquad\qquad\qquad = 60,700 \times 60 \times 0 \cdot 24$ calories

With the water carrying off 80% of the heat with a temperature rise of 20° C., the weight of water required

$$= \frac{60,700 \times 60 \times 0 \cdot 24 \times 80}{20 \times 100} \text{ grm. per min.}$$

$$= 34,980 \text{ grm.} = 34 \cdot 98 \text{ litres per min.} \quad Ans.$$

5. 27·6 cub. metres per sec.; 265 gallons per min.
6. (a) 9·9 cub. mt. at 760 mm. and 25° C.; (b) 19·44 h.p.
7. 29·4 cub. mt. per sec.; 26·1 cub. mt. per sec.
8. 79·6 kW. Synchronous induction motor.

EXAMPLES 46

1. 140 tons-ft.   **2.** 544 kg.-mts.
3. Maximum power before pulling out of synchronism (see M2)
$\quad V =$ Bus-bar Volts; $E =$ Machine E.M.F. Volts
$\quad R =$ Resistance and $Z =$ Impedance inside machine
Cos $\alpha = R/Z$ for the machine

Maximum Power input to machine $= P_1 = \dfrac{E}{Z} (E \cos \alpha + V)$

Maximum Power output to load $= P_2 = \dfrac{V}{Z} (E - V \cos \alpha)$

53,000 kW.; 6,400 amp.; 0·686 in machine, 0·728 in load.
4. 7·81 amp.
5. $E_1 - V = I_1(0 \cdot 2 + j2)$
$\quad\;\; E_2 - V = I_2(0 \cdot 2 + j2)$
$\qquad\quad V = (I_1 + I_2)(3 + j4)$

Using $E_1 = 2000$ and $E_2 = 2200 + j100$, then

$$I_1 = 68 \cdot 2 - j102 \cdot 5$$
$$I_2 = 127 - j196 \cdot 4$$
$$I = I_1 + I_2 = 195 \cdot 2 - j298 \cdot 9$$
$$V = IZ = I(3 + j4) = 1781 - j115 \cdot 9$$

Output $VI_1 =$ "dot" product of $(1781 - j115 \cdot 9)$ and $(68 \cdot 2 - j102 \cdot 5) = 121 \cdot 2 + 11 \cdot 87$ kW. $= 133 \cdot 07$ kW. per phase or $399 \cdot 2$ kW. total.

$$\left. \begin{array}{l} \text{Tan}^{-1}\ 102 \cdot 5/68 \cdot 2 = 56°24' \\ \text{Tan}^{-1}\ 115 \cdot 9/1781 = 3°43' \end{array} \right\}\ \text{Cos } 52°41' = 0 \cdot 6062.$$

Output $VI_2 = (1781 - j115 \cdot 9)(127 - j196 \cdot 4)$ dot $= 226 \cdot 2 + 22 \cdot 77 = 248 \cdot 97$ kW. per phase, or $746 \cdot 9$ kW. total.

Cos $(57°6' - 3°43') = 0 \cdot 596$.

6. 2000 kW.   **7.** $788 \cdot 8$ amp.; 7200 volts; $0 \cdot 556$.

8. 360 amp. at $0 \cdot 611$ p.f.; 15,427 kW.; 1785 amp. at $0 \cdot 7865$ leading.

9. 3089 kW.; 461 amp. at $0 \cdot 588$ p.f. **10.** 2864 kW., 787 amp. at $0 \cdot 551$ power factor. **11.** 384,000 lb.-ft.^{2} **12.** $96 \cdot 75$ volts, 405 watts, 635 watts. **13.** $1 \cdot 32$ sec.

EXAMPLES 47

1. 3421 volts. **2.** As a motor, 121 amp.; as a generator, 76 amp. **3.** 124 amp. **4.** $34 \cdot 4\%$ up.

5. See Figs. 5 and 6. Explanation of the solution and drawing—

The O.C. volts curve should be plotted as *phase volts* against excitation.

$$\text{Full-load current} = \frac{600,000}{\sqrt{3} \times 3300} = 105 \text{ amp.}$$

Demagnetizing ampere-turns per pole for full-load and zero power factor

$$= \frac{200}{8} \times 105 \times 1 \cdot 06 = 2780$$

At full-load the reactance internal volts will be 7% of $3300/\sqrt{3} = 133$. In Fig. 5 the terminal volts of $3300/\sqrt{3} = 1910$ volts are set off as OV. The internal reactance drop of 133 volts is set off as VA at an angle corresponding to $0 \cdot 8$ power factor lagging. Had the internal resistance been specified, the drop occasioned by it would have been set off as AA' at right angles to the reactance drop. Then the resultant OA (or OA') gives the generated volts (1987 volts). From the O.C. volts curve is read off the excitation ampere-turns required for this generated voltage and is found to be 5100, and along OA is set off $OB = 5100$. The 2780 demagnetizing ampere-turns are then set off as BC in the wattless direction (i.e. parallel to VA) and the resultant OC ampere-turns—7240—will be the effective ampere-turns when the full-load is thrown off. From the O.C. volts curve, this corresponds to an E.M.F. of 2240 volts per phase or 3880 line volts. The " regulation up " is thus

$$\frac{3880 - 3300}{3300} = \frac{580}{3300} = 17 \cdot 6\% \quad Ans.$$

Short-circuit Characteristic. Internal resistance not being specified, and certainly low, assume zero power factor on short-circuit. Then demagnetizing ampere-turns for full-load current = 2780 as above. Reactance drop internal at full-load current = 133 volts. The

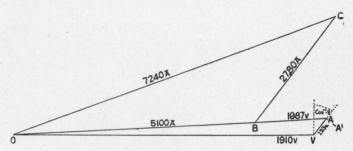

FIG. 5. ALTERNATOR REGULATION

ampere-turns to generate this voltage is about 300, from O.C. volts curve. Hence total excitation is 2780 + 300 = 3080 ampere-turns for full-load short-circuit current, and this is a point on the short-

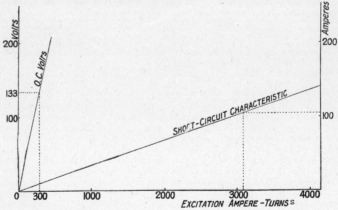

FIG. 6. ALTERNATOR SHORT-CIRCUIT CHARACTERISTIC

circuit characteristic, assumed to be a straight line through the origin. See Fig. 6.

6. 84% ; 0·827. **7.** 20% up. **8.** 96·6 amp. ; 70·3 amp.

9. (Ref. M1, pp. 96–106.) By Potier Method, armature reaction is

15,700 ampere-turns; reactance drop is 640 volts per phase. Full-load current = 788 amp. Armature reactance = $640/788 = 0.812$ ohms. Short-circuit A.T. = 18,000, which corresponds to an E.M.F. of 4850 volts. Hence synchronous reactance (Behn-Eschenberg method) = $4850/788 = 6.15$ ohms.

By drawing similar to Fig. 5, OV = phase volts = 6350 volts. VA = reactance drop = 640 volts. OA = generated volts on load. OB = rotor ampere-turns necessary to generate OA = 30,800. BC = armature reaction at full-load = 15,700 A.T. OC = effective A.T. when full-load (at 11 kV.) is thrown off = 42,800 A.T., and this generates 7540 volts on open-circuit. Hence regulation up is $(7540 - 6350)/6350 = 18.8\%$.

From the short-circuit characteristic current would be about 1880 amp. at an excitation of 42,800 A.T., and a generated voltage of 7540 volts, so that the synchronous reactance under full-load 0.8 p.f. conditions would be about $7540/1880 = 4$ ohms.

EXAMPLES 48

3. $A = 1.41$.

EXAMPLES 49

2. 0.532. 3. Voltages generated will be proportional to the following values—

Degrees	Phase	Line	Degrees	Phase	Line
0	0	25·6	100	26·5	36
20	9·5	36	120	25·6	25·6
40	18·2	44·7	140	18·2	8·7
60	25·6	51·2	160	9·5	– 8·7
80	26·5	44·7	180	0	– 25·6

5. 8.5×10^6 lines. 6. $21 \sin \theta - 2.64 \sin 3\theta + 2.64 \sin 7\theta$. 15.1 volts. 7. Flux per pole, 8 megalines; 18·5 volts; 50 c/s.

EXAMPLES 50

1. 72 slots. 2. Try 180 slots; 4 conductors per slot. 3. Try 288 or 216 slots, 2592 conductors. 4. 72 coils each winding, one the odd numbers, other the evens. Coil table $1 - 25 - 49 - 73 - 97 - 121 - 143$ (by a shortened step, i.e. 5 of 24 and 1 of 22) $- 23$, etc. Rings at 1, 137 and 129; star point 115, 107 and 99. For duplicate winding, add 1 throughout the above. 5. 36 coils each winding. Use pitches of 36 and 34 alternately, so that one winding may contain odd coils only, other the evens. Coil table: $1 - 37 - 71 - 35$, etc. Ring 1, 61, 49; star point 27, 15 and 3. Add 1 throughout for duplicate winding. 5. *Alternative.* Symmetrical singly closed duplex wave winding with step of 35. Winding divided into six phases, and opposite sections connected in series thus:

Red. 1 to 26 joined to 62, thence to 37 star.

Yellow. 49 to 2 joined to 38, thence to 13 star.

Blue. 25 to 50 joined to 14, thence to 61 star.

For parallel running, connect thus:

Red. 1 to 26 star. Red. 62 to 37 star.

Yellow. 49 to 2 star. Yellow. 38 to 13 star.

Blue. 25 to 50 star. Blue. 14 to 61 star.

7. About 3·4 in. × 0·5 in. Space factors 0·71 and 0·63.

8. Try 3 slots per pole per phase, 12 conductors per slot.

9. For 3-phase from 6-phase sections—

Red. Ring 1 –   – 125 join to 24 –   – 102 star.

Yel. Ring 96 –   – 35 join to 69 –   – 12 star.

Blue. Ring 91 –   – 80 join to 119 –   – 57 star.

15·5 per cent higher voltage.

EXAMPLES 51

1. 4400 amp.; 1050 amp.

EXAMPLES 52

1. Try $D = 87$ cm.; $L = 30$ cm.; $S = 72$. **2.** (a) 684 cond. in 57 slots; about 40 mm.^{2} each. (b) 4·9 kW. (c) About 18,000 gauss at max. **3.** $B_{max} = 9000$; $ac = 280$; $D = 130$; $L = 33$. **4.** Approx., $D = 1$ m.; $L = 260$ cm. **5.** 28,000 kVA. **6.** Approx., $D = 218$ cm., $L = 35$ cm., 180 slots 9 cond. per slot. **7.** 20 cm. $89\frac{1}{2}$ turns; 0·211 cm. thick. **8.** $D = 162$; $L = 70$. **9.** About 3·3 cm. thick, and 84 turns. Use strip about $33 \times 1·6$ mm. **10.** 17,000 kVA. **11.** $B_{av} = 4930$, $ac = 627$, new $L = 252$ cm.

EXAMPLES 53

1. (a) 97·5%; (b) 97%.

2. Constant iron losses = 975 watts.

Full-load copper loss   = 1050 watts

Full-load impedance volts (primary side) = 22

Full-load current (primary side)   = 100 amp.

Equivalent impedance referred to the primary side
$$= 0·22 \text{ ohm}$$

Equivalent resistance referred to the primary side
$$= 1050/100^2$$
$$= 0·105 \text{ ohm}$$

Equivalent reactance referred to the primary side
$$= \sqrt{0·22^2 - 0·105^2}$$
$$= 0·193 \text{ ohm}$$

(a) Hence % resistance drop = 1·05 (i.e. $0·105 \times 100 \times 100/10000$)

% impedance drop = 2·2.

% reactance drop = 1·93. *Ans.*

(b) A $\frac{3}{4}$ full-load current at 0·8 p.f. = 75 amp.

Copper losses will be = $1050 \times \left(\dfrac{75}{100} \right)^2 = 590$ watts.

Total losses will be $590 + 975 = 1565$ watts.

$$\text{Efficiency} = \frac{75,000 \times 0.8}{75,000 \times 0.8 + 1565} = \frac{60,000}{61,565} = 97.45\% \ Ans.$$

(c) % full-load drop at 0.9 p.f. $= 1.05 \times 0.9 + 1.93 \times \sqrt{0.19}$

$\qquad\qquad\qquad\qquad\qquad = 0.945 + 0.841 = 1.786\% \ Ans.$

3. 329 volts, 0.2 p.f. **4.** 50.2 volts.

5. First, 96.5%; Second, 97.2%.

6. (a) 0.3 amp., 0.632 amp.; (b) 96.4%, 3.26% down.

7. $R_0 = 18,000$; $X_0 = 6360$; $\overline{R}_1 = 2.32$; $\overline{X}_1 = 4.56$ ohms.

9. $R_0 = 781$; $X_0 = 264$; $\overline{R}_1 = 0.174$; $\overline{X}_1 = 0.378$ ohms, all on 250 V. side.

10. $R_0 = 108$ ohms, $X_0 = 22.1$ ohms, $\overline{R}_2 = 0.01$ ohm, $\overline{X}_2 = 0.0356$ ohm. **11.** 1540 volts, 6 kW. **12.** 90.5%.

EXAMPLES 54

1. Each sec. for 400 volts, one tapped at 100 and 200 volts, the other at 27, 200 and 373 volts. **2.** 98.5; 98; 98.4; 98.2%. **3.** 772 volts between corresponding terminals, 207 and 565.6 volts, possible values.

4. Allotting the 500 kW. to the Teaser and 800 kW. to the Main Transformer, we have, for unity p.f.—

Teaser primary current $\dfrac{500,000}{11,000 \times 0.866} = 52.5$ amp.

Main primary current $\dfrac{800,000}{11,000} = 72.7$ amp.

Hence current in line feeding Teaser is 52.5 amp. This current, on reaching the centre tap of the Main, will divide equally, each half flowing outwards from the centre tap, along the two supply lines to the source of supply. Hence the current in these lines and in each half of the Main is composed of the above 72.7 amp., together with $52.5/2 = 26.25$ amp. displaced 90°, the resultant being

$$\sqrt{72.7^2 + 26.25^2} = 77.1 \text{ amp.}$$

Hence one 3-phase line carries 52.5 amp., and the other two 77.1 amp each. At 0.5 p.f., each of the component currents is doubled ; hence also the resultant, giving line currents of 105 amp. in one and 154.2 in the others.

5. Using net iron $= 0.9$ of gross, primaries 830, main secy. 62, teaser secy. $18 + 36 = 54$.

6. One transformer has two equal windings of 83 turns each, the other has two sections containing 96 and 48 turns respectively.

EXAMPLES 55

1. 195 amp.; 422 amp.

2. See Fig. 7. Explanation of the drawing—

For a full explanation of this graphical method, see the Author's *Electrical Transformer Theory* (Pitman).

The two impedance triangles are constructed by measuring off the reactance horizontally, such as $OD = 8$ units and $OC = 4$ units, and then erecting the resistance values such as $DF = \frac{1}{2}$ unit and $CE = \frac{3}{4}$ unit. Thus ODF is the impedance triangle for the first transformer (A), and OCE for the second transformer (B). The impedance of each is then swung over by compass on to the other's line, i.e. OE on to A's impedance to give OG, and OF on to B's impedance line (produced) to give OH. Then OG represents the

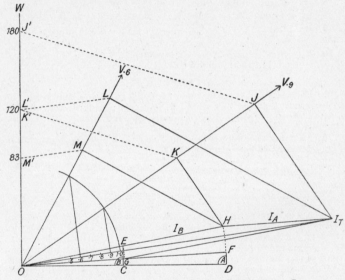

Fig. 7. Transformers in Parallel—Sharing of Loads

current in transformer A and OH that in transformer B, in their relative sizes and vector directions. By vectorially combining these we get the total load current OI_T. It will be noted that HI_T, equal and opposite to OG, has been labelled I_A, which it is in direction and size.

It is now necessary to place in the voltage lines. The construction of lines at power factors of 0·9 and 0·6 is effected by the usual quadrant method shown. It is clear that the total current I_T is lagging behind $OV_{.9}$ by a power factor of 0·9, and is similarly 0·6 behind the voltage $OV_{.6}$. By projecting the individual and total currents on to these voltage lines, we obtain the watts, individual and total. Thus at the 0·9 power factor, the total watts OJ are shared as OK on transformer B and KJ on transformer A. Similarly at the 0·6 power factor, there are OM watts on B, with the balance ML on A. The given loads have to be shared in these proportions. To do this graphically, draw any other line OW and scale it off in kilowatts. Thus J' represents 180 kilowatts. Join JJ', and draw KK' parallel to it, cutting the watts line in 120 kW. Thus the 180 kW. load at 0·9 power factor is shared as 120 kW. on transformer B, with 60 kW. on A. Similarly, by joining L to the 120 kW. point L', and drawing MM' parallel to it to cut the watts line in M' at 83 by scale, we find that a total load of 120 kW. at 0·6 power factor is shared as 83 kW. on B, with the balance of 37 kW. on A. (NOTE. It is quite an accident that the point L' coincides with K'.)

    3. 263 kVA. at 0·77; 237 kVA. at 0·63.

    4. Let I_1 and I_2 = currents in respective transformers.

        Z_1 and Z_2 = leakage impedances of respective transformers, then, in parallel, each must have the same internal volt drop, i.e. $I_1 Z_1 = I_2 Z_2$.

    But $Z_1 = 0·1 + j0·2$ and $Z_2 = 0·05 + j0·4$

    $Z_1 + Z_2 = 0·15 + j0·6$

whence $\dfrac{I_1}{I_1 + I_2} = \dfrac{0·05 + j0·4}{0·15 + j0·6}$

    I = total current = $I_1 + I_2$

     = 1000 amperes at 0·8 p.f. lagging

     = $800 - j600 = 800\,(1 - j0·75)$.

Then $I_1 = \dfrac{800(1 - j0·75)(0·05 + j0·4)}{0·15 + j0·6}$

     = $564·5 - j325·5$,

and $I_2 = \dfrac{800(1 - j0·75)(0·1 + j0·2)}{0·15 + j0·6}$

     = $235·5 - j274·5$,

totalling $800 - j600$.

whence $I_2 = 235·5 - j274·5 = 362$ amp.

and $I_1 = 564·5 - j325·5 = 652$ amp.

    The ratio of the kW. outputs is given by the in-phase components of the currents $= 235·5/564·5 = 1/2·4$.

    5. 583 kVA. at 0·843; 426 kVA. at 0·735.

    6. 498 kW. at 0·83; 703 kW. at 0·78.

    7. 2180 volts.

    8. 727 kW. at 0·834; 873 kW. at 0·76.

EXAMPLES 56

    1. 10,400 gauss; 0·39 amp.

    2. Hysteresis loss 60·5 watts, eddy current loss 8·0 watts.

    3. (a) 21° C.; (b) 63° C.

    4. Load current = 12·5 amp., in common turns 21·7 amp., input 34·2 amps. **5.** 0·932 of turns. **6.** 354 watts. **7.** 4 kW.

8. $3\cdot31/1$. **9.** $7\cdot25°$ C. **11.** $1\cdot34 \times 10^6$; 29,820 volts.
13. 517, about 6 mm. (3 layer). **14.** 250 watts, 50 watts.
15. 1500, 87.

EXAMPLES 57

The following values are suggested as a basis for suitable designs.

1. $A_i = 380$ cm.^{2} Volts per turn, 12.

   $d = 25$, $D = 34$, $L = 24$ cm.

2. $A_i = 54\cdot6$ cm.^{2} Volts per turn, $1\cdot21$.

   $d = 11$, $D = 22\cdot4$, $L = 30$ cm.

3. $A_i = 460$, $A_w = 304$; copper about 300 lb., stampings only about 850 lb.

4. $A_i = 1364$ cm.^{2} Volts per turn, $42\cdot5$

   $d = 50$, $D = 74$, $L = 72$ cm.

   Overall length of yoke about 194 cm.

5. $A = 0\cdot851d = 27\cdot8$;

   $B = \sqrt{d^2 - A^2} = 17\cdot2$.

6. Turns 1183 and 46 per limb; areas 2 and $52\cdot5$ sq. mm.; $A_i = 210$.

7. $A_i A = \dfrac{1000 \times 10^{11}}{2\cdot22 \times 50 \times 13000 \times 280 \times 0\cdot33} = 757,000$ cm.^{4}

   Volts per turn $= 0\cdot75 \sqrt{1000} = 23\cdot7$ V.

   $$\Phi_m = \frac{23\cdot7 \times 10^8}{4\cdot44 \times 50} = 10\cdot7 \text{ megamaxwells.}$$

At $B = 13,000$, this gives $A_i = 822$ cm.^{2}
Taking diameter of core as $d = \sqrt{A_i/0\cdot6} = 38$ cm.
Window area $= 757,000/822 = 920$ cm.^{2}
Taking distance between centre of limbs as $D = 56$ cm., gives 18 cm. for window width, with thus a length of $L = 920/18 = 51$ cm.
Turns suitable are $S_2 = 400/23\cdot7 = 17$, as $8\frac{1}{2}$ on each limb, and $S_1 = 17 \times 66/4 = 280$, as 140 on each limb.
(For suitable coils, see Ref. S3.)

8. $A_i = 350$. $D = 38$, $L = 30$. Turns 810/54.

9. $D = 36$, $d = 22$, overall of core about 95×70.

EXAMPLES 58

1. As examples, electric clock, time switch, gramophone turntable, etc. **2.** $0\cdot67$ leading. **4.** $0\cdot965$ leading. **5.** 4320 lb.-ft.

6. Explanation of " V " curve constructions—

Constant Input, Fig. 8.

   Impedance of armature $= \sqrt{1^2 + 5^2} = \sqrt{26} = 5\cdot1$ ohm.

The scale of current must be so chosen that the length of the resultant voltage vector is the same as the length of the armature current vector caused to flow by that voltage, i.e an ampere will be represented by the same length as 5·1 volts. Hence the following scales employed—

$$1'' = 100 \text{ volts} = 100/5\cdot1 = 19\cdot62 \text{ amperes}$$

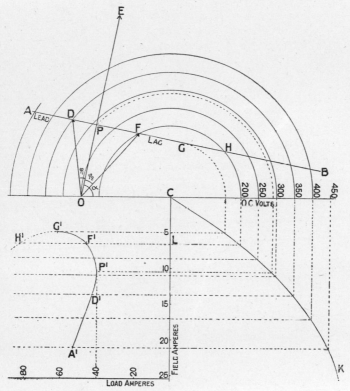

Fig. 8. Synchronous Motor " V " Curve for Constant Input

In the drawing, OE is erected at an angle $a = \tan^{-1} r/x = 1/5$, i.e. the internal angle of lag in the armature.

$OC = 250$ volts and $OP = 40$ amp. (i.e. 10 kW./250 volts)

$\qquad\qquad = 204$ volts in length

APB is perpendicular to OE and is the locus of the current vectors for constant power input. Semicircles are drawn with C as centre and generated volts as radii, and to the same scale the O.C. volts curve is drawn as *CK* against field amperes.

Now *OF* and *OH* are armature currents flowing when the excita-

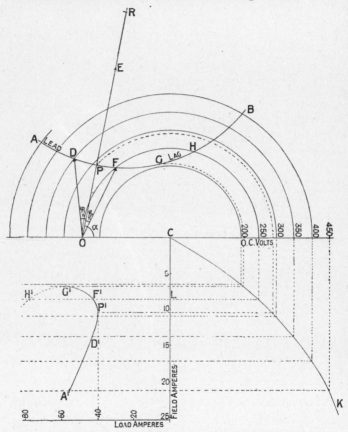

FIG. 9. SYNCHRONOUS MOTOR " V " CURVE FOR CONSTANT OUTPUT

tion is such as to produce a back E.M.F. of 200 volts, i.e. *CL*, and ordinates LF^1 and LH^1 are set up equal in length to the current vectors *OF* and *OH*, and the axis is scaled off in amperes in accordance with the above scale. The angle of lag of OF is φ_2 and cos φ_2 can be ascertained by a power factor quadrant with O as centre. (See Examples 64, Ques. 6, Fig. 10.) The curve of excitation against power factor can thus be plotted if wanted. The point H, giving LH^1 in the " V " curve, is in the unstable region after the motor has " stalled " at G^1, which latter point corresponds to the minimum permissible excitation for the given load input. The point P^1, corresponding to OP, is obviously the unity power factor current and hence the minimum, i.e. 40 amp. Leading power factors are obtained to the left of OP, e.g. OD, at cos φ_1, the excitation now being such as to produce a back E.M.F. of 350 volts.

7. *Constant Output*, Fig. 9. The same letters apply as in Fig. 8, but the locus for constant (total) mechanical output is an " O " curve obtained as follows—

Diameter of the maximum " O " curve, i.e. zero output, is given by volts/resistance $= 250/1 = 250$ amp., and the centre R is at a radius of 125 amp., which is equivalent to $125 \times 5 \cdot 1 = 637 \cdot 5$ on the volt scale, i.e. $6 \cdot 375''$. OP as before is 40 amp. $= 2 \cdot 04''$, and the locus for constant output is the " O " curve APB with centre at R.

8 and 9. The following are points on the " V " curves—

Field amp.		2	4	6	8	10
Armature amp. :	stable	23·1	20·2	20·4	22·0	25·1
(Const. input)	stalling	40·3	48·0			
Armature amp. :	stable		20·7	22·3	24·6	
(Const. output)	stalling		41·0	48·0		

Power factor (Ques. 9)—

	Const. input	Const. output
Minimum excitation (amp.)	1·42	2·54
Armature amp. at ditto	30·5	28·2
Excitation for unity p.f. (amp).	4·5	4·34

10. About 146 amp. at 0·9 p.f. leading.

EXAMPLES 59

1. 40·8 b.h.p.; 90%; 0·909 p.f. 2. 676 kVA.; 0·74.
3. (a) 0·005; (b) 75 W.; (c) 16·5 kW.; (d) 22 amp.; (e) 15.
4. (a) 1·82; (b) 217 r.p.m. 5. 1·65%.
7. 727·5 r.p.m.; $s = 0·03$, or 22·5 r.p.m. 8. 576 watts.

EXAMPLES 60

1. (a) 0·139; (b) 0·312. 2. 1·236 amp.
3. 13·5 amp., at 0·48 p.f.; 27 amp., at 0·47 p.f.
4. 1·29 ohms; 1·0 p.f.
5. $R_1 =$ total resistance in circuit on first stud,

   $r_2 =$ rotor resistance per phase,

   $s_r =$ fractional slip when taking upper limit starting current on the last stud,

n = number of steps in the startor, then

$R_1 = r_2/s_r = 0.015/0.02 = 0.75$ ohm.

$r_2 = R_1 (\delta)^n$ or $0.015 = 0.75 (\delta)^5$, whence

$\delta = 0.4573$.

$R_2 = \delta R_1 = 0.4573 \times 0.75 = 0.343$

$R_3 = \delta R_2 = 0.4573 \times 0.343 = 0.157$

$R_4 = \delta R_3 = 0.4573 \times 0.157 = 0.0717$

$R_5 = \delta R_4 = 0.47573 \times 0.0717 = 0.0328$

$r_2 = \delta R_5 = 0.4573 \times 0.0328 = 0.015$ as given.

Sections between studs are 0.407, 0.186, 0.0853, 0.0389 and 0.0178. These, with the 0.015, total 0.75 for R_1. (Ref. M7.)

6. (a) 1.836; 0.378; (b) 3.06, 0.378 times full-load for current and torque respectively. **7.** 25 lb.-ft. per phase. **9.** 6.584 ohms (added 6.25 ohms). **10.** (a) 3.42 amp.; (b) 2.14 amp.

11. 63.3% tap; 0.4 and 0.16 × f.l. torque.

EXAMPLES 61

2. 0.44 ohm. **4.** 600 r.p.m.; 40 h.p.

EXAMPLES 62

(The following are suggested as suitable answers.)

1. 2 slots per pole per phase, 46 cond. per slot, total 1104.

2. Single-layer winding, short-pitched, 3-tier end-turns. Sections in parallel for 50 cycles, in series for 25 cycles. (Ref. C. 5.)

4. $D = 18$ cm., $L = 16$ cm., slots = 36, cond. per slot = 34. No. 12 s.w.g.

5. Try 36 slots, 32 cond. per slot, full-pitched hemi-tropic coils. Pole flux about 1 megaline.

6. Concentric winding, 36 slots, 12 cond. per slot, pole flux about 790,000. **9.** Use $y_c = 58$ or 59, groups of 20 and 19 coils.

11. Red   1–33 thence   5–29
    Yellow 31–7   ,,   35–14
    Blue   16–3   ,,   20–44

EXAMPLES 63

(The following are suggested as suitable answers.)

1. 69 slots, wave winding, slot pitch 17.

2. (a) 5 to 1; (b) 1/4.8. **4.** 27 kVA. (output)

5. 120 slots, 2 cond. per slot, 395 V., 120 amp. (Ref. C5.) *Alternative:* 63 slots, 4 cond. per slot, 412 V., 120 amp. for 6-phase wave.

6. 2.13 kW. **7.** 17.7%. **8.** 392; 1150 amp. **9.** 3.45/1.

10. (a) 62.5 amp.; (b) 94.4 amp.

EXAMPLES 64

1. *Construction of the Circle Diagram* (Fig. 10).

The diagram must be drawn for one phase only in the case of a polyphase motor. In this case phase volts = $440/\sqrt{3} = 254$ V.

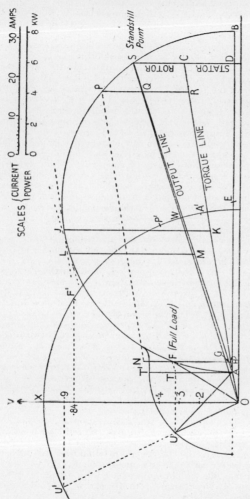

FIG. 10. THE APPROXIMATE CIRCLE DIAGRAM FOR AN INDUCTION MOTOR

Choosing a current scale, say $1'' = 10$ amp., then $1''$ will represent 10×254 watts $= 2\cdot54$ kW. on the power scale. Note that on the standstill test, 23 amp. at 110 V. $= 92$ amp. at 440 V., at the same power factor of $0\cdot3$.

Draw OV vertically to represent the volts line. Draw a quadrant of radius $OX = 1$ unit, say $5''$, and mark off $0\cdot2$ and $0\cdot3$ of this unit, i.e. $1''$ and $1\cdot5''$ from O. Draw horizontals through these points to cut the quadrant, e.g. W is level with $0\cdot3$ point. Then OW is at a power factor of $0\cdot3$ to OV. Produce it to S, making $OS = 92$ amp. $= 9\cdot2''$. Similarly, draw $OA = 8$ amp. $= 0\cdot8''$ at the $0\cdot2$ power factor. Points A and S lie on the required circle locus of rotor currents, the base being AB. Hence join AS and perpendicularly bisect it with a line cutting AB in E, the centre of the circle. (*Note.* Any load condition other than the standstill test point S can be used as the second point on the circle, and used accordingly.)

For any point on this semicircle, e.g. P, OP is the stator current and AP the corresponding rotor current. OS is the standstill stator current, and AS the equivalent standstill rotor current (with, of course, the rotor short-circuited, if of the wound type). If OS were projected on to the volts line OV, the perpendicular height, equal in length to SD', would be the watts absorbed by the motor on standstill (at full voltage). Of this, the constant portion DD' is considered to represent the core or iron loss, and the balance SD represents the total copper loss, stator and rotor. Hence, divide SD at C so that $DC/CS =$ the given ratio of these losses, so that $DC =$ stator copper loss and $CS =$ rotor copper loss on standstill test. (*Note.* If the stator and equivalent rotor resistances per phase are given, then SD is divided at C in the proportion of these resistances, thus assuming that stator and rotor currents are equal on standstill test. The *equivalent rotor resistance* is the *actual rotor resistance per phase* $\times$ *square of ratio of transformation*, in this case 13.)

Join AC then the vertical intercept anywhere between the circle and AC line, e.g. PR, is the input to the rotor in synchronous watts, i.e. $2\pi \times$ *synchronous speed* $\times$ *torque* $=$ rotor input. Hence, all such intercepts as PR are proportional to the rotor torque; hence, AC is called the *Torque Line*. But the portion QR represents the copper heat loss in the rotor for the particular point P, so that the balance PQ is the rotor output, in watts, or horse-power by division by 746. Hence AS is called the *Output Line*.

(a) *Full-load Conditions.* With centre O and radius $OF = 20$ amp. $= 2''$, cut the circle in F, to give the full-load position. Producing OF to cut the power factor quadrant in F', and projecting this point back on to the OX base, it is found that this gives the full-load power factor as $0\cdot84$. By measurement, $FH = 1\cdot48'' = 1\cdot48 \times 2540$ watts. The synchronous speed for a 4-pole 50 cycle motor is 1500 r.p.m. If $T =$ torque in lb.-ft., and $N =$ synchronous speed in r.p.m., then

$$\frac{2\pi NT}{33,000} \times 746 = 1\cdot48 \times 2540 \text{ watts,}$$

whence $T = 17.7$ lb.-ft. per phase, or 53.1 lb.-ft. total for the motor. Further, $FG = 1.44'' = 1.44 \times 2540$ watts per phase $= 4.9$ h.p., or 14.7 h.p. total for the motor on full-load. The full-load efficiency would thus be

$$\frac{1.44 \times 2540 \times 3 \text{ watts output}}{\sqrt{3} \times 440 \times 20 \times 0.84 \text{ watts input}} = 85.5\%$$

The slip at full-load is given by

$$\frac{\text{rotor copper loss}}{\text{rotor input}} = \frac{GH}{FH} = \frac{.04''}{1.48''} = 2.7\%$$

The measurement here is difficult and does not afford a very accurate result. Among other methods of getting the slip from the diagram more accurately, the following may be used—

$$\text{Slip} = \frac{AH}{AC} \times \frac{SC}{FH}, \text{ by measurement} = \frac{0.27}{8.1} \times \frac{1.28}{1.48} = 2.88\%$$

(*Note.* It will be seen from the diagram that there is a best possible power factor at which the machine can work, given by the tangent to the circle from O. Full-load should agree fairly closely with this position of maximum power factor.)

(*b*) *Maximum Torque and Output.* By drawing tangents to the circle parallel to the Torque Line and the Output Line, the maximum for each of these items is obtained. Thus JK is the maximum or stalling torque, and by measurement this is $3.75''$, giving a total maximum torque for the motor of

$$\frac{3.75 \times 2540 \times 3 \times 33,000}{2n \times 1500 \times 746} = 134 \text{ lb.-ft.}$$

Similarly LM gives the maximum horse-power output. By measurement, it is found to be $3.2''$, corresponding to a total maximum horse power of

$$\frac{3.2 \times 2540 \times 3}{746} = 32.8 \text{ h.p.}$$

(*c*) *Standstill Torque* is given by $SC = 1.28''$, corresponding to a total torque of 45.7 lb.-ft., or 86.5% of full-load torque.

(*d*) *Rotor Resistance for* 150% *Full-load Torque.* Produce HF to N, making $FN = HF/2$, so that HN is 150% of full-load torque, and project this across by a parallel to the Torque Line until it cuts the circle in P.

This point P will be the new standstill or starting point giving $PR = 150\%$ full-load torque on starting. But at standstill, PR will be the rotor copper loss, divided as QR in the rotor itself and PQ on resistance external to the rotor. By measurement, $PQ = 1.04''$ $= 2640$ watts. The corresponding rotor current is given by AP $= 8'' = 80$ amp., whence the equivalent external resistance must be $2640/80^2 = 0.413$ ohm per phase. This resistance is the equivalent resistance, as referred to the stator. The actual resistance to be inserted in each phase of the rotor circuit will be $0.413/13 = 0.0318$

ohms. Alternatively, the equivalent rotor current being 80 amp., the actual rotor current is $80 \times 3 \cdot 6 = 288$ amp., and the watts to be absorbed, 2640, by resistance, will necessitate a resistance of $2640/288^2 = 0 \cdot 0318$ ohm. The current AP cuts the power factor circle in P', which when projected on to OX gives a power factor of about $0 \cdot 4$ for this new starting condition.

By drawing through F a line parallel to the Output Line to give AT the full-load output, and again projecting this by a horizontal to U, on the $0 \cdot 9$ leading power factor line OU', we obtain data for this motor to work at such a leading power factor. See Examples 69, page 89 for further particulars.

2. $173 \cdot 5$ watts. **3.** 31 amp.; $0 \cdot 915$; $0 \cdot 035$.

4. $24 \cdot 3$ amp.; $0 \cdot 88$; 29 h.p.

5. Starting torque, 135 synch. kW. Added resistance $0 \cdot 05$ ohm per phase. On short-circuit, 118 amp. at $0 \cdot 28$ p.f. Resistance starting, 112 amp. at $0 \cdot 45$ p.f. **6.** $0 \cdot 85$ p.f.; $0 \cdot 032$ ohm.

7. (a) 515 kW.; (b) 450 kW.; (c) $R = 5 \cdot 6$ ohms (all per phase).

8. (a) $28 \cdot 2$ amp. at $0 \cdot 844$ p.f.; (b) $37 \cdot 3$ h.p.; (c) $11 \cdot 62$ syn. kW. per phase.

9. 49 amp. at $0 \cdot 88$ p.f.; $78 \cdot 4$ synch. kW. or $2 \cdot 575 \times$ full-load torque; 94 h.p.

10. $0 \cdot 064$ ohm. **11.** (a) 70 amp. at $0 \cdot 885$; (b) 604lb.-ft., 102 h.p.

12. (a) $31 \cdot 7$ amp.; (b) $0 \cdot 915$; (c) $89 \cdot 5\%$; (d) $67 \cdot 8$ h.p.

13. $0 \cdot 99$. **14.** (a) 197 lb.-ft.; (b) $1 \cdot 08$; (c) $7 \cdot 3$ approx.

15. $3 \cdot 4$ amp. at $0 \cdot 93$ p.f.

17. $7 \cdot 65$ h.p.; $12 \cdot 2$ amp.; $82 \cdot 5\%$; $0 \cdot 82$.

18. (a) $26 \cdot 6$ amp., at $0 \cdot 85$; (b) $28 \cdot 8$ lb.-ft.

EXAMPLES 65

(The following are suggested as suitable answers.)

1. $D = 19$ cm., $L = 10$ cm., $Z = 828$ (36 slots).

2. Stator 36 slots, 25 or 26 cond. in each. Rotor 41 or 47 slots and bars.

3. 130 lb.-ft.

4. $D = 16$ cm., $L = 14$ cm., $Z = 792$ cond. in 24 slots.

5. 6×10^5 lines; slot about $2 \cdot 4 \times 0 \cdot 95$ cm.

6. $D = 19$ cm., $L = 19 \cdot 5$ cm.

7. $D = 17$ cm., $L = 17$ cm. Turns $= 528$, $S = 24$.

EXAMPLES 65A

1. (i) ratio $1 : 7$, (ii) $145°$, (iii) 350 volts to 467 volts.

3. 5 kVA.

4. 136 kVA.

5. $17 \cdot 7$ volts; 1050 amp.; about 110 kVA.

EXAMPLES 66

1. (a) $15 \cdot 55$, 212 volts; (b) 983 amp.; (c) 164 amp. **2.** A.C., 70 amp., 763 amp.; D.C. 1600 amp., 1400 amp. **4.** 657 to 602 volts.

6. (a) 250 volts; (b) 306 volts. **7.** $4 \cdot 44$ kW.

9. (a) 596; (b) 561; (c) 632 volts.

10. 0·72.

11. (a) 70·7 volts, 165 amp.; (b) 61·2 volts, 110·4 amp.; (c) 35·4 volts, 55·2 amp.

12. 821 amp.; 279 kVAR.

13. H.T. current input = 50·2 amp. at 0·96 p.f. leading. Considering overall efficiency of 91% as 94% for the induction motor and 97% for the rotary convertor, the rotor current per connector = 152 amp. A.C. in convertor mesh = 292 amp. (r.m.s.). D.C. output, 833 amp.

14. 377 amp. each line connector.

15. 6600 volts, 31·2 amp. phase, 389 volts, 530 amp.

16. 45%. **17.** 0·0154 ohm.

18. 428 r.p.m., 214 kW., 115 amp.

EXAMPLES 67

1. About 3500 (capable of considerable variation, according to assumptions made). **5.** (a) 8-pole, 12-phase; (b) 12-pole, 6-phase.

7.

Rings	1	2	3
Conductors	1	73	145
	217	289	361
	433	505	577

8. 0·095 ohm.

EXAMPLES 68

4. 1330 r.p.m. **5.** 126; 58; 162 volts.

8. (a) 516 r.p.m., 0·69 p.f.; (b) 723 r.p.m., 0·933 p.f.

9. 268 volts; 0·94 p.f.

EXAMPLES 69

1. 92 kVAR.; 263 h.p.; 398 h.p.

2. Sync. $= 1·35 \times Tf.l.$
Stall. $= 2·2 \times Tf.l.$
p.f. $= 0·63$ leading
Current $= 33$ amp.

3. 116 amp. **4.** 0·9 leading. **5.** 5 kW.

6. 153 amp.; 329 lb.-ft. **7.** 137 amp.; 1·46.

8. 116 amp. **9.** 162 amp.; 39·7 kW.

10. 288 amp.

EXAMPLES 70

1. 6 lb.; 1375 lb.

3. $CO_2 = 11·4$; $SO_2 = 0·027$; $N_2 = 80·2$; $O_2 = 8·4\%$. (Water vapour neglected.) **4.** 17·4%; £39,600.

5. $a = 50,000$; $b = 1·67$; $c = 0·000342$. **6.** (a) 0·786 lb.; (b) 14·3 lb. **7.** 2000 kW. **8.** 52·5%. **9.** $A = 23·7$ MW., $B = 23$ MW.; (i) $A = 5·385 \times 10^6$ lb., $B = 5·351 \times 10^6$ lb., (ii) 77·5%. **10.** 520 tons.

EXAMPLES 71

1. 106·8 kW. **2.** About 200 volts.
3. About 1370 volts; 2·8%.
4. Turn ratio = 10·5 per limb (separate rectifier each half of D.C. system). **6.** 16·15 kW. **8.** 15°. **9.** 1·55 × D.C. output.

EXAMPLES 72

2. Heavier load on + *ve* side; + *ve*, 215·7 volts, – *ve*, 201·44 volts.
3. 287 amp.; 365 amp.; 1018 kW.
4. + *ve*, 167 volts; – *ve*, 333 volts.
5. $P = 233·125$, $Q = 232·375$, $R = 232·81$, $S = 233·81$.

EXAMPLES 73

1. 1/1·11/1·03. **2.** 1·17 tons, 1·27 tons.

EXAMPLES 74

1. 532 amp. per in.^{2} **2.** Assume eff. of 0·9 for the motor. Units = 436,000 per an., cost = £3082. **3.** 0·29 in.^{2} **4.** 59% load factor. Use the first at load factors above this. **5.** £3870. **6.** 1560. **8.** 0·989d. per unit. **9.** 0·73 and 0·76d. per unit at 10% capital charges. **10.** (a) 0·53d.; (b) 0·28d. per unit. **11.** £2518; £2600; £2384. **12.** 656 amp. per in.^{2} **13.** 0·043 sq. in. **14.** 585 amp. per in.^{2} 0·45%. **15.** 0·846. **16.** Equal at 3250 kW., £17,212·5. $A = £8175$, $B = £8100$. **17.** 0·129 in.^{2} **18.** £952; 1·14d.; (a) same, (b) 1·3d. **19.** 0·574 in.^{2} **20.** 0·25 sq in. (Kelvin total, £56·1). **22.** 0·19 sq. in. **23.** 0·078 sq. in.

EXAMPLES 75

1. 238·66 volts. **2.** 92·76 amp., 87·24 amp., 245·97 volts on 35 amp. load.
3. Current entering positive feeder from left = 89·5 amp.

      ,,   ,,   ,,   ,,   ,, right = 85·5 amp.
      ,,   ,,   negative ,,   ,, left = 89·5 amp.
      ,,   ,,   ,,   ,,   ,, right = 85·5 amp.

P.d. minimum on positive side is 224·83 volts on the 50 amp. load.
P.d. minimum on negative side is 225·85 volts on the 60 amp. load.
4. $OC = 1·33$; $CA = 0·835$; $CB = 0·5$ sq. in.
5. P.D.'s: $B = 217·1$; $C = 216·14$; $D = 216·15$; $E = 216·93$ volts.
Currents: $AB = 29·04$ amp., etc.
P.D.'s: $B = 217·23$; $C = 216·35$; $D = 216·27$; $E = 216·83$ volts.
Currents: $AB = 27·49$ amp.; $EC = 9·76$ amp.
6. In 900 yd., 272·7 amp.; in 600 yd., 327·3 amp.; 545·5 yd. from the 900 yd. feeder point.
7. Working single line, in milli-ohms and millivolts—

Moments about A			Moments about B		
40 × 4 = 160			50 × 2·5 = 125		
20 × 12·5 = 250	'total 410		30 × 7·5 = 225	total 350	
(30 × 17·5 = 525	935)		20 × 12·5 = 250	600	

Load at minimum potential is the 20 amp. Of this current, let x enter from the end A and therefore $(20-x)$ from the end B.

Then equating moments, we have
$$160 + 12 \cdot 5x = 350 + (20 - x)\, 12 \cdot 5$$
$$\text{or} \quad 25x = 600 - 160 = 440, \text{ whence } x = 17 \cdot 6 \text{ amp}$$

Hence total current from $A = 57 \cdot 6$ amp., and
Ditto $\qquad\qquad B = 82 \cdot 4$ amp.

Drop to 20 amp. load $= 160 + 17 \cdot 6 \times 12 \cdot 5 = 380$ millivolts **on**

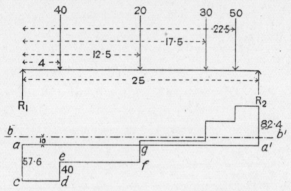

FIG. 11. DISTRIBUTOR LOADING DIAGRAMS

each line, or 20 amp. load is at a p.d. of 0·76 volt lower than the feeder points.

Raising the p.d. at end A by 0·5 volt causes a circulating current of
$$\frac{0 \cdot 5 \text{ volt}}{0 \cdot 05 \text{ ohm}} = 10 \text{ amp.}$$

to be superimposed on the above currents, thus giving total current entering from A as 67·6 amp., and from B as 72·4 amp. The load to be divided is now the 30 amp. load, of which 7·6 amp. will come from A and 22·4 from B. The drop to this load is now $125 + 22 \cdot 4 \times 7 \cdot 5 = 293$ millivolts on each line, causing that load to be at a p.d. 0·586 volts below B.

Using the loaded beam method, with lengths of beam proportional to resistances and loads proportional to currents, and end reactions R_1 and R_2 to represent the total currents entering from each end, we have

$$25R_2 = 4 \times 40 + 12 \cdot 5 \times 20 + 17 \cdot 5 \times 30 + 22 \cdot 5 \times 50$$

whence $R_2 = 82 \cdot 4$, and $R_1 = 140 - 82 \cdot 4 = 57 \cdot 6$. (See Fig. 11.)

Drawing the shearing force diagram, the B.M. is a maximum

when S.F. is zero, and the voltage drop is equal to the area *acdefg*
$= 57 \cdot 6 \times 12 \cdot 5 - 40 \times 8 \cdot 5 = 0 \cdot 38$ volt.

Superimposing 10 amp. raises the base line by 10, giving S.F. zero
at the 30 amp. load and drop below B as $72 \cdot 4 \times 7 \cdot 5 - 50 \times 5$
$= 0 \cdot 293$ volt.

8. (a) $0 \cdot 51$ sq. in.; (b) $0 \cdot 1275$ sq. in. **9.** $P = 18$ amp.; $R =$
$98 \cdot 5$ amp.; $Q = 28 \cdot 5$ amp. Volts at $b = 214 \cdot 8$.

10. Voltages, A, $247 \cdot 26$; B, $246 \cdot 78$; C, $248 \cdot 74$. Currents,
$OA = 54 \cdot 8$ amp.; $OB = 32 \cdot 2$ amp.; $OC = 63$ amp.; $AB = 4 \cdot 8$
amp.; $CB = 13$ amp.

11. $AB = 53 \cdot 94$, $BC = 33 \cdot 94$, $CD = 8 \cdot 35$, $ED = 16 \cdot 65$, $AE =$
$71 \cdot 06$, $FC = 4 \cdot 42$, $EF = 24 \cdot 42$.

12. $160 \cdot 63$ and $131 \cdot 87$ amp., 540 yd. load.

13. (a) $239 \cdot 1$ volts at 200 yd.; (b) $207 \cdot 6$ volts at B.

14. Currents $AB = 27 \cdot 7$ amp.; $FC = 3 \cdot 3$ amp. P.D.'s at B
$= 248 \cdot 6$; $C = 248$; $D = 247 \cdot 87$; $E = 248 \cdot 18$; $F = 248$ volts.

15. $232 \cdot 3$ volts at 25 amp. load.

16. 73 yd.; $0 \cdot 817$ volts. **17.** $CD = 4 \cdot 75$ amp.; $CE = 7 \cdot 34$ amp.
and then $CD = 1 \cdot 56$ amp.

EXAMPLES 76

1. $0 \cdot 3185 \mu$F. **2.** $0 \cdot 0354 \mu$F. **3.** $0 \cdot 000192 \mu$F. **4.** $36 \cdot 66$ kV.

5. $\dfrac{L}{82 \cdot 7 \log a/r}$; $I_c = 0 \cdot 822$ amp.

6. Number the porcelain units, from earth down to line, as
1, 2, 3, 4, and let the capacity of each be C farads. Call the capacities
to earth of each successive metal link a, b, c, and then each capacity
will be $0 \cdot 2 C$ farad. Let the voltage across the first main unit be
V kV. The calculation is then best carried out in tabular form,
working down in zigzag fashion, thus—

Condenser	Volts Across	Current Across
1	V	$\omega C V$
(a)	V	$0 \cdot 2\omega C V$
2	$1 \cdot 2V$	$1 \cdot 2\omega C V$
(b)	$2 \cdot 2V$	$0 \cdot 44\omega C V$
3	$1 \cdot 64V$	$1 \cdot 64\omega C V$
(c)	$3 \cdot 84V$	$0 \cdot 768\omega C V$
4	$2 \cdot 408V$	$2 \cdot 408\omega C V$
Total	$6 \cdot 248V = 60$ kV.	

whence $V = 9 \cdot 6$ kV.

The distribution of voltage across the successive units is therefore
$1 = 9 \cdot 6$; $2 = 1 \cdot 2 \times 9 \cdot 6 = 11 \cdot 5$; $3 = 1 \cdot 64 \times 9 \cdot 6 = 15 \cdot 7$; $4 = 2 \cdot 408$
$\times 9 \cdot 6 = 23 \cdot 2$; total 60 kV. The string efficiency is
$$60/(4 \times 23 \cdot 2) = 60/92 \cdot 8 = 64 \cdot 7\%.$$

7. $3 \cdot 5$.

8. From earth end, 31%, $30 \cdot 3\%$, and $38 \cdot 7\%$. Eff. $= 86\%$.
9. $7 \cdot 07$ per sq. cm., 424 volts. **10.** $3 \cdot 55$ kVA.
11. (a) $26 \cdot 7$ kV., $94 \cdot 5\%$; (b) $35 \cdot 7$ kV., $84 \cdot 1\%$. **12.** $2 : 1$.
13. (a) 260 kV., (b) 366 kV.

EXAMPLES 77

1. (a) 0.2193μF. ; (b) 0.2922μF. ; (c) 0.525 amp. **2.** 3.23 amp.
3. 15 amp. **4.** 120 amp. **5.** 4.3 amp. **6.** (a) $0.6\ \mu$F. per mile;
(b) 754 kVA.

EXAMPLES 78

1. 92.3 kV. **2.** 1.44 kV. and 18.6 kV. **3.** 24 amp.
4. $E_T = 174$ kV., $I_T = 435$ amp.; $E_R = 74$ kV., $I_R = 1233$ amp.

EXAMPLES 79

1. 0.0684 henry. **2.** 3 ft. **3.** 1336 volts.

EXAMPLES 80

1. 34 MW. **2.** 25.5 MW. **3.** 12,670 volts; 13,120 volts.
4. 122 kV.; 195.8 amp.; 0.71; 29,360 kW. **5.** 138 kV.; 95.6 %.
6. At 0.707 power factor, load-end volts in-phase and in quadrature
with current $= 10,000\ /(\sqrt{3}\ \sqrt{2}) = 4083$ volts.

Line current $= 10,000\ /(\sqrt{3} \times 10 \times 0.707) = 816$ amp.

Resistance drop, in phase with current $= 0.22 \times 816 = 179.5$
volts.

Reactance drop, in quadrature with current $= 314 \times 0.0025$
$\times 816 = 640$ volts.

Total volts in phase $= 4262.5$ volts.

Total volts in quadrature $= 4723$ volts.

Hence sending end volts $= \sqrt{4262.5^2 + 4723^2} = 6390$ volts per
phase $= 11$ kV. line. (*Ans.*)

At 0.866 p.f., $I = 666.6$ amp.

Resistance drop $= 146.6$ volts.

Reactance drop $= 523$ volts.

In-phase load volts $= 5000$.

In-quadrature load volts $= 2882$.

Total volts in-phase $= 5146.6$ and in-quadrature $= 3405$ volts,
whence sending-end volts $= 6173$ phase or 10.69 kV. line. (*Ans.*)

Idle current originally $= 577.5$ and when improved $= 333.3$ amp.
or a leading current of 244.2 taken by the condensers per line.
Hence at the load, the condenser bank will be $\sqrt{3} \times 10 \times 244.2$
$= 4230$ kVAR. (*Ans.*)

7. (a) 10,810 volts; (b) 9683 volts.
8. 36,000 volts; 33,400 volts.
9. 252.8 volts; $2°\ 7'$.
10. (i) 2500 kVA.; (ii) 12.6 kV.
11. 90.3 amp.; 82 amp.
12. 3859 volts. **13.** 143.3 kV.
14. 49.75 kV.; 33 MVA.; 54.5 MW.

EXAMPLES 81

1. 14.2 ft. **2.** 24.4 ft. **3.** 5.37 (using wind 0.6 for round surface).
4. 18.2 ft. **5.** 1170 lb. **6.** 18.86×10^{-6}; 12.43×10^6 lb per in.^{2}

EXAMPLES 82

3. 11·3 kV. **4.** 162·6 kV.; 80 kV. in paper; 107 kV. in oil; 40 kV. in porcelain. **5.** 67·7; 65; 81·9 kV/cm. **6.** 281 amp. **7.** (a) 0·286 μF.; (b) 2·78 × 10⁵ ohms; (c) 1·0 amp; (d) 435 watts. **8.** 2·16 cm.; 0·59 cm.; 65 kW. **9.** 313 amp. **10.** 136·5 kV/cm. **11.** 65·2%. (By volume, 83·3%.) **12.** 5·55 × 10¹⁰ ohm–cm. **13.** 3 cm.; 57 kV. **14.** 260 μF.; 0·035; 0·43 ohm.

15. (a) $S = \dfrac{V^1}{R_1 \log_e R_2/R_1}$ where $\dfrac{V^1}{V - V^1} = \dfrac{\varepsilon_1 \times \log_e R_2/R_1}{\varepsilon_2 \times \log_e R_1/r}$

where V^1 = intermediate voltage,

    r, R_1, R_2 = inner, intermediate, and outer radii,

    $\varepsilon_1, \varepsilon_2$ = inner and outer dielectric constants.

(b) 12,430 volts/cm. **16.** 0·094 megohms per mile.

17. 0·245 μF. At 30 kV./cm., voltage = 6600.

18. 10; 10·9; 11·97; 13·35; 15; 17·12; 20; 24·05; 30·2; 40·4 cm.

EXAMPLES 83

1. 640 ohms. $F = (V_1 - V_2)/I$.

2. Total leak current is zero, and since leakage on negative side is greater than on positive, the neutral will be positive with respect to earth. Let it be at v volts, and equate sum of leakage currents to zero thus—

$$\frac{230 + v}{15} + \frac{v}{10} + \frac{v - 230}{12} = 0$$

i.e. $4(230 + v) + 6v + 5(v - 230) = 0$

$$15v = 230 \text{ or } v = 15·33 \text{ volts.}$$

Neutral ammeter thus reads 1·533 amp. and positive outer is at a potential of + 245·33 and negative at − 214·67 volts.

3. Equate the leakage currents, taking f_1 and f_2 as the insulation resistances of the two mains, in 1000's of ohms. In the first case, with the first main at + 80 volts, and the second therefore at − 170 volts, we have

$$\frac{80}{80} + \frac{80}{f_1} = \frac{170}{f_2}$$

In the second case, the second main is at − 30 volts, so that the first is at + 220 volts, and we thus have

$$\frac{220}{f_1} = \frac{30}{80} + \frac{30}{f_2}$$

The solution of these equations is $f_1 = 373·333$ and $f_2 = 140$, so that the insulation resistances of the mains are 373,333 and 140,000 ohms respectively.

4. 2·745 × 10¹¹ ohms. **5.** 64·7 megohms. **6.** 17·75 megohms. **7.** 3000 and 1000 ohms. **9.** 0·95 megohms. **10.** 9·637 ohms at 186·3 yd. **11.** 105 yd.

EXAMPLES 84

1. 157·2 μF. **2.** 0·84; 5960 kW. **3.** 170 kVA.; 227 kVA., both without losses. **4.** 57·8 kVA. **5.** 1983 kVA. at 0·82. **6.** 277 μF.; 4·6 kVA. **7.** 0·9927. **8.** Power factor = 0·752 leading, kVA. = 66·5. **9.** 118 μF. **10.** £518. **11.** £8 15s. using 0·707 and 0·866. **12.** £222·2; £179·7. **13.** 0·72 leading. **14.** 1800 kVAR.

EXAMPLES 85

1. 6 ohms per phase. **2.** 11·5°. **3.** 1·9 ohms. **5.** $r = 10·5$ and 500/1. **6.** 0·0163 henry. **9.** 236 ohms (50 f.). **15.** 3° 26′.

EXAMPLES 86

3. 36·8 mins.
4. Assuming a star-delta transformer, 263 amp. and 10,500 amp.
5. 8·54 units.

EXAMPLES 87

1. 0·77; $A = 35$ amp. at 0·75 p.f.; $B = 19·7$ amp. at 0·8 p.f. **2.** 11·6 miles from A, 8·57 miles from B, and 16 miles from C. (Taking BC as base line, B as origin, the C. of G. is represented by $x = 6·66$ miles and $y = 5·39$ miles.) **3.** 11,270 volts; 3° 27′. **4.** 0·87; 4,400 volts. **6.** 5284 and 6716 kW. **7.** 2612 and 2388 kW. **8.** 13,000 volts; 6°. **9.** 2550 kW. **10.** $R = 0·794$; $X = 1·7$ ohms. **11.** 2080 kW., 3500 kVA.; 2920 kW., 3960 kVA. **12.** 130 amp., 26·5 amp., 125·5 amp., 333 volts line. **13.** $10·6 + j13·47$.

EXAMPLES 88

2. 9 ft.
3. 110 kilovolts between lines.

EXAMPLES 89

1. (a) 250,000; (b) 500,000 kVA. **2.** (a) 438; (b) 320 amp. **3.** 84,500 kVA. **4.** 2780 amp. **5.** (a) 160,000; 200,000; (b) 140,000 kVA. **6.** 6900 amp. **7.** 12%. **8.** 1,302,000; 968,000 kVA. **9.** 995 amp., 19·9 amp. **10.** 36 MVA. **11.** 10%.

EXAMPLES 90

2. 0·578 kWh. (10 sec. each series and parallel). **3.** 475·2 volts. **4.** 681·48 volts at ends. 632·5 volts at centre. **5.** 33 kWh. **6.** Highest potential 7·05 volt; at B, 6 volts; feeder current 767 amp. **7.** 37·7 kW., 2·32 volts. **8.** 8·3 volts; 21 kW. **9.** 75 amp. **10.** 106 tons. **11.** 62 tons; 3 driving axles; 6 motors of about 360 h.p. each. **12.** 2210 lb. **13.** 18·22 kWh. **14.** 22·2 kWh.

EXAMPLES 91

1. 208 amp. **2.** 33·55 m.p.h.
3. (a) 1·33 m.p.h.p.s. (b) 1560 h.p.
4. 1·73 m.p.h.p.s.
5. (a) 1·25 m.p.h.p.s. (b) 0·116 m.p.h.p.s.
   (c) 18·32 m.p.h. (d) 20 m.p.h.
6. (a) 24·7 m.p.h. (b) 550 amp.
7. 25·4 m.p.h.

Time (sec.)	0	11·5	23	29·3	41	58
T.E. (lb.)	16470	16470	16470	10500	7400	3630

8. 800 h.p.; 24·8 m.p.h. **9.** 18·65 m.p.h.

10.
Time (sec.)	22*	32	97†	103
Speed (m.p.h.)	27·5	32·5	12·6	0
Distance (yds.)	148	294·8	1011·5	1030

Schedule speed, 17·1 m.p.h.

11. 20·6 m.p.h.; 25 Wh/ton-mile. **12.** 1·2 m.p.h.p.s.
13. (a) 25 m.p.h.; (b) 0·1075 m.p.h.p.s.; (c) 25·8 Wh. per ton-mile.

EXAMPLES 92

1. 6·35 ohms.

2.
Current (amp.)	50	100	150	200	250
Trac. Eff. (lb.)	343	1200	2125	3050	4000
Speed (m.p.h.)	40·3	26·3	22·5	20·4	19·3

3.
Current (amp.)	100	150	200	250
Trac. Eff. (lb.)	640	1350	2160	2975
Speed (m.p.h.)	49·2	35·4	28·9	26

4. (a) 275 amp.; 3085 lb.; (b) 258 amp.; 2820 lb.

5.
Current (amp.)	40	60	80	100	120	160	200
Trac. Eff. (lb.)	150	555	1048	1575	2100	3180	4260
Speed (m.p.h.)	89·5	47	33·6	27·6	25·2	21·3	19·7

6.
Current (amp.)	45	675	90	1125	135	180	225
Trac. Eff. (lb.)	180	620	1170	1780	2380	3600	4720
Speed (m.p.h.)	94·5	53·1	38·5	31	27·9	23·8	22·2

7. (a) 1246 and 754 h.p. (b) 302 h.p. on A as motor and 202 h.p. from B as generator.

8. 11·43 m.p.h.; 7050 lb.

9. 40,400 lb.; 16·5 m.p.h.

10.
Current (amp.)	100	150	200	250	300	400
Trac. Eff. (lb.)	580	1215	2100	3070	4200	6400
Speed (m.p.h.)	58	44	34·3	28·4	24·2	21·1

11.
Amperes	50	100	150	200	250	300
m.p.h.	38·3	24·9	20·9	19·0	17·55	16·5
T.E. lb.	3580	10850	19200	27900	37400	47500

12. (a) 11·25 m.p.h.; (b) 1400 lb. and 1600 lb.

* Power off. † Brakes applied.

13. 280 lb. ft.

14. 922 h.p.

15. (a) 1320 kW., 270 amp.; (b) 515 kW., 133 amp. input to mains.

16.

Amperes			44	66	110	155	200
m.p.h.			65	44·2	30·7	24·9	22·4
T.E. lb.			380	771	1940	3290	4600

52 amp. increase

17. 22·4 kWh.

18. 0·54, 0·47, 0·4, 0·35, with motors 0·24 total 2·0 ohms.

$i = 222$ amp.

19.

Amperes			100	150	200
r.p.m.			17·2	20·9	28·3
T.E. lb.			1350	1695	1695

20.

Amperes			100	150	200
r.p.m.			16·3	14·16	12·6
T.E. lb.			1350	2290	3370

EXAMPLES 93

1. 0·69 Wh. per ton-mile (input).

2. 615 Wh. (output); 11·54 m.p.h.

3. 68 Wh. per ton-mile (input).

4. (a) 18·2 kWh. (output); (b) 138 Wh. per ton-mile (input).

5. (a) 47·25 m.p.h.; (b) 46 Wh. per ton.

6. 61·7 Wh. per ton-mile (output).

7. (a) 39·4 Wh. per ton mile; (b) 279 kW.

8. (a) 7·35 kWh. per train-mile; (b) 155 amp.; (c) 25 m.p.h.

9. 4·5 kWh.

10. 81·5. Wh. per ton-mile (input).

11. 26·4 Wh. per ton-mile.

12. 21 kWh.

13. 55·8 Wh. per ton-mile; 49·2%.

14. (a) 107 Wh.; (b) 81 Wh. per ton-mile.

15. 60·6 Wh. per ton-mile.

LOGARITHMIC TABLES

LOGARITHMS

	0	1	2	3	4	5	6	7	8	9	1 2 3	4 5 6	7 8 9
10	·0000	0043	0086	0128	0170	0212	0253	0294	0334	0374	4 8 12	17 21 25	29 33 37
11	·0414	0453	0492	0531	0569	0607	0645	0682	0719	0755	4 8 11	15 19 23	26 30 34
12	·0792	0828	0864	0899	0934	0969	1004	1038	1072	1106	3 7 10	14 17 21	24 28 31
13	·1139	1173	1206	1239	1271	1303	1335	1367	1399	1430	3 6 10	13 16 19	23 26 29
14	·1461	1492	1523	1553	1584	1614	1644	1673	1703	1732	3 6 9	12 15 18	21 24 27
15	·1761	1790	1818	1847	1875	1903	1931	1959	1987	2014	3 6 8	11 14 17	20 22 25
16	·2041	2068	2095	2122	2148	2175	2201	2227	2253	2279	3 5 8	11 13 16	18 21 24
17	·2304	2330	2355	2380	2405	2430	2455	2480	2504	2529	2 5 7	10 12 15	17 20 22
18	·2553	2577	2601	2625	2648	2672	2695	2718	2742	2765	2 5 7	9 12 14	16 19 21
19	·2788	2810	2833	2856	2878	2900	2923	2945	2967	2989	2 4 7	9 11 13	16 18 20
20	·3010	3032	3054	3075	3096	3118	3139	3160	3181	3201	2 4 6	8 11 13	15 17 19
21	·3222	3243	3263	3284	3304	3324	3345	3365	3385	3404	2 4 6	8 10 12	14 16 18
22	·3424	3444	3464	3483	3502	3522	3541	3560	3579	3598	2 4 6	8 10 12	14 15 17
23	·3617	3636	3655	3674	3692	3711	3729	3747	3766	3784	2 4 6	7 9 11	13 15 17
24	·3802	3820	3838	3856	3874	3892	3909	3927	3945	3962	2 4 5	7 9 11	12 14 16
25	·3979	3997	4014	4031	4048	4065	4082	4099	4116	4133	2 3 5	7 9 10	12 14 15
26	·4150	4166	4183	4200	4216	4232	4249	4265	4281	4298	2 3 5	7 8 10	11 13 15
27	·4314	4330	4346	4362	4378	4393	4409	4425	4440	4456	2 3 5	6 8 9	11 13 14
28	·4472	4487	4502	4518	4533	4548	4564	4579	4594	4609	2 3 5	6 8 9	11 12 14
29	·4624	4639	4654	4669	4683	4698	4713	4728	4742	4757	1 3 4	6 7 9	10 12 13
30	·4771	4786	4800	4814	4829	4843	4857	4871	4886	4900	1 3 4	6 7 9	10 11 13
31	·4914	4928	4942	4955	4969	4983	4997	5011	5024	5038	1 3 4	6 7 8	10 11 12
32	·5051	5065	5079	5092	5105	5119	5132	5145	5159	5172	1 3 4	5 7 8	9 11 12
33	·5185	5198	5211	5224	5237	5250	5263	5276	5289	5302	1 3 4	5 6 8	9 10 12
34	·5315	5328	5340	5353	5366	5378	5391	5403	5416	5428	1 3 4	5 6 8	9 10 11
35	·5441	5453	5465	5478	5490	5502	5514	5527	5539	5551	1 2 4	5 6 7	9 10 11
36	·5563	5575	5587	5599	5611	5623	5635	5647	5658	5670	1 2 4	5 6 7	8 10 11
37	·5682	5694	5705	5717	5729	5740	5752	5763	5775	5786	1 2 3	5 6 7	8 9 10
38	·5798	5809	5821	5832	5843	5855	5866	5877	5888	5899	1 2 3	5 6 7	8 9 10
39	·5911	5922	5933	5944	5955	5966	5977	5988	5999	6010	1 2 3	4 5 7	8 9 10
40	·6021	6031	6042	6053	6064	6075	6085	6096	6107	6117	1 2 3	4 5 6	8 9 10
41	·6128	6138	6149	6160	6170	6180	6191	6201	6212	6222	1 2 3	4 5 6	7 8 9
42	·6232	6243	6253	6263	6274	6284	6294	6304	6314	6325	1 2 3	4 5 6	7 8 9
43	·6335	6345	6355	6365	6375	6385	6395	6405	6415	6425	1 2 3	4 5 6	7 8 9
44	·6435	6444	6454	6464	6474	6484	6493	6503	6513	6522	1 2 3	4 5 6	7 8 9
45	·6532	6542	6551	6561	6571	6580	6590	6599	6609	6618	1 2 3	4 5 6	7 8 9
46	·6628	6637	6646	6656	6665	6675	6684	6693	6702	6712	1 2 3	4 5 6	7 7 8
47	·6721	6730	6739	6749	6758	6767	6776	6785	6794	6803	1 2 3	4 5 5	6 7 8
48	·6812	6821	6830	6839	6848	6857	6866	6875	6884	6893	1 2 3	4 4 5	6 7 8
49	·6902	6911	6920	6928	6937	6946	6955	6964	6972	6981	1 2 3	4 4 5	6 7 8
50	·6990	6998	7007	7016	7024	7033	7042	7050	7059	7067	1 2 3	3 4 5	6 7 8
51	·7076	7084	7093	7101	7110	7118	7126	7135	7143	7152	1 2 3	3 4 5	6 7 8
52	·7160	7168	7177	7185	7193	7202	7210	7218	7226	7235	1 2 2	3 4 5	6 7 7
53	·7243	7251	7259	7267	7275	7284	7292	7300	7308	7316	1 2 2	3 4 5	6 6 7
54	·7324	7332	7340	7348	7356	7364	7372	7380	7388	7396	1 2 2	3 4 5	6 6 7

LOGARITHMS

	0	1	2	3	4	5	6	7	8	9	1	2	3	4	5	6	7	8	9
55	·7404	7412	7419	7427	7435	7443	7451	7459	7466	7474	1	2	2	3	4	5	5	6	7
56	·7482	7490	7497	7505	7513	7520	7528	7536	7543	7551	1	2	2	3	4	5	5	6	7
57	·7559	7566	7574	7582	7589	7597	7604	7612	7619	7627	1	2	2	3	4	5	5	6	7
58	·7634	7642	7649	7657	7664	7672	7679	7686	7694	7701	1	1	2	3	4	4	5	6	7
59	·7709	7716	7723	7731	7738	7745	7752	7760	7767	7774	1	1	2	3	4	4	5	6	7
60	·7782	7789	7796	7803	7810	7818	7825	7832	7839	7846	1	1	2	3	4	4	5	6	6
61	·7853	7860	7868	7875	7882	7889	7896	7903	7910	7917	1	1	2	3	4	4	5	6	6
62	·7924	7931	7938	7945	7952	7959	7966	7973	7980	7987	1	1	2	3	3	4	5	6	6
63	·7993	8000	8007	8014	8021	8028	8035	8041	8048	8055	1	1	2	3	3	4	5	5	6
64	·8062	8069	8075	8082	8089	8096	8102	8109	8116	8122	1	1	2	3	3	4	5	5	6
65	·8129	8136	8142	8149	8156	8162	8169	8176	8182	8189	1	1	2	3	3	4	5	5	6
66	·8195	8202	8209	8215	8222	8228	8235	8241	8248	8254	1	1	2	3	3	4	5	5	6
67	·8261	8267	8274	8280	8287	8293	8299	8306	8312	8319	1	1	2	3	3	4	5	5	6
68	·8325	8331	8338	8344	8351	8357	8363	8370	8376	8382	1	1	2	3	3	4	4	5	6
69	·8388	8395	8401	8407	8414	8420	8426	8432	8439	8445	1	1	2	2	3	4	4	5	6
70	·8451	8457	8463	8470	8476	8482	8488	8494	8500	8506	1	1	2	2	3	4	4	5	6
71	·8513	8519	8525	8531	8537	8543	8549	8555	8561	8567	1	1	2	2	3	4	4	5	5
72	·8573	8579	8585	8591	8597	8603	8609	8615	8621	8627	1	1	2	2	3	4	4	5	5
73	·8633	8639	8645	8651	8657	8663	8669	8675	8681	8686	1	1	2	2	3	4	4	5	5
74	·8692	8698	8704	8710	8716	8722	8727	8733	8739	8745	1	1	2	2	3	4	4	5	5
75	·8751	8756	8762	8768	8774	8779	8785	8791	8797	8802	1	1	2	2	3	3	4	5	5
76	·8808	8814	8820	8825	8831	8837	8842	8848	8854	8859	1	1	2	2	3	3	4	5	5
77	·8865	8871	8876	8882	8887	8893	8899	8904	8910	8915	1	1	2	2	3	3	4	4	5
78	·8921	8927	8932	8938	8943	8949	8954	8960	8965	8971	1	1	2	2	3	3	4	4	5
79	·8976	8982	8987	8993	8998	9004	9009	9015	9020	9025	1	1	2	2	3	3	4	4	5
80	·9031	9036	9042	9047	9053	9058	9063	9069	9074	9079	1	1	2	2	3	3	4	4	5
81	·9085	9090	9096	9101	9106	9112	9117	9122	9128	9133	1	1	2	2	3	3	4	4	5
82	·9138	9143	9149	9154	9159	9165	9170	9175	9180	9186	1	1	2	2	3	3	4	4	5
83	·9191	9196	9201	9206	9212	9217	9222	9227	9232	9238	1	1	2	2	3	3	4	4	5
84	·9243	9248	9253	9258	9263	9269	9274	9279	9284	9289	1	1	2	2	3	3	4	4	5
85	·9294	9299	9304	9309	9315	9320	9325	9330	9335	9340	1	1	2	2	3	3	4	4	5
86	·9345	9350	9355	9360	9365	9370	9375	9380	9385	9390	1	1	1	2	3	3	4	4	5
87	·9395	9400	9405	9410	9415	9420	9425	9430	9435	9440	0	1	1	2	2	3	3	4	4
88	·9445	9450	9455	9460	9465	9469	9474	9479	9484	9489	0	1	1	2	2	3	3	4	4
89	·9494	9499	9504	9509	9513	9518	9523	9528	9533	9538	0	1	1	2	2	3	3	4	4
90	·9542	9547	9552	9557	9562	9566	9571	9576	9581	9586	0	1	1	2	2	3	3	4	4
91	·9590	9595	9600	9605	9609	9614	9619	9624	9628	9633	0	1	1	2	2	3	3	4	4
92	·9638	9643	9647	9652	9657	9661	9666	9671	9675	9680	0	1	1	2	2	3	3	4	4
93	·9685	9689	9694	9699	9703	9708	9713	9717	9722	9727	0	1	1	2	2	3	3	4	4
94	·9731	9736	9741	9745	9750	9754	9759	9763	9768	9773	0	1	1	2	2	3	3	4	4
95	·9777	9782	9786	9791	9795	9800	9805	9809	9814	9818	0	1	1	2	2	3	3	4	4
96	·9823	9827	832	9836	9841	9845	9850	9854	9859	9863	0	1	1	2	2	3	3	4	4
97	·9868	9872	9877	9881	9886	9890	9894	9899	9903	9908	0	1	1	2	2	3	3	4	4
98	·9912	9917	9921	9926	9930	9934	9939	9943	9948	9952	0	1	1	2	2	3	3	4	4
99	·9956	9961	9965	9969	9974	9978	9983	9987	9991	9996	0	1	1	2	2	3	3	3	4

ANTI-LOGARITHMS

	0	1	2	3	4	5	6	7	8	9	1	2	3	4	5	6	7	8	9
·00	1000	1002	1005	1007	1009	1012	1014	1016	1019	1021	0	0	1	1	1	1	2	2	2
·01	1023	1026	1028	1030	1033	1035	1038	1040	1042	1045	0	0	1	1	1	1	2	2	2
·02	1047	1050	1052	1054	1057	1059	1062	1064	1067	1069	0	0	1	1	1	1	2	2	2
·03	1072	1074	1076	1079	1081	1084	1086	1089	1091	1094	0	0	1	1	1	1	2	2	2
·04	1096	1099	1102	1104	1107	1109	1112	1114	1117	1119	0	1	1	1	1	2	2	2	2
·05	1122	1125	1127	1130	1132	1135	1138	1140	1143	1146	0	1	1	1	1	2	2	2	2
·06	1148	1151	1153	1156	1159	1161	1164	1167	1169	1172	0	1	1	1	1	2	2	2	2
·07	1175	1178	1180	1183	1186	1189	1191	1194	1197	1199	0	1	1	1	1	2	2	2	2
·08	1202	1205	1208	1211	1213	1216	1219	1222	1225	1227	0	1	1	1	1	2	2	2	3
·09	1230	1233	1236	1239	1242	1245	1247	1250	1253	1256	0	1	1	1	1	2	2	2	3
·10	1259	1262	1265	1268	1271	1274	1276	1279	1282	1285	0	1	1	1	1	2	2	2	3
·11	1288	1291	1294	1297	1300	1303	1306	1309	1312	1315	0	1	1	1	2	2	2	2	3
·12	1318	1321	1324	1327	1330	1334	1337	1340	1343	1346	0	1	1	1	2	2	2	2	3
·13	1349	1352	1355	1358	1361	1365	1368	1371	1374	1377	0	1	1	1	2	2	2	3	3
·14	1380	1384	1387	1390	1393	1396	1400	1403	1406	1409	0	1	1	1	2	2	2	3	3
·15	1413	1416	1419	1422	1426	1429	1432	1435	1439	1442	0	1	1	1	2	2	2	3	3
·16	1445	1449	1452	1455	1459	1462	1466	1469	1472	1476	0	1	1	1	2	2	2	3	3
·17	1479	1483	1486	1489	1493	1496	1500	1503	1507	1510	0	1	1	1	2	2	2	3	3
·18	1514	1517	1521	1524	1528	1531	1535	1538	1542	1545	0	1	1	1	2	2	2	3	3
·19	1549	1552	1556	1560	1563	1567	1570	1574	1578	1581	0	1	1	1	2	2	3	3	3
·20	1585	1589	1592	1596	1600	1603	1607	1611	1614	1618	0	1	1	1	2	2	3	3	3
·21	1622	1626	1629	1633	1637	1641	1644	1648	1652	1656	0	1	1	2	2	2	3	3	3
·22	1660	1663	1667	1671	1675	1679	1683	1687	1690	1694	0	1	1	2	2	2	3	3	3
·23	1698	1702	1706	1710	1714	1718	1722	1726	1730	1734	0	1	1	2	2	2	3	3	4
·24	1738	1742	1746	1750	1754	1758	1762	1766	1770	1774	0	1	1	2	2	2	3	3	4
·25	1778	1782	1786	1791	1795	1799	1803	1807	1811	1816	0	1	1	2	2	2	3	3	4
·26	1820	1824	1828	1832	1837	1841	1845	1849	1854	1858	0	1	1	2	2	3	3	3	4
·27	1862	1866	1871	1875	1879	1884	1888	1892	1897	1901	0	1	1	2	2	3	3	3	4
·28	1905	1910	1914	1919	1923	1928	1932	1936	1941	1945	0	1	1	2	2	3	3	4	4
·29	1950	1954	1959	1963	1968	1972	1977	1982	1986	1991	0	1	1	2	2	3	3	4	4
·30	1995	2000	2004	2009	2014	2018	2023	2028	2032	2037	0	1	1	2	2	3	3	4	4
·31	2042	2046	2051	2056	2061	2065	2070	2075	2080	2084	0	1	1	2	2	3	3	4	4
·32	2089	2094	2099	2104	2109	2113	2118	2123	2128	2133	0	1	1	2	2	3	3	4	4
·33	2138	2143	2148	2153	2158	2163	2168	2173	2178	2183	0	1	1	2	2	3	3	4	4
·34	2188	2193	2198	2203	2208	2213	2218	2223	2228	2234	1	1	2	2	3	3	4	4	5
·35	2239	2244	2249	2254	2259	2265	2270	2275	2280	2286	1	1	2	2	3	3	4	4	5
·36	2291	2296	2301	2307	2312	2317	2323	2328	2333	2339	1	1	2	2	3	3	4	4	5
·37	2344	2350	2355	2360	2366	2371	2377	2382	2388	2393	1	1	2	2	3	3	4	4	5
·38	2399	2404	2410	2415	2421	2427	2432	2438	2443	2449	1	1	2	2	3	3	4	4	5
·39	2455	2460	2466	2472	2477	2483	2489	2495	2500	2506	1	1	2	2	3	3	4	5	5
·40	2512	2518	2523	2529	2535	2541	2547	2553	2559	2564	1	1	2	2	3	4	4	5	5
·41	2570	2576	2582	2588	2594	2600	2606	2612	2618	2624	1	1	2	2	3	4	4	5	5
·42	2630	2636	2642	2649	2655	2661	2667	2673	2679	2685	1	1	2	2	3	4	4	5	6
·43	2692	2698	2704	2710	2716	2723	2729	2735	2742	2748	1	1	2	3	3	4	4	5	6
·44	2754	2761	2767	2773	2780	2786	2793	2799	2805	2812	1	1	2	3	3	4	4	5	6
·45	2818	2825	2831	2838	2844	2851	2858	2864	2871	2877	1	1	2	3	3	4	5	5	6
·46	2884	2891	2897	2904	2911	2917	2924	2931	2938	2944	1	1	2	3	3	4	5	5	6
·47	2951	2958	2965	2972	2979	2985	2992	2999	3006	3013	1	1	2	3	3	4	5	5	6
·48	3020	3027	3034	3041	3048	3055	3062	3069	3076	3083	1	1	2	3	4	4	5	6	6
·49	3090	3097	3105	3112	3119	3126	3133	3141	3148	3155	1	1	2	3	4	4	5	6	6

ANTI-LOGARITHMS

	0	1	2	3	4	5	6	7	8	9	1	2	3	4	5	6	7	8	9
·50	3162	3170	3177	3184	3192	3199	3206	3214	3221	3228	1	1	2	3	4	4	5	6	7
·51	3236	3243	3251	3258	3266	3273	3281	3289	3296	3304	1	2	2	3	4	5	5	6	7
·52	3311	3319	3327	3334	3342	3350	3357	3365	3373	3381	1	2	2	3	4	5	5	6	7
·53	3388	3396	3404	3412	3420	3428	3436	3443	3451	3459	1	2	2	3	4	5	6	6	7
·54	3467	3475	3483	3491	3499	3508	3516	3524	3532	3540	1	2	2	3	4	5	6	6	7
·55	3548	3556	3565	3573	3581	3589	3597	3606	3614	3622	1	2	2	3	4	5	6	7	7
·56	3631	3639	3648	3656	3664	3673	3681	3690	3698	3707	1	2	3	3	4	5	6	7	8
·57	3715	3724	3733	3741	3750	3758	3767	3776	3784	3793	1	2	3	3	4	5	6	7	8
·58	3802	3811	3819	3828	3837	3846	3855	3864	3873	3882	1	2	3	4	4	5	6	7	8
·59	3890	3899	3908	3917	3926	3936	3945	3954	3963	3972	1	2	3	4	5	5	6	7	8
·60	3981	3990	3999	4009	4018	4027	4036	4046	4055	4064	1	2	3	4	5	6	6	7	8
·61	4074	4083	4093	4102	4111	4121	4130	4140	4150	4159	1	2	3	4	5	6	7	8	9
·62	4169	4178	4188	4198	4207	4217	4227	4236	4246	4256	1	2	3	4	5	6	7	8	9
·63	4266	4276	4285	4295	4305	4315	4325	4335	4345	4355	1	2	3	4	5	6	7	8	9
·64	4365	4375	4385	4395	4406	4416	4426	4436	4446	4457	1	2	3	4	5	6	7	8	9
·65	4467	4477	4487	4498	4508	4519	4529	4539	4550	4560	1	2	3	4	5	6	7	8	9
·66	4571	4581	4592	4603	4613	4624	4634	4645	4656	4667	1	2	3	4	5	6	7	9	10
·67	4677	4688	4699	4710	4721	4732	4742	4753	4764	4775	1	2	3	4	5	7	8	9	10
·68	4786	4797	4808	4819	4831	4842	4853	4864	4875	4887	1	2	3	4	6	7	8	9	10
·69	4898	4909	4920	4932	4943	4955	4966	4977	4989	5000	1	2	3	5	6	7	8	9	10
·70	5012	5023	5035	5047	5058	5070	5082	5093	5105	5117	1	2	4	5	6	7	8	9	11
·71	5129	5140	5152	5164	5176	5188	5200	5212	5224	5236	1	2	4	5	6	7	8	10	11
·72	5248	5260	5272	5284	5297	5309	5321	5333	5346	5358	1	2	4	5	6	7	9	10	11
·73	5370	5383	5395	5408	5420	5433	5445	5458	5470	5483	1	3	4	5	6	8	9	10	11
·74	5495	5508	5521	5534	5546	5559	5572	5585	5598	5610	1	3	4	5	6	8	9	10	12
·75	5623	5636	5649	5662	5675	5689	5702	5715	5728	5741	1	3	4	5	7	8	9	10	12
·76	5754	5768	5781	5794	5808	5821	5834	5848	5861	5875	1	3	4	5	7	8	9	11	12
·77	5888	5902	5916	5929	5943	5957	5970	5984	5998	6012	1	3	4	5	7	8	10	11	12
·78	6026	6039	6053	6067	6081	6095	6109	6124	6138	6152	1	3	4	6	7	8	10	11	13
·79	6166	6180	6194	6209	6223	6237	6252	6266	6281	6295	1	3	4	6	7	9	10	11	13
·80	6310	6324	6339	6353	6368	6383	6397	6412	6427	6442	1	3	4	6	7	9	10	12	13
·81	6457	6471	6486	6501	6516	6531	6546	6561	6577	6592	2	3	5	6	8	9	11	12	14
·82	6607	6622	6637	6653	6668	6683	6699	6714	6730	6745	2	3	5	6	8	9	11	12	14
·83	6761	6776	6792	6808	6823	6839	6855	6871	6887	6902	2	3	5	6	8	9	11	13	14
·84	6918	6934	6950	6966	6982	6998	7015	7031	7047	7063	2	3	5	6	8	10	11	13	15
·85	7079	7096	7112	7129	7145	7161	7178	7194	7211	7228	2	3	5	7	8	10	12	13	15
·86	7244	7261	7278	7295	7311	7328	7345	7362	7379	7396	2	3	5	7	8	10	12	13	15
·87	7413	7430	7447	7464	7482	7499	7516	7534	7551	7568	2	3	5	7	9	10	12	14	16
·88	7586	7603	7621	7638	7656	7674	7691	7709	7727	7745	2	4	5	7	9	11	12	14	16
·89	7762	7780	7798	7816	7834	7852	7870	7889	7907	7925	2	4	5	7	9	11	13	14	16
·90	7943	7962	7980	7998	8017	8035	8054	8072	8091	8110	2	4	6	7	9	11	13	15	17
·91	8128	8147	8166	8185	8204	8222	8241	8260	8279	8299	2	4	6	8	9	11	13	15	17
·92	8318	8337	8356	8375	8395	8414	8433	8453	8472	8492	2	4	6	8	10	12	14	15	17
·93	8511	8531	8551	8570	8590	8610	8630	8650	8670	8690	2	4	6	8	10	12	14	16	18
·94	8710	8730	8750	8770	8790	8810	8831	8851	8872	8892	2	4	6	8	10	12	14	16	18
·95	8913	8933	8954	8974	8995	9016	9036	9057	9078	9099	2	4	6	8	10	12	15	17	19
·96	9120	9141	9162	9183	9204	9226	9247	9268	9290	9311	2	4	6	8	11	13	15	17	19
·97	9333	9354	9376	9397	9419	9441	9462	9484	9506	9528	2	4	7	9	11	13	15	17	20
·98	9550	9572	9594	9616	9638	9661	9683	9705	9727	9750	2	4	7	9	11	13	16	18	20
·99	9772	9795	9817	9840	9863	9886	9908	9931	9954	9977	2	5	7	9	11	14	16	18	20

PITMAN'S
NATIONAL CERTIFICATE SERIES

These books meet the requirements of students preparing for the National Certificate Examinations.

FIRST YEAR ENGINEERING SCIENCE
(MECHANICAL AND ELECTRICAL)
By G. W. Bird, Wh.Ex., B.Sc., A.M.I.Mech.E., A.M.I.E.E. Revised by B. J. Tams, M.Sc.Tech., A.M.I.Mech.E.
In demy 8vo, cloth gilt, 140 pp. **5s.** net.

SECOND YEAR ENGINEERING SCIENCE
(MECHANICAL)
By G. W. Bird, Wh.Ex., B.Sc., A.M.I.Mech.E., A.M.I.E.E. Revised by Struan A. Robertson, B.Sc., B.Com., A.M.I.Mech.E.
In demy 8vo, cloth gilt, 260 pp. **8s. 6d.** net.

MECHANICS FOR ENGINEERING STUDENTS
By G. W. Bird, B.Sc., Wh.Ex., A.M.I.Mech.E., A.M.I.E.E. Revised by G. W. T. Bird, B.Sc.
In demy 8vo, cloth gilt, 158 pp. **6s.**

ELEMENTARY PRACTICAL MATHEMATICS
(Book I—First Year)
By E. W. Golding, M.Sc.Tech., A.M.I.E.E., and H. G. Green, M.A.
In demy 8vo, cloth, 168 pp. **6s.** net.

ELEMENTARY PRACTICAL MATHEMATICS
(Book II—Second Year)
By E. W. Golding, M.Sc.Tech., A.M.I.E.E., Mem.A.I.E.E., and H. G. Green, M.A.
In demy 8vo, cloth gilt, 202 pp. **6s. 6d.** net.

ELEMENTARY PRACTICAL MATHEMATICS
(Book III—Third Year)
By E. W. Golding, M.Sc.Tech., A.M.I.E.E., Mem.A.I.E.E., and H. G. Green, M.A.
In demy 8vo, cloth gilt, 171 pp. **7s. 6d.** net.

A FIRST YEAR ENGINEERING DRAWING
By A. C. Parkinson, A.C.P. (Hons.), F.Coll.H., F.I.E.D.
In crown 4to, quarter cloth, 175 pp. **6s. 6d.**

INTERMEDIATE ENGINEERING DRAWING
By A. C. Parkinson.
In crown 4to, 186 pp., illustrated. **7s. 6d.** net.

Sir Isaac Pitman & Sons, Ltd., Parker Street, Kingsway, W.C.2

DEFINITIONS AND FORMULAE FOR STUDENTS

THIS series of booklets is intended to provide engineering students with all necessary definitions and formulae in a convenient form.

ELECTRICAL
By PHILIP KEMP, M.Sc., M.I.E.E., Mem.A.I.E.E.

ELECTRICAL INSTALLATION WORK
By F. PEAKE SEXTON, A.R.C.S., A.M.I.E.E., A.I.E.E.

HEAT ENGINES
By ARNOLD RIMMER, B.Eng.

APPLIED MECHANICS
By E. H. LEWITT, B.Sc., A.M.I.Mech.E.

PRACTICAL MATHEMATICS
By LOUIS TOFT, M.Sc.

CHEMISTRY AND PHARMACY
By W. GORDON CAREY, F.I.C.

BUILDING
By T. CORKHILL, F.B.I.C.C., M.I.Struct.E.

AERONAUTICS
By JOHN D. FRIER, A.R.C.Sc., D.I.C.

COAL MINING
By M. D. WILLIAMS, F.G.S.

TELEGRAPHY AND TELEPHONY
By E. MALLETT, D.Sc., M.I.E.E.

LIGHT AND SOUND
By P. K. BOWES, M.A., B.Sc.

METALLURGY
By E. R. TAYLOR, A.R.S.M., F.I.C., D.I.C.

RADIO AND TELEVISION ENGINEERING
By A. T. STARR, M.A., Ph.D., A.M.I.E.E.

AUTOMOBILE ENGINEERING
By H. KERR THOMAS, M.I.Mech.E., M.I.A.E.

MODERN PHYSICS
By E. E. WIDDOWSON, Ph.D., M.Sc.

THEORY OF MACHINES
By R. E. SMITH, B.Sc., A.M.I.M.E.

Each in pocket size, about 32 pp. **8d.**

SIR ISAAC PITMAN & SONS, LTD., PARKER ST., KINGSWAY, W.C.2